595

D1499621

CARPENTRY
and
BUILDING

formerly
Questions and Answers
for Carpenters and Builders

by Harry F. Ulrey

THEODORE AUDEL & CO.
a division of
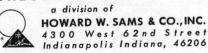
HOWARD W. SAMS & CO., INC.
4300 West 62nd Street
Indianapolis Indiana, 46206

FIRST EDITION

1971 PRINTING

Copyright © 1966 by Howard W. Sams & Co., Inc., Indianapolis, Indiana. Printed in the United States of America.

All rights reserved. Reproduction or use, without express permission, of editorial or pictorial content, in any manner, is prohibited. No patent liability is assumed with respect to the use of the information contained herein.

Library of Congress Catalog Card Number 66-29074

Foreword

The questions appearing in this text are quite typical of those which have come to the attention of the author during his career as a designing engineer and engineering consultant for a nationally recognized trades magazines. Many of these questions have been asked repeatedly. Some were brief and to the point, requiring only brief and undetailed explanations; some were involved and complex, and some questions were highly technical.

All the answers given are in accord with good engineering practices. Some of the answers are based on the personal experiences and observations of the author, and some are founded on dependable and unbiased laboratory testing results. None of the answers is based soley on the universal claims of the advertisers of competitive commercial products.

The author hopes that carpenters and builders will recognize this book as a truly honest attempt to help them solve some of the problems that have plagued others at one time or another and to assist them in achieving the goal of all good carpenters and builders—to erect better buildings.

HARRY F. ULREY

Contents

CHAPTER 1

Contents

Contents

CHAPTER 4

Contents

Contents

Contents

Heat-conduction through electrical-outlet boxes, 188
Shredded redwood-bark insulation, 189
Insulating of plaster on radiant ceilings, 190
Molds and mildews on walls, 191
Effect of dampness on casein glues, 192

CHAPTER 7

CHAPTER 8

CHAPTER 9

CONCRETE 227

Contents

CHAPTER 10

CHAPTER 11

CHAPTER 12

Contents

CHAPTER 13

Contents

CHAPTER 1

Layout

Layout for an Elliptic Curve

Ques. How can an elliptic curve—the type that is often used for plastered arches be laid out?

Ans. The easiest method is to make a template of wallboard or thin plywood. Make the width equal to the rise of the arch, and the length equal to one-half the span. With a compass, step off the same number of equal spaces on a side and an edge, and connect the points with straight lines, as shown in the sketch (Fig. 1). If the spaces are made relatively short, the formed curve can be cut out with very little "doctoring."

Correct Proportions for a Fireplace

Ques. Is there a correct relation to maintain between the area of a fireplace opening and the area of the chimney if the fireplace is to work satisfactorily? What is the correct height of the opening?

Ans. In general, the cross-sectional area of fireplace flues should be not less than 1/10 the area of the fireplace opening; for the sake of appearance, recommended proportions between height, width, and depth should be maintained (Fig. 2). These proportions also are essential for satisfactory fireplace operation.

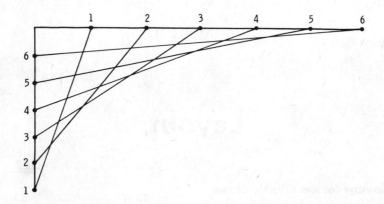

Fig. 1. Laying out a curve that resembles an ellipse. This method may be used to lay out a template that may be used for plastered arches or similar projects.

In designing a fireplace, the type of fuel to be burned should be considered. In addition, the design should harmonize with the room in both proportion and detail. In the days of the early settlers of our land, wood was plentiful and fireplaces with openings as large as 7 feet wide and 5 feet high were common. These were often used for cooking as well as heating. Needless to say, they consumed huge amounts of fuel and were more likely to be smoky than not.

Where cordwood (4 ft. long) is readily available, a 30-inch wide opening is desirable for a fireplace. The wood is cut in half to provide pieces 24 inches long. If coal is to be burned, however, the opening can be narrower. Thirty inches is a practical height for any fireplace having an opening less than 6 feet wide. It will be found that, in general, the higher the opening, the greater is the chance the fireplace will smoke. The dimensions in Table 1 are generally satisfactory for the construction of fireplaces.

Fitting Baseboard in Corners

Ques. What is the recommended method of fitting baseboard around inside corners? When using square-edged stock, the common method is to butt one board against the other, but this method results in an unsatisfactory appearance. Since the corners are rarely

Table 1. Recommended Dimensions for Fireplaces

Opening		Depth (inches)	Minimum back (horizontal) (inches)	Vertical back wall (inches)	Inclined back wall (inches)	Outside dimensions of standard rectangular flue lining (inches)	Inside diameter of standard round flue lining (inches)
Width (inches)	Height (inches)						
24	24	16-18	14	14	16	8½ X 8½	10
28	24	16-18	14	14	16	8½ X 8½	10
24	28	16-18	14	14	20	8½ X 8½	10
30	28	16-18	16	14	20	8½ X 13	10
36	28	16-18	22	14	20	8½ X 13	12
42	28	16-18	28	14	20	8½ X 18	12
36	32	18-20	20	14	24	8½ X 18	12
42	32	18-20	26	14	24	13 X 13	12
48	32	18-20	32	14	24	13 X 13	15
42	36	18-20	26	14	28	13 X 13	15
48	36	18-20	32	14	28	13 X 18	15
54	36	18-20	38	14	28	13 X 18	15
60	36	18-20	44	14	28	13 X 18	15
42	40	20-22	24	17	29	13 X 13	15
48	40	20-22	30	17	29	13 X 18	15
54	40	20-22	36	17	29	13 X 18	15
60	40	20-22	42	17	29	18 X 18	18
66	40	20-22	48	17	29	18 X 18	18
72	40	22-28	51	17	29	18 X 18	18

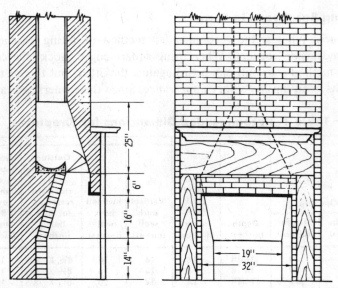

Fig. 2. Illustrating a well-proportioned fireplace. Details of fireplace construction often vary widely.

plumb and square, it is difficult to obtain a fit with straight miters; with a round-edge baseboard, the thin finger in a coped joint often breaks off.

Ans. Set the first board, with the end squared, and nail it firmly in place (Fig. 3). Butt the opposite board, against the first board,

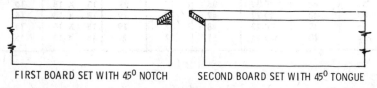

FIRST BOARD SET WITH 45° NOTCH   SECOND BOARD SET WITH 45° TONGUE

Fig. 3. Illustrating method of cutting baseboard to fit inside corners, in order to give the appearance of a miter joint without mitering the entire widths of the boards.

and scribe it to fit; allow approximately 3/4 inch for cutting off. From the cutoff line, saw a miter cut across the top, but make the miter only about 3/16 inch deep, and then saw the board square along the scribed line from the bottom edge, upward to the miter

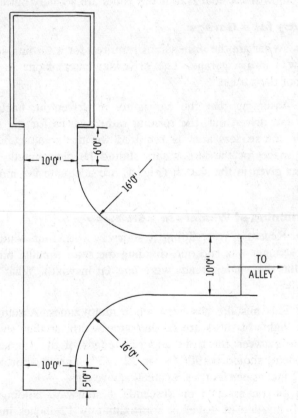

Fig. 4. Method of calculating turning space for a driveway that enters the garage from an alley at the side of the garage. A driveway with the dimension given accommodates most modern cars, but turning radii vary widely.

cut. Then set the second board in place, with its mitered tongue extending over the top edge of the first board, and mark the miter cut on the top edge of the first board. Cut this miter 1/4-inch deep, or more, with a sharp chisel. These joints show a miter cut at the top edges of the boards, but the joints are actually butted joints.

Driveway for a Garage

Ques. What are the dimensions required for a turning space for a driveway into a garage. The driveway enters from an alley at the side of the garage.

Ans. Assuming that the car is to be driven in, backed out, turned, and driven out, the turning radius varies for the different cars. Of course, less area is required for the compact cars, but turning space for the larger cars should be determined. The dimensions given in the sketch (Fig. 4) are adequate for most automobiles.

Proportioning of Winders in a Stairway

Ques. Recently, in building a stairway with four winders, the outside stringer was laid out, dividing the span equally, but it was found that the winder treads were uneven in width. What mistake was made?

Ans. This mistake has been made many times. Assuming that the two flights of stairs are of the same width, as they should be, the angle between the front and rear edges of the winder treads (all of them) should be 90°/4, or 22-1/2°. This is approximately 4-31/32 inches per foot, using steel-square cuts.

As a person ascends or descends a stairway, holding to the handrail, his line of travel is approximately 12 inches inside the handrail line. If the stairway is to be safe, it is important that the widths of the winder treads in this line of travel should have the

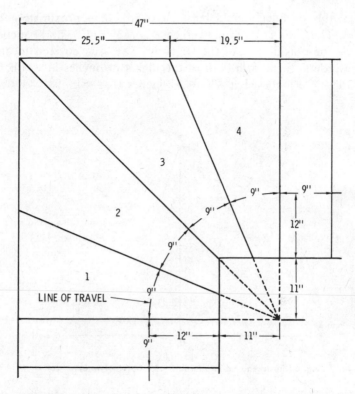

Fig. 5. Proportioning the winders in stairway landings. In a stairway landing that has four winder treads, note that the cut against the wall is wider in treads No. 2 and 3 than in treads No. 1 and 4.

same widths as the treads in the remainder of the stairway. This means that the lines of the edges of the winders do not converge in the corner where the flights change direction, but they do converge at a point some distance outside the corner. With four winders, the distance from the line of travel to this point of convergence should be 2.56 times the width of the treads. If the width is 9 inches, this distance should be (9 × 2.56), or approximately 23 inches. Thus, the point of convergence is (23 − 12), or 11 inches outside the outside line of the stairway. The area covered by the four winders, then, with both of the flights 36 inches in width, is not 36 × 36 inches, but 47 × 47 inches (Fig. 5).

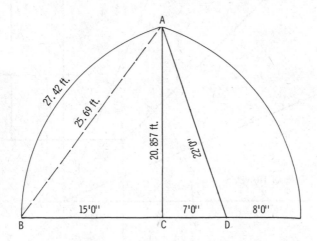

Fig. 6. Illustrating the proportions of a Gothic-style barn roof.

The cut ends of treads *2* and *3*, then, should be wider than the cut ends of treads *1* and *4*, at the wall ends. The cut ends of treads *1* and *4* should have a length equal to *tan* 22-1/2° × the width of the area covered; or, if the stair is 36 inches wide, the length of the cut end should be (.414 × 47), or approximately 19-1/2 inches. The lengths of the cut ends of treads *2* and *3* should be (47 − 19-1/2), or 27-1/2 inches. The wall-side stringer should be cut to these dimensions. The height of the risers should be the same throughout both flights, including the risers in the winders.

Proportioning a Gothic-Style Barn Roof

Ques. Are the proportions given in the sketch (Fig. 6) correct for a Gothic-style barn roof? The width of the building is to be 30'0", and a 22-ft. radius has been used. What are the lengths of the chord AB and the arc?

Ans. Apparently, there is no standard for these roofs, but designers often use either two-thirds or three-fourths of the span as a radius for the arcs. In the true Gothic arch, the radius is equal to the span, but the arch is too high for most barn roofs, although it may be appropriate for church and cathedral arches. The dimensions can be calculated as follows:

1. Height AC = square root of $(22)^2 - (7)^2 = 20.8567$ feet.
2. Length of chord AB = square root of $(20.857)^2 + (15)^2$ = 25.69 feet.

3. Tangent of angle CD-$CA = \dfrac{20.857}{7} = 2.979$, which is the tangent of $71.42°$.
4. Length of arc $AB = .01745 \times 71.42 \times 22 = 27.42$ feet.

Unusual Method for Calculating Rafter Lengths

Ques. When calculating rafter lengths for a 6" $\times$ 12" roof, the width of the building multiplied by 0.559 gives the correct rafter length. What are the decimals that can be used for the other pitches, ranging from 2" $\times$ 12" to 8" $\times$ 12"?

Ans. This is a rather unusual method for calculating rafter lengths, but it should be entirely satisfactory. The desired decimals that can be used to calculate rafter lengths are listed as follows:

for 2" × 12" pitch, multiply by 0.507
for 3" × 12" pitch, multiply by 0.5155
for 4" × 12" pitch, multiply by 0.527
for 5" × 12" pitch, multiply by 0.542
for 6" × 12" pitch, multiply by 0.559
for 7" × 12" pitch, multiply by 0.579
for 8" × 12" pitch, multiply by 0.601

Safe Loadings on Wooden Columns

Ques. How can safe loadings for wooden columns be estimated?

Ans. Several column formulas are commonly used; the local building code probably includes the formula that should be used. In the absence of code regulations the following formula is dependable, but all column formulas are slightly cumbersome. Column formulas should not be used to determine loadings for very short columns, which may fail from actual crushing action of the wood. For yellow pine and Douglas fir columns, all grades, the recommended formula is:

$$P = \frac{528,000 \times A \times d^2}{L^2}$$

in which;

P is allowable loading, pounds
A is area of section, square inches
d is shortest side, inches
L is unsupported length, inches.

For example, the safe loading for a standard dressed 4" × 4" column: length, 8'0", or 96 in.; shortest side, 3.625 in.; and cross-sectional area, 13.14 sq. in. can be calculated as follows:

$$P = \frac{528{,}000 \times 13.14 \times 3.625 \times 3.625}{96 \times 96} = 9893 \text{ pounds}$$

Roof Pitches

Ques. Is the pitch of a gabled roof whose rafters are constructed with 12 inches rise per foot considered to be "full" pitch, or "one-half" pitch?

Ans. A gabled roof whose rise is one-half the width (span) of the building is "one-half" pitch; likewise, a roof whose rise is equal to one-third of the building width (span) is "one-third" pitch. This indicates that the rafters rise 12 in. per foot and 8 in. per foot, respectively. This is an old method of defining roof pitches, possibly centuries old; and, in all probability, it originated in England. At least, the method is mentioned in *Molesworth's Formulae,* first published in London in 1862 and in *Trautwine's Reference Book,* first published in the United States in 1871. It seems that this usage is fairly well established. The term "full" pitch, then, indicates rafters with 24 inches of rise per foot of run, which is almost unknown in this country; however, this was by no means unknown in England, where straw-thatched roofs were common.

It is less confusing to specify gable roof pitches and rafter slopes in inches of rise per foot of span, such as 12″ × 12″, 8″ × 12″, etc.; then there is less possibility for confusion.

Proportioning Risers and Treads of Stairways

Ques. What are the rules for proportioning the risers and treads of stairways.

Ans. Several different rules for determining the most satisfactory dimensions for stair risers and treads are in common use, and all are fairly satisfactory. Some of these rules are as follows:

1. Double the rise, and add the tread width. The result should range from 24 to 25.
2. Multiply the riser height by the tread width. The product should be not less than 70, nor more than 75.
3. Add the riser height to the tread width. The sum should range from 17 to 18.

In all of the above rules, the tread width does not include the width of the nosing, which may range upward to 1-1/2 inches. Rule No. 1 is the most satisfactory rule for most residential stairways. In some instances, none of the rules seem to work well, but they do provide a basis for calculations. In general, a riser should

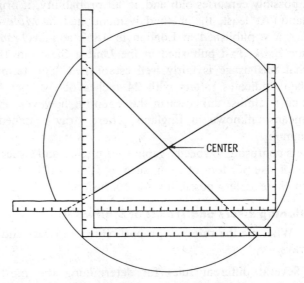

Fig. 7. Illustrating a method of locating the center point of a circle by means of a carpenter's steel square. The hypotenuse of any right triangle inscribed inside a circle passes through the center point of the circle.

be not more than 7-3/4 inches, and a tread, exclusive of the nosing, should be not more than 9-1/2 inches.

Using a Steel Square to Locate the Center Point of a Circle

Ques. Is it possible to locate the center point of a circle by means of a carpenter's square?

Ans. It can be done quite readily. Lay the square on the circle so that the heel touches the circumference of the circle, and mark the points where the blade and tongue cross the circumference. A line drawn between these two points passes through the center point. Then lay the square on the circle in another position, preferably one-quarter of the distance around the circle, and draw another diameter. The point where the two diameters intersect is the center point of the circle. The markings on the square are of no consequence (see Fig. 7).

Determining Rafter Lengths by the Feet-per-Foot-of-run Method

Ques. A carpenter friend determines rafter lengths by multiplying one-half the building width by a number. Is this method accurate, and can it be used for all pitches?

Ans. The method is accurate; it can be used for roofs of all pitches, if the correct factor is used. These numbers can be found on many different makes of special rafter squares, but the rafter lengths are usually given in inches and decimals, instead of in feet. The correct numbers to use for even-inch pitches ranging from $3'' \times 12''$ to $12'' \times 12''$ are as follows:

$3'' \times 12''$, for common rafters, use 1.0308;
for hips and valleys, use 1.4361
$4'' \times 12''$, for common rafters, use 1.0541;
for hips and valleys, use 1.453

5″ × 12″, for common rafters, use 1.0833;
for hips and valleys, use 1.4743

6″ × 12″, for common rafters, use 1.118;
for hips and valleys, use 1.5

7″ × 12″, for common rafters, use 1.1577;
for hips and valleys, use 1.5298

8″ × 12″, for common rafters, use 1.2019;
for hips and valleys, use 1.5635

9″ × 12″, for common rafters, use 1.25;
for hips and valleys, use 1.6008

10″ × 12″, for common rafters, use 1.3017;
for hips and valleys, use 1.6415

11″ × 12″, for common rafters, use 1.3566;
for hips and valleys, use 1.6853

12″ × 12″, for common rafters, use 1.4142;
for hips and alleys, use 1.7321

The above numbers are given in *feet-per-foot-of-run.* For example, if the roof pitch is to be 4″ × 12″ and the half-width of the building is to be 12′ 3″, or 12-1/4 feet, the calculation is as follows: 12-1/4 × 1.0541 = 12.91 feet.

To change the decimal foot to inches, multiply by 12 as follows: .91 × 12 = 10.92 inches, or, to the nearest tenth, 10-9/10 inches.

Since one edge of the square is laid out in tenths, the fraction may be converted easily.

Mitering Members of Different Widths

Ques. How can a miter cut be made to fit when the two members are of different widths?

Ans. Lay one of the members over the other in the same positions that they will occupy when the miter is completed, and mark the edges of each board. The diagonals of these marks represent the miter cut. It may be advantageous for a good joint, to mark and cut one board first; then lay it over the other board, and mark the other side of the miter directly. Most good carpenters know this trick, and use it in numerous ways (Fig. 8).

A Mathematically Correct Way to Draw an Ellipse

Ques. How can an ellipse be drawn, using two nails and a piece of string?

Ans. This method of drawing an ellipse is mathematically correct, but it is slightly tricky, because strings usually stretch a bit; however, this is more satisfactory than merely guessing.

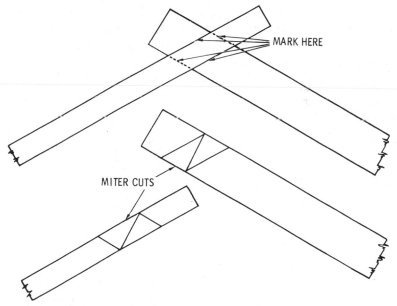

MARK HERE

MITER CUTS

Fig. 8. Illustrating a method of laying out miter cuts when the two members are of different widths. This method may be used in numerous places.

Layout

As shown in the sketch (Fig. 9), lay out the two axes of the curve. The width is marked *3 - 4,* and the height is *1 - 2.* Then using length *2 - 3* (or *2 - 4*) as a radius, and point *1* as a center, strike arcs, intercepting the horizontal line *3 - 4* at points *A* and *B*. These are the correct positions for the nails. It may be advantageous to drive a nail temporarily at point *1,* until the length of the string is adjusted.

Space Standards for Poultry Houses

Ques. What is the size of laying house required for 150 laying hens? How many nests are required, and what length of roosts should be provided?

Ans. For the heavier breeds of hens, 4 square feet of floor space per hen is the usual allowance, which is 600 square feet for 150 hens. For the smaller breeds this can be reduced to 2-2/3 square feet per hen, or 400 square feet for 150 hens. In mild climates where the birds have free outside range, these spaces

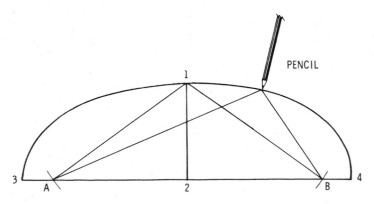

Fig. 9. This is a mathematically correct way to draw an ellipse. This curve is one of the conic sections; it is often used for masonry and plastered arches.

may be reduced. Allow one nest for five to eight hens. For roosts, allow at least 10 inches of roost space per bird, and for the larger breeds allow not less than 15 inches of roost space.

Inches Expressed as Decimals of a Foot

Ques. Is there a table showing decimals of a foot for each inch and fraction that can be used in calculating rafter lengths?

Ans. The following list indicates decimals for calculating rafter lengths:

⅛ in. = .0104 ft.	5 in. = .4167 ft.
¼ in. = .0208 ft.	6 in. = .5000 ft.
½ in. = .0417 ft.	7 in. = .5833 ft.
¾ in. = .0625 ft.	8 in. = .6667 ft.
1 in. = .0833 ft.	9 in. = .7500 ft.
2 in. = .1667 ft.	10 in. = .8888 ft.
3 in. = .2500 ft.	11 in. = .9167 ft.
4 in. = .3333 ft.	12 in. = 1.0000 ft.

Outside Walls vs. Inside Walls for Bathrooms

Ques. A building permit to install a new bathroom in an old house has been refused, because there is no outside wall for a window. The building code requires an outside window for all bathrooms. Why cannot forced ventilation be installed instead?

Ans. That is a mystery. As for window ventilation, no one leaves a window open while taking a bath in winter. Most bathrooms, although they do have a window, remain practically unventilated during the entire winter. Lighting is not a problem; since most of the bathroom use is at other than during daylight hours, adequate artificial lighting is imperative.

An inside bathroom with forced ventilation draws tempered air into the bathroom from heated rooms in the house. Cold drafts from the outside do not occur through an open window, and bathroom odors and steam are not diffused throughout the house, but they are exhausted to the outside air. Since there are no cold outside walls, the inside bathroom is easy to heat, and condensation and dampness are eliminated. Considering all factors, the argument is much in favor of the inside bathroom.

Relieving the Arches in Brickwork

Ques. What is the correct method for laying out the centering for relieving the arches in brickwork?

Ans. This job is often bungled. The common method for laying out the curve is to make the radius equal to the span, which makes

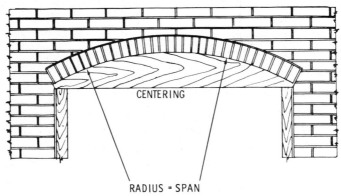

CENTERING

RADIUS = SPAN

Fig. 10. A common design for centering the relieving arches in brick walls.

the height of the arch vary with the length of the span (Fig. 10). The centering should be shored up from below, and wedges should be placed underneath the shores to make removal of the centering material easier. After the arches are laid, the loading on the centering material is greatly reduced.

Slopes for Ramps

Ques. What is the recommended slope for a ramp from the first floor to the second floor in a store building? It is to be used chiefly for foot traffic by customers, but, undoubtedly, heavy and bulky merchandise will be moved up and down the ramp.

Ans. The slope of a ramp is sometimes governed by the space which is available, since it takes up much more room than is occupied by stairways. In the larger cities, the maximum slope for a ramp is usually fixed by the code (Fig. 11). If they are to be used as fire exits, which is common, all the usual requirements of fire safety for stairways apply.

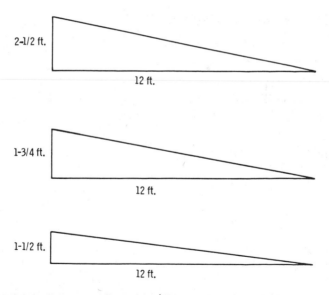

Fig. 11. Slopes of ramps. A slope of 2-1/2 ft. in 12 ft. is nearly the steepest slope that is practical for use by lift trucks with rubber tires. Building codes usually specify a slope of approximately 1-1/2 ft. in 12 ft.

If the ramps are to be used by rubber-tired lift trucks, the usable limit to the slope of a ramp is approximately 2-1/2 in. per foot; however, the maximum slope preferably is not more than 1-3/4 in. per foot, and 1-1/2-inch rise per foot is even better. If the ramp is to be used for heavy foot traffic, the maximum slope recommended is 1-1/2 in. per foot, and some codes require a maximum slope of 1 inch in 10 inches, or 1.2 in. per foot.

Outside ramps have long been in use in factories and mills; in general they are a problem, and even dangerous, when they are wet or icy. Inside ramps, with a slope of not more than 1-1/2 in. per foot, should have some type of nonskid surface; this is mandatory under some codes.

Miter Cuts for the Regular Polygons

Ques. What are the steel-square cuts that can be used for the corners of the regular polygons?

Ans. The following steel-square cuts can be used for mitering the corners of the regular polygons (3 to 10 sides) accurately to the nearest 1/32 inch. Cut on the last figure:

equilateral triangle (3 sides)	12 × 20-25/32
square (4 sides)	12 × 12
pentagon (5 sides)	12 × 8-25/32
hexagon (6 sides)	12 × 6-15/16
heptagon (7 sides)	12 × 5-25/32
octagon (8 sides)	12 × 4-31/32
nonagon (9 sides)	12 × 4-3/8
decagon (10 sides)	12 × 3-7/8

The lengths of the sides of a regular polygon must be identical for accuracy.

Layout of Flat Curves

Ques. Difficulty in making a layout for the curves in the top chords of bowstring trusses has been experienced. Several of these trusses, mostly for pole buildings, have been made; they are often built on a floor where enough space to strike a radius is lacking. Is there any way to avoid this difficulty?

Ans. A recommended method for laying out flat curves under the described conditions is shown in Fig. 12. Lay out the lower chord line *AB;* erect the center line *CD* and the line *AE* of indefinite length, but accurately perpendicular to line *AB*. Stretch a line from point *B* through point *C* until it intercepts line *AE*. Then divide both lines *AE* and *AD* into the same number of equal parts (any convenient number). Construct lines at right angles upward from the division points on line *AB*. Then draw the lines from point *B* to the division points on line *AE*. The points where these lines intercept the vertical lines are the points on the curve.

There are other ways of making this layout without taking up too much space, but the above method is easiest. Calculations are not

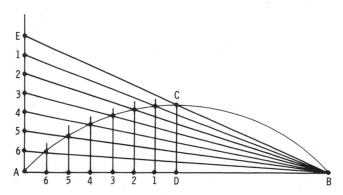

Fig. 12. This sketch illustrates a method for layout of circular arcs in an area lacking space for striking a radius.

necessary, and a chalkline and a 6-ft. rule are the only equipment needed. For accuracy in these layouts, a fishing line has been found to be better than a standard heavy chalkline.

Calculating the Radius of a Circular Arc

Ques. How can the radius of a circular arc be determined, if the height and the length of the chord are given?

Ans. A recommended method, using the geometric relations of similar triangles (Fig. 13), is as follows: A triangle inscribed in

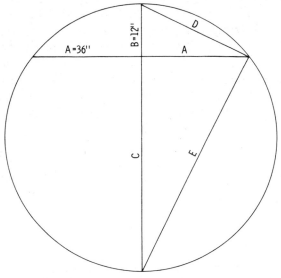

Fig. 13. Illustrating a method for determining the radius of a circular arc.

a semicircle is a right triangle. If the triangle $(C + B)DE$ is a right triangle, triangle DAB is similar, and:

$$\frac{B}{A} = \frac{A}{C} \text{ ; or C} = \frac{A^2}{B}$$

substituting and solving;

$$\frac{36^2}{12} = 108 \text{ inches}$$

Then the diameter $C + B = 108 + 12 = 120$ inches, and the radius of the curve is 120/2, or 60 inches.

Another solution that can be used is:

$$\text{radius} = \frac{4B^2 + (2A)^2}{8B} = \frac{576 + 5184}{96} = 60 \text{ inches}$$

Steel-Square Cuts and Angles in Degrees

Ques. Is there any method that can be used to measure an angle, such as the pitch of a roof, in degrees, by using the steel square?

Ans. It cannot be done directly. Steel-square cuts are triangular measure, and angles in degrees are circular measure. The illustration shows how they are related (Fig. 14). Only one of the whole-inch steel square cuts is in whole degrees. This is 12 $\times$ 12, which is 45 degrees, or 1/8 of a circle.

Rafters are generally measured with 12 inches representing a horizontal run, or the base of a triangle. By applying the principles of similar triangles, the cuts of rafters, lengths of rafters, and other lines and angles in a roof may be determined by using the steel square. Rafters can be framed, in degrees, by using a pro-tractor to lay out the angles and by using a table of trigonometric functions to determine the lengths. Although the uses of the steel

41

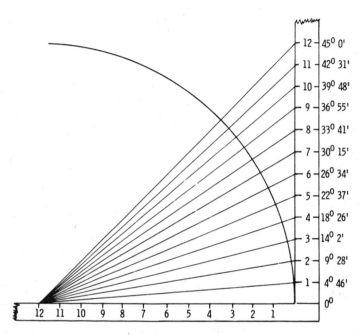

12	45° 0'	
11	42° 31'	
10	39° 48'	
9	36° 55'	
8	33° 41'	
7	30° 15'	
6	26° 34'	
5	22° 37'	
4	18° 26'	
3	14° 2'	
2	9° 28'	
1	4° 46'	
	0°	

Fig. 14. Showing the relation between steel-square cuts and angles that are measured in degrees.

square have definite limitations, it is the simplest and most generally understood instrument for rafter framing.

Plywood-Web Arch Ribs

Ques. The design and construction principles of plywood-web box and I-beam sections are reasonably well understood. Many of them have been constructed for local builders, but is it practical to build curved-arch ribs in the same way, nail-gluing narrow laminations for the flanges?

Ans. That is a practical idea, and it has been done, but it must be determined whether the cost is worthwhile. They are probably rather expensive. If one is unfamiliar with the design of arch ribs, professional help for the designs probably should be obtained, at least until the problems involved become familiar. The easiest design is for a three-hinged arch; a tentative sketch of this type of arch rib which has been used for spans as long as 40 feet is shown in Fig. 15. The rib is recommended for a three-hinged arched roof; it is built up with a plywood web and glue-laminated flanges. This type of arch rib needs sidewise stiffening, which can be done by means of plywood gussets at the purlins.

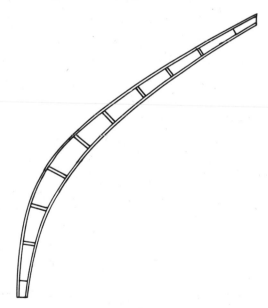

Fig. 15. A rib that is recommended for a three-hinged arched roof; this type of rib is built up with a plywood web and glue-laminated flanges.

Space Requirements for Spectator Seating

Ques. What are the space requirements per person for seats in bleachers and grandstands for baseball parks, race tracks, reviewing stands, outdoor theaters, and basketball gymnasiums?

Ans. Grandstand seats are usually a sturdy type of individual seat, or chair, because this type of seating is frequently reserved. Their back-to-back spacing is approximately 30 inches minimum, and the seat width may vary from 18 to 20 inches, depending on the length of the rows. The average occupied space is approximately 4 sq. ft. per seat, not including the aisles. The number of seats in a row is governed by law in most states. The state of Indiana allows only 20 seats per row, but some states allow as

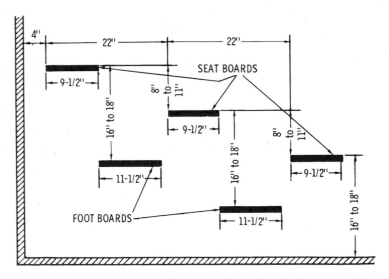

Fig. 16. Recommended spacing of bleacher seats for high-school basketball gymnasiums. With the 16-in. seat widths, the dimensions allow only 2.44 sq. ft. per seat, which is barely adequate for normal adults.

many as 40 seats per row. The aisles or spaces between the ends of the rows are approximately 3-1/2 feet wide. The stepping may be a convenient dimension, with a maximum width of 30 inches and a rise ranging from 8-1/2 to 11-1/2 inches.

Bleacher seating for high-school basketball gymnasiums is usually a factory-built movable type, which allows more efficient use of the space. When the seats are folded back, space for two basketball courts is available for routine physical education classes, and with the seats extended, a standard basketball floor with spectator seating is provided for competitive games. The number of spectator seats available is usually based on the number of pupils in the school. The average demand for high-school basketball games is approximately 2-1/2 seats per student; or, for important games, it is approximately 3 seats per student—the highest demand of record being approximately 5-1/2 seats per student. The needs of a community may demand that the room be made available for banquets, concerts, shows, and public meetings of all types. Removable, loose, folding chairs are used in these instances. If a stage is provided, a rolling partition is usually placed across its front.

For high-school gymnasium bleacher seating, the spacing of the seatboards is usually 22 in., and the seats are marked in 16-in. widths (Fig. 16). This provides only 2.44 sq. ft. per seat, which seems small, and in fact, it *is* small, but hundreds of these installations are used satisfactorily. The 16-in. seat width is hardly adequate for the average adult, but since this type of seating is rarely reserved and since the seatboards are continuous, the matter usually adjusts itself satisfactorily.

The live-load allowance that is used in grandstand and bleacher designs is often specified at 100 lbs. per horizontal sq. ft.; the safety factor is usually about 4. The risers in factory-built bleacher seats are usually enclosed, to prevent a stray basketball from falling through the bleachers. The space beneath the seats *must* be made accessible for cleaning, since an accumulation of popcorn bags, peanut shells, and similar materials, is a serious fire hazard; probably no fire is more dangerous than a fire that has begun in a bleacher or grandstand.

Correct Position for Columns

Ques. In a recently built porch, the columns were set so that the column capitals did not project out beyond the face of the

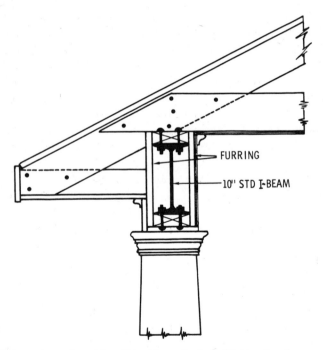

Fig. 17. A porch cornice with a 10-in. I-beam in the soffit, showing the proper position of a column. The column design is known as the Tuscan Order.

FURRING

10' STD I-BEAM

soffit above. Is this architecturally incorrect? What is the correct position of the columns relative to the soffit above?

Ans. According to accepted ideas of good architecture, the columns were not set correctly. The classic "orders" were established centuries ago by the Greeks and Romans, and these have never been improved on; or, at least, the appearance of the classic orders has become so familiar to everyone that they are established as correct.

In the classic orders, the diameter of the neck of the column is identical to the width of the soffit above; the column is set so that its center line coincides with the center point of the soffit, and the moldings of the capital project at the front and rear. For good appearance, the column should set so that its center line coincides with the center point of the soffit above, even when there is necessarily a difference in the column diameter and the width of the soffit (Fig. 17).

Correct Rafter Measurements

Ques. Several different methods for layout of rafters have been tried, but poor joints invariably result, especially on short runs. Perhaps, the measuring is being done incorrectly. On what line should the measurement be made?

Ans. The measuremnet is probably being taken along the line indicated in Fig. 18A. This results in rafters which are too long, and the joint at the ridge is open at the top; this is especially noticeable on short rafters.

Some carpenters prefer to mark, or scribe, a "measuring line" on the pattern rafter, as shown in Fig. 18B; this is an excellent practice, although it is not always entirely necessary. The notch for the plate is, of course, cut to the depth of the measuring line. Most workmen prefer to mark a plumbline on the side of the pattern at the edge of the plate notch, as shown in Fig. 18C, and measure along the back of the rafter. The measurement is the same as when a measuring line is used.

The vertical height of the rafter above the plate is shown as X, in Fig. 18C. If the rafter tails are ripped, the tail of the hip rafter is slightly wider than those of the common rafters, as shown in Fig. 18D.

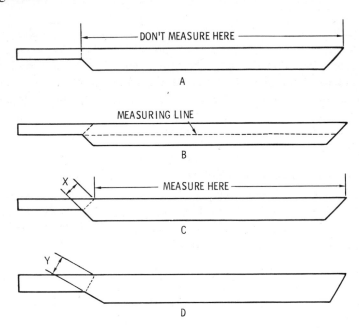

Fig. 18. Illustrating correct methods of taking measurements in the layout of rafters.

Dividing the Areas of Circles

Ques. Several 24-in. wallboard targets are to be made for the local rifle club. How can their areas be divided into equal parts?

Ans. It is likely that the concentric circles are not intended to divide the target into equal areas, but are intended to indicate the distances from a common center (Fig. 19A). For a 24-in. target, the divisions are, probably, a 6-in. bullseye, a 12-in. circle, and an 18-in. circle indicating, respectively, 3, 6, and 9 inches

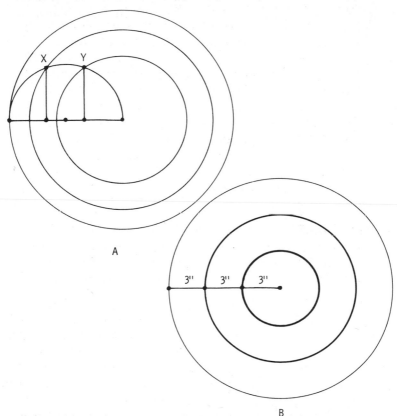

A

3″ 3″ 3″

B

Fig. 19. In sketch "A," the area of the circle is divided into three equal areas; however, in sketch "B," the radius is divided into equal divisions.

from the exact center point in all directions, as indicated in Fig. 19B.

If it is truly desired to divide the target area into equal areas, the job can be done mathematically, using the geometric axiom that the areas of circles are proportional to the squares of their respective radii. The area of the entire target is proportional to $(12)^2$, or 144. If it is desired to divide the circle into three equal areas by means of concentric circles, the radius of the inner circle is equal to the square root of 144/3, or 48, which is 6.9282 inches; the radius of the second circle is equal to the square root of $2 \times 144/3$, or 96, which is 9.789 inches.

This is easily done graphically, as shown in Fig. 19A. First, divide the radius into the number of equal parts desired, and draw a semicircle on the radius. From each division point on the radius, erect perpendiculars extending to the semicircle. The distances from the center point of the circle to the points of intersection, marked X and Y, are the radii of the desired circles which divide the target area into three equal areas.

Effect of Curvature of the Earth on Precise Leveling

Ques. When leveling long lines, for example a drain that is one-half mile in length, should a correction be made for the curvature of the earth, as indicated in the sketch (Fig. 20)?

Ans. As shown in the upper sketch (see Fig. 20) the instrument is not in the correct position; if it is possible, avoid this type of setup. The rear sight should always be the same length as the front sight, as shown in the lower sketch; then it is not necessary to allow for curvature of the earth. When it is necessary to allow for earth curvature, the allowance is approximately $2/3d^2$, in which d is equal to the length of the line of sight, in miles, and the result is in feet. For a rule of thumb, it is approximately 3 inches per one-half mile.

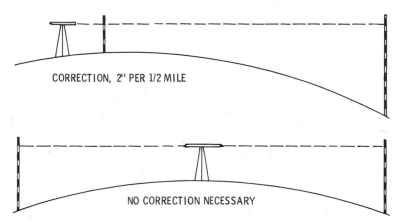

CORRECTION, 2″ PER 1/2 MILE

NO CORRECTION NECESSARY

Fig. 20. These illustrations show why a correction (top) allowing for the curvature of the earth may be necessary in leveling long lines, and showing how it is possible to avoid making the correction for earth curvature (bottom) by properly positioning the leveling instrument.

In reality, earth curvature is not the only problem encountered in leveling long lines. Refraction or bending of the line of sight is often more serious. This is slightly dependent on the temperature, and, in some instances, it may reach a maximum of 1/10 ft. in a 200-ft. line. Refraction bends the sight line *downward,* and the amount of the bending changes rapidly with temperature changes. The heat waves which are so troublesome in extremely hot weather indicate rapidly changing refraction. This need not be considered if the rear sight and front sight lines are approximately the same length; precise leveling is preferably done on cloudy days.

Steel Square as a Calculating Device

Ques. Is it possible to use a steel square to determine the circumference of a sheet-metal pipe, the diameter being known? Can you tell me how this is done?

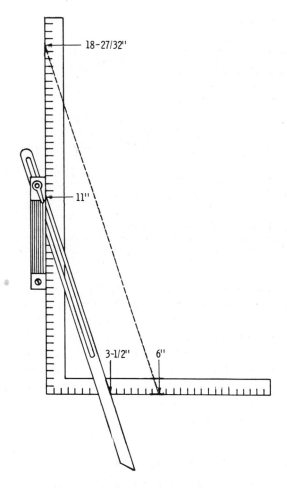

18–27/32"

11"

3-1/2"   6"

Fig. 21. Illustrating a method by which a steel square and a long-bladed adjustable T-bevel may be used to solve simple problems of proportion. The method can be used as a substitute for a slide rule, in this instance.

Ans. A method of solving this problem by a simple application of a steel square is not known, but it can be done, and quite accurately, by means of a steel square and a long-bladed adjustable T-bevel (Fig. 21). First set the bevel to read "3-1/2" on the tongue and to read "11" on the blade. Then, by moving the bevel to the known diameter on the tongue, the circumference of the pipe may be read directly at the point where the bevel intersects the scale on the blade. For example, if the diameter is 6 in., the circumference is found to be, to the nearest 1/32 in., approximately 18-27/32 in. This is accurate enough for most practical work, in fact, within 0.007 in. This is actually using the steel square as a substitute for a slide rule; other simple proportions may be solved in the same manner.

CHAPTER 2

Foundations

Concrete Blocks for Foundation Walls

Ques. It is worthwhile to anchor the sills of a house to only a concrete-block foundation?

Ans. This is a moot question if the foundation walls are constructed of common 8" hollow blocks (Fig. 1). In some instances, builders have used lightweight blocks. In many instances, the rel-

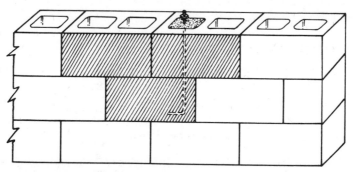

Fig. 1. Anchor bolts may be set in hollow-block foundation walls. Only the three shaded blocks provide an appreciable resistance to uplift, and lateral resistance is almost negligible.

atively recent hurricanes in the East and Southeast have demonstrated that walls constructed of 8″ blocks lack the necessary stability to resist windstorm damage appreciably, but 12″ concrete-block walls, with the cores filled with concrete as the walls were laid, proved satisfactory in some instances. However, all codes that permit 8″ hollow-block foundations require anchor bolts. The *F.H.A.* regulations require 1/2″ bolts with 2″ washers, embedded 15″, and fully grouted in; maximum spacing is 8′0″, with not less than two bolts per piece of sill, placed not more than 12″ from the ends. In regions where earthquakes are prevalent, bolt spacing should be not more than 6 feet.

It is difficult to understand the reasoning behind these specifications. In effect, the specifications permit bolts with a tensile strength of approximately 2250 pounds to be embedded in a wall having an uplift resistance of approximately 150 pounds; or equivalent to the weight of approximately three blocks; the lateral, or sidewise, resistance is so small that a bolt may be kicked sidewise accidentally with a workman's foot. It seems that the above specifications are lacking in windstorm resistance. Many cities with realistic codes do not permit the use of 8″ hollow concrete blocks for foundations.

An Eccentric Chimney Footing

Ques. A chimney approximately 18 feet in height is to be built. It is shaped approximately as shown in the sketch (Fig. 2). The base of the chimney is to be approximately 48″ × 48″. A concrete terrace is already located where the flue is to be built. Can a footing be laid directly on the old slab?

Ans. From the sketch (see Fig. 2), it appears that approximately 70 cu. ft. of masonry is required, which weighs 4 to 5 tons. Almost any type of soil, except black loam soil, can safely bear a weight

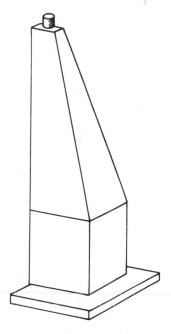

Fig. 2. The center point of the loading on the footing for this chimney is not located in the center of the slab—and it cannot be so designed. There is little advantage to be gained by increasing the size of the footing, unless it is heavily reinforced. If the bearing soil is good, the chimney should not require footing.

of 1 ton per square foot. Since the base of the flue is approximately 4 ft. sq., a larger footing is unnecessary, even though the loading on the footing is to be slightly eccentric. However, the footing should not be set on the old slab, because of the unknown material in the area directly beneath it. It is better practice to break up a 4-sq. ft. area of the old slab, remove the topsoil, or fill, if any, and examine the base. Although frost heaving is not necessarily a problem (in Alabama), it is better practice to lower the footing slightly. In the northern states, the footing should be placed below the frost line. If the chimney is to be placed against a house or a building, settlement should be considered; probably, the building has completely settled, but some settlement of the chimney is almost certain. The chimney should be tied to the building in a manner that allows for future settlement. A narrow steel band placed around the chimney should be sufficient. If a corbel for a thimble that extends through the building wall is placed tightly over a strong header, the masonry may be cracked as settlement occurs.

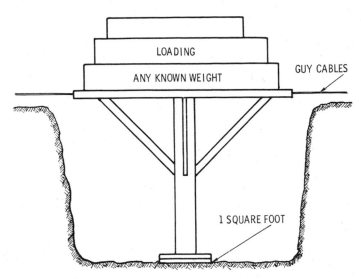

LOADING

ANY KNOWN WEIGHT

GUY CABLES

1 SQUARE FOOT

Fig. 3. A practical test for the load-carrying capacity of soils. This is one of the most severe tests, and the results are usually on the conservative side. A nail is placed in the center of the platform for the leveling rod, and the loading is piled around it.

Test for Load-Bearing Capacity of a Soil

Ques. When uncertain as to the bearing qualities of a soil, how can this be determined for designing a building? How are the soil tests made?

Ans. Excavate as far as the depth of the footings; then cut a strong timber or log for erecting a column of sufficient height to extend from the bottom of the hole to slightly above ground level (Fig. 3). For the base of the column, construct a $12'' \times 12''$ pad made of crossed planks, and erect the column in the hole. At the top of the column, construct a strong and well-braced platform (at least 4-feet square), bracing or guying it to hold the column vertically in the excavation, but allowing the column to sink without restraint. Load the platform with brick, pig iron, bagged cement, or a known weight, leaving an opening in the center of the pile for a nail for the leveling rod. Load the column at the rate of 2 tons per hour, taking level readings for each one-half ton of loading material. There should be no stoppage of the loading for eating lunch or other purpose, or a slight recovery occurs. When the post begins to sink rapidly—out of proportion to the loading—the yield point has been reached, and the safe-loading weight is one-half the loading weight at that point. The exact distance of settlement at the safe-loading point should be noted, and the fact that the soil may be subject to alternate wetting and drying may be significant. The test platform may be left in position for some time, if desired.

Never Place a Back-Fill in Water

Ques. In a house with a basement, the foundation walls were constructed of concrete blocks. Considerable back-filling was necessary, and after the house was set on the foundation, the fill was begun, permitting a 3/4-inch stream of water to run for several hours in order to settle the fill. The next morning, one wall was broken up at the mortar joints. At the point where the bulldozer ran, a slab floor must be laid for a garage. If water cannot be used to settle the fill, is it advisable to build the garage floor on the fill? How can the broken-up wall be saved?

Ans. The wall is lost and nothing can be done, except to needle and shore the house; the wall should be taken down and relaid. Securely held at both top and bottom, concrete-block basement walls usually, but not always, provide satisfactory service, but this is impossible with a broken-up wall.

Fluid pressure has been placed on the wall, approximating 120 to 140 pounds per cubic foot. Clear water exerts only one-half as much pressure. *Never* place an earth fill in water. At best, watering is not an efficient method of providing settlement for a fill.

A slab floor cannot be built safely on a 4- to 6-ft. earth fill for several months. If an attempt is made to pack the fill with a bulldozer, the wall may be pushed in again. However, if the job must be attempted, use clean gravel, tamping it in 6-in. layers. Even this may not pack the fill sufficiently, and care must be taken not to damage the wall. One of the small vibrating-pad types of tamping machines may be used for the job.

Settlement of New Foundations

Ques. How should the foundations and footings of masonry additions that are added to existing masonry buildings be designed to prevent the cracks which invariably appear between the old and the new work? This is especially exasperating when new brick veneer is joined to the old brick veneer.

Ans. This depends largely on the compressibility of the soils underneath the footings. Practically all types of soils compress to some extent beneath the footings when the weight of the entire structure is placed on them. This may be either a large or a small settlement. It is the duty of the designer to make certain that the footings are proportioned properly, to provide uniform stresses and uniform settlement. The settlement may continue for an indefinite period, possibly for years.

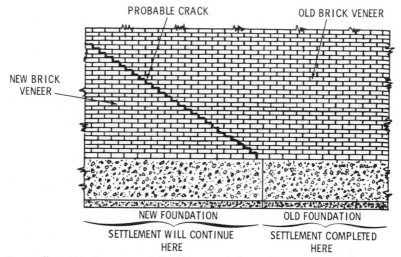

Fig. 4. Illustrating the cause of breaking up of the walls in veneered brickwork, when an extension of new foundations is added to an existing structure.

In the older structure, settlement may have been completed, or nearly so. In the new addition, the settlement has not occurred. If the bearing soil is dry clay, hardpan, or a good grade of sand or gravel, the initial settlement may be very small; therefore, the new structure may be joined rigidly to the old structure. Unless the soil is a nearly incompressible type of bearing soil, this should not be attempted. Allowance for the settlement in the new masonry should be provided by leaving a vertical joint between the masonry of the two structures; this joint can be filled with an elastic joint compound. This is the only safe method for preventing breaking up of the masonry at the junction of the two structures (Fig. 4).

Allowable Loads on Soils Beneath Foundations

Ques. Without making actual tests, how much pressure is usually permitted on the soils beneath foundations and footings?

Ans. The allowable pressure on soils of different types are given in the codes of most of the larger cities; they vary slightly, but the following pressures are approximately average:

medium-soft clay................................1-1/2 tons per square foot
medium-stiff clay..............................2-1/2 tons per square foot
fine, loose sand..2 tons per square foot
loose gravel or compact coarse sand........4 tons per square foot
compact sand-gravel mixture...................6 tons per square foot
hardpan ....10 tons per square foot
sound hard shales, or sandstones...........15 tons per square foot
sound schist, or slate ....40 tons per square foot
sound massive bed rock ....100 tons per square foot

In all instances, the widths of footings should be adjusted so that the loadings are distributed uniformly, to assure uniform settlement.

Let an Expert do the Blasting

Ques. A 10-in. concrete wall located on one side of an old barn is to be removed. The barn is empty and clean, and it can easily be protected from fire. Can small charges of dynamite be used to break up the wall? This can save much labor.

Ans. This can, and has, been done. Anyone who is experienced in handling high explosives can do the job, but anyone who is *not experienced* should talk to an explosives dealer and ask him to recommend an expert. It is true that dynamite is one of the "safest" explosives, but in a ticklish place, this is no "do-it-yourself" job for a novice.

The job can be done in this manner. Dig a trench along the inside of the wall, extending downward to the bottom but not underneath the wall. Set small charges (one-half stick of low-nitro) tightly against the wall (and we do mean *tightly*) at points where they can do the most good, probably 8 to 10 ft. apart, on the outside. If the soil is tight and the holes are stemmed well, the charges may not blow out; if the soil is gravelly, some type of mat should be used. A flattened-out roll of used wire fencing that a tractor has run over may make a good mat. Light charges of dynamite are not extremely noisy; they may not be heard in the next block. Do not try to shatter the wall, but attempt to merely break it up so that the pieces can be handled with a tractor. The charges should be exploded one at a time, so that all the props are not blown from the building at one time. In one instance, this type of job was performed on the second lot from a school, while the school was in session, and officials and students were not aware of the operation until the job was completed.

CHAPTER 3

Framing

Air-Dried vs. Kiln-Dried Lumber

Ques. Is it true that air-dried lumber is more satisfactory than kiln-dried lumber for building purposes?

Ans. If both the air-drying and the kiln-drying operations are done properly, there is no difference in the utility of the lumber. Kiln-drying, however, is faster, and if it is not done properly, may cause serious warping and checking. If it is done correctly, kiln-dried lumber is much cleaner and brighter than air-dried lumber, and for trim that is to have a natural finish, it is preferred. It is free from the "blue sap" and "sap stain" that are so common in air-dried stock. These discolorations do not actually impair the utility of the lumber, but they are unsightly. Discoloration is actually caused by decay-producing organisms that require moisture to live and grow, but their growth is arrested by the drying operation before they can do serious damage. The kiln-drying operation kills the organisms before they can begin to multiply.

Necessity for Bridging of Joists

Ques. Is it necessary to bridge between the floor joists? What function does the bridging perform?

Ans. The necessity for bridging the floor joists is questionable. Some testing has been done, and it has been found that the effect of bridging is negligible when the joists carry a double floor. When a floor is placed above the joists and a ceiling is placed below the joists, it is probable that bridging is not beneficial. It is believed that bridging the joists is a relatively "modern" innovation. The joists in many of the old houses were not bridged, but in the old houses, the joists were relatively heavy and they were spaced wider. Regardless of the origin, the American builder has adopted the practice and no one has taken time to investigate the matter for approximately the last hundred years. It is certain that bridging is not detrimental.

Lumber from Dead Trees

Ques. Is it true that lumber which has been sawed from fire-killed trees is particularly susceptible to dry-rot?

Ans. Lumber from fire-killed trees is not inferior. Lumber is sawed from the dead wood for the most part. Only the sapwood of the tree is composed of living cells, and the sapwood is the least desirable part of the log. It is quite common for specifications to call for "lumber cut from living trees," but lumber cut from dead trees, unless the trees have been standing so long that decay has begun, is indistinguishable from lumber cut from living trees. Strictly speaking, there is no such thing as "dry rot" in wood. Rot, or decay, of wood is the work of certain low-order, but living, organisms called fungi. All fungi require the presence of water, and plenty of it, for living, multiplying, and eventually destroying the wood structure.

The Queen-Post Truss

Ques. A type of truss with a form, as shown in the sketch (Fig. 1A), was proposed for a job because of the large unobstructed area

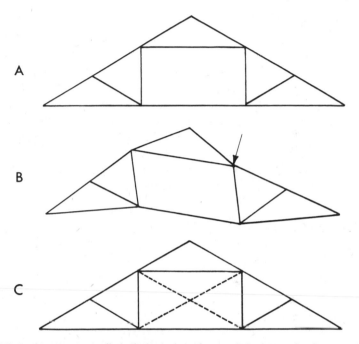

(A) As this truss is usually built, both the rafters and the lower chord are necessarily continuous through the joints.
(B) Showing how bending stresses are developed in the rafters and lower chord when placed under a loading that is applied on only one side.
(C) The dotted lines show the positions of "counters" that are designed to prevent bending stresses in the rafters and the chord when they are placed under unsymmetrical loadings.

Fif. 1. The Queen-post truss. In its usual form, this truss is not well adapted to modern light-duty wood framing.

in the attic. They are often used, but the building inspector does not approve trusses of this type. Why?

Ans. The inspector is correct. This is not truly a truss, or rather, it is an incomplete type of truss. Formerly, it was often used for framing. The truss has been referred to as the "Queen-rod," the "King-and-Queen," or the "Queen-post" truss. It is statically determinate. Stresses in the various members can be calculated by common statics, but under nonuniform loadings, the truss is unstable. In the second sketch (see Fig. 1B), none of the members is distorted, but the joints permit some rotation, and bending stresses are developed if the top and bottom chord members are continuous through the joints—or if the joints are rigid. To achieve stability, the crossed members, as indicated by the dotted lines in the third sketch (see Fig. 1C), are necessary. In bridge trusses of this type, the additional members are called "counters," and they usually consist of threaded rods.

Framing Unequal-Length Hip and Valley Rafters

Ques. For framing a hip or valley between roofs that have different pitches, is there a method that can be used to lay out these rafters—other than the time-consuming method in which it is necessary to cut, try, measure, trim, and shim each rafter as the framing progresses.

Since the tables on the framing squares are based on the assumption that the pitches of both sides of the hips are identical, they cannot be used to determine the length of jack rafters, side cuts, etc. for shed roofs or porch roofs that are continuous around corners—because the runs of the rafters and, consequently, the pitches of the roofs are different.

Ans. It is true that the framing of a hip or valley between roofs that have different pitches is a chore and that framing squares are of little value for this purpose. The most practical method is to use either a protractor or one of the framing devices that measure angles in degrees; this method requires a knowledge of trigonometry, and is only slightly less time consuming than the measure, cut, and try method.

The most difficult part of the entire job is to make the projecting cornices meet properly. For example, if the pitch of the roof on one side of the hip is 4 × 12 and the pitch on the opposite side of the hip is 5 × 12 (rise of one roof is 1 in. per foot more than the other roof), with eaves that are 24 inches wide, the rafter tails will be 2 inches out of alignment, when the rafters are set on a plate which is level around the corner. Then, if the plate is raised on the steeper side to align the rafters, the 5 × 12 pitch is no longer maintained; therefore, the cuts are incorrect.

Measure the rafters from the back of the fascia, as indicated in the drawing (Fig. 2). If a 4-1/2 × 12 pitch is obtained on one side of the hip and a 4 × 12 pitch is obtained on the other side, raise the plate on the steeper side a distance of 1 inch; then the vertical depths of the seat cuts are identical on both sets of rafters. If the difference in the two pitches is slight, the depths of the seat

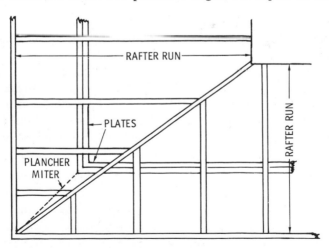

Fig. 2. A hip between roofs having unequal pitches. Note how the rafter runs are measured from the inside edge of the fascia, and that the hip rafter does not cross the plates precisely at the corner.

notches can be changed slightly to overcome the difference in pitches.

In this method, the hip rafter does not cross at a point directly above the corner of the plate, and is set off toward the side with the steeper pitch. If the cornice is open, the job is unsightly, but this cannot be avoided. If the plancher is closed and level, a short length of framing can be nailed for the mitered ends of the plancher finish—whether it is beaded ceiling, plywood, or hardboard.

Additional problems involve the difference in length of jack rafters on the two sides of the hip and the difference in side cuts. However, if one pair of jacks is fitted and measured, the correct figures can be determined.

If the peculiarities of hip framing are fixed firmly in the mind, the job is not likely to be bungled. After one roof has been framed satisfactorily, it is much easier to frame the succeeding roof jobs.

Trussed Roof for Chicken House

Ques. In building a 22 ft. $\times$ 44 ft. chicken house, can the trussed rafters (Fig. 3) be used satisfactorily?

Ans. The trusses may be used satisfactorily. The stress diagrams for the trusses (Fig. 3) show the stresses in the several members under a design loading of 40 lbs. per sq. ft., which should be adequate for most of the Midwest. The trusses can be held by means of well-nailed joints, without connectors.

Installing New Lap Siding Over the Old Siding

Ques. How should new lap siding be applied over the old siding, other than by nailing a filler strip on the underside of the laps? Should building paper be placed beneath the new siding?

Ans. Attempting to place new lap siding over the old siding does not often result in a satisfactory job, regardless of the method. It

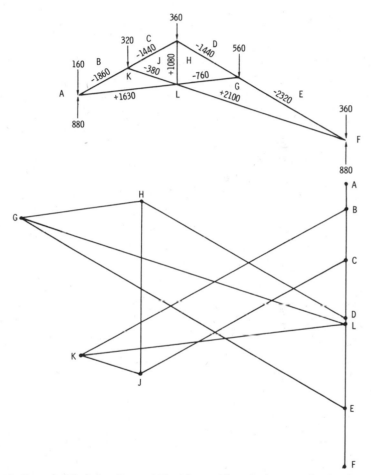

Fig. 3. Trussed-roof design for a chicken house. The scissors-type of trussed roof (top) is designed for a 22-ft. span, set on 24-in. centers. Stresses are calculated at 40 lb. per sq. ft., design loading. Members marked with negative sign (−) are under compression; those marked with positive sign (+) are under tension. Bow's notation is used to designate stresses on the standard stress diagram (lower) for the entire truss design.

is necessary to "furr out" the casings, corner strips, and even the window sills in most instances. When placing new lap siding over old tongue-and-grooved siding (with casings set over the siding), this can be done very easily and often the casings need not be changed. When placing new lap siding over old lap siding, vertical furring strips are usually placed over the studding. Tarred felt may be placed beneath the new siding to insure against leaks.

Collar Joists for Roof Support

Ques. The proposed construction for the roof of a narrow factory building that is to be built is shown in the sketch in Fig. 4A. The carpenter, however, thinks that 2″ × 6″ collar joists can be placed one-half the distance upward on the rafters to dispense with both the joists at the plate line and the columns (Fig. 4B). Is this practical? If necessary, can the joists and columns be installed later; or can the roof be trussed adequately at a later date?

Ans. The use of collar joists placed one-half the distance upward on the rafters is never recommended if they are the sole means of keeping the roof from spreading, especially for the flatter types of roofs. In due time, the weight of the roof invariably causes sagging which pushes the walls outward. The joist-and-column construction that is proposed is recommended; and if the posts are undesirable, the roof can be trussed. A type of truss that may be used is shown in Fig. 4C.

Do not be too optimistic about attempting to truss the roof if the carpenter's idea is proved inadequate. The roof is almost certain to settle unevenly and at a quick rate; a roof that has settled unevenly is extremely difficult to straighten. This sometimes may be done, but it is often impossible. Timbers which have settled and seasoned unevenly often break before they can be straightened. Since the sketch is not dimensioned, calculations cannot be made.

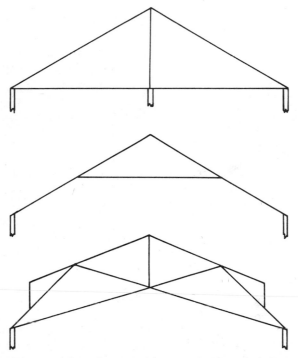

Fig. 4. Alternative designs for the roof of a factory building. Both the original design (top) and the recommended truss design (bottom) are satisfactory, but the carpenter's proposal (center) is not considered to be good construction.

Construction for Wind Resistance

Ques. Is the roof design (see sketch in Fig. 5) suitable for a trussed-rafter roof above an 18-ft. living room in a region that is subject to high winds?

Ans. The design is entirely adequate and should prove to be completely satisfactory for wind-uplift resistance. In addition, do not forget to anchor the walls adequately to a solid foundation.

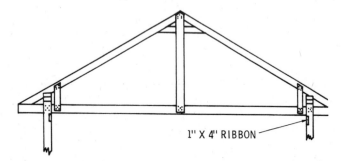

1" X 4" RIBBON

Fig. 5. A roof designed to resist wind uplift. This is an excellent type of construction.

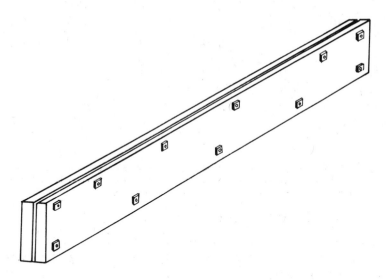

Fig. 6. A flitch-plate beam, constructed by bolting a 1/2" steel plate between two 2" × 12" planks. In strength, this beam nearly equals a 10" × 4" × 17# light-weight I-beam, but the weight of the steel plate alone in the flitch-plate girder is approximately 19.55 lb. per foot. The flitch-plate girder is not economical because of the weight of the steel plate.

Flitch-Plate Girders

Ques. Is it practical to build a beam by bolting a steel plate between two planks (Fig. 6)?

Ans. These beams, usually called flitch-plate beams, are not in common use at present, because they are inefficient and are usually more expensive than steel I-beams of comparable strength and stiffness. An axiom exists among structural engineers: "When forces may travel more than one path to reach points of support, they are divided among the paths in direct proportion to their relative rigidities."

In the flitch-plate girder, two dissimilar paths exist; the forces may travel either the wooden path with low rigidity or the path of extremely rigid steel. When these beams are loaded, the wooden portions bend readily, supporting only a small portion of the loading, and the greater portion is supported by the more rigid steel. The two materials cannot work together, and, in some instances, the wooden members are supporting practically no load. It is only after the steel portion has been overstressed and begins to fail that the wooden members begin to bear a portion of the load.

Weathered Redwood Siding

Ques. A house was built about six months ago; it was intended that the siding should be permitted to weather naturally, with no paint or any other type of finish. Redwood siding was used because it is supposed to be resistant to rot. However, the siding is checking slightly and the grain is rising, especially on the south side of the house. How can this be prevented? Will the checks and raised grain cause the siding to decay?

Ans. If it is intended to let the siding weather naturally, redwood is one of the best timbers that can be used, but weathering causes all timbers to check, and some warping and cupping are inevitable. Edge-grained boards are recommended, with a thickness not less than approximately one-eighth the width of the boards. If the siding has no pockets which retain moisture, lumber without great natural resistance to decay, such as yellow poplar and white pine, lasts almost indefinitely. Lumber weathers very slowly, losing probably no more than 1/4-inch thickness in an entire century.

Some woods attain a very attractive silvery sheen during weathering action, but, unfortunately, redwood is not one of them. It usually attains a rather unattractive mottled appearance first, but gradually attains a more uniform dark gray color. Uncoated iron and steel nails should not be used, because they make unsightly blue stains. For a few years, it may be necessary to drive the nails down occasionally, because cupping and warping of the boards may pull them slightly. Corner strips, window and door casings, and other outside trim are usually painted.

Scissors-Type Trusses Are Often a Problem

Ques. Is the church roof framing shown in the sketch (Fig. 7) recommended? Will trusses of this type, set on 24-in. centers, sag enough to affect the walls?

Ans. A scissors-type truss is not recommended. Probably no other type of roof framing has caused so much serious trouble. Scissors-type trusses sometimes give satisfaction, but they are often unsatisfactory. With the best designs and with good workmanship, the mechanical fastenings in the highly-stressed joints of wooden framing *always* slip slightly, especially as the timbers become dried out; however, there is a place where the fastenings apparently "catch hold" and the movement ceases. This action is typical in joints with nearly all types of fastenings—bolts, ring connectors,

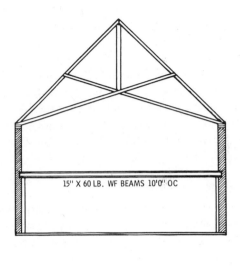

15" X 60 LB. WF BEAMS 10'0" OC

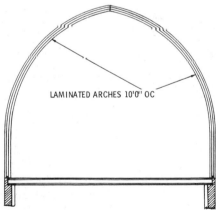

LAMINATED ARCHES 10'0" OC

Fig. 7. Scissors-type trussed roofs are often a problem. A proposed scissors-type trussed roof (top) for a church is shown. Under the conditions illustrated, scissors-type trusses are often unsatisfactory. A more satisfactory arrangement (bottom) uses glued laminated arches which are usually built to order at the factory.

77

and to some extent, nailed joints. This is always a problem when scissors-type trusses are used, and is typical of all trusses with highly cambered lower chords.

The design should be reconsidered. The laminated three-hinged arches, as shown in Fig. 7, are recommended. The masonry should be stopped at the floor level. Placed on 10-ft. centers, the laminated Gothic arches are ideal; the appearance is as good as, or better than the scissors-type, and there is no question of structural integrity.

Holding Power of Blunt Nails

Ques. If the sharp points of finish nails are either nipped off or blunted with a hammer, they do not split bone-dry finish lumber nearly so readily. Does blunting the nails reduce their holding power?

Ans. Blunt-pointed nails do not have the holding power of nails with sharp points. When sharp-pointed nails are driven, the points merely push the fibers of the wood aside without cutting them, and thus the nails are wedged fast; blunt-pointed nails cut the fibers. The nail with the greatest holding power has a long, sharp point, and it has a much greater tendency to split the wood.

The old-fashioned cut iron nail with a rectangular blunt point did not split the wood readily when it was set with the length of the point *across* the grain. The fibers of the wood were cut, and the cut ends were wedged tightly against the two slanting sides. When set with the length of the point placed *with* the grain, the nails were miniature wedges, splitting the wood readily. If the cut nail should be withdrawn only slightly, the ends of the cut fibers lose their solid contact with the flat sides of the wedge-shaped shanks, and the nails withdraw the remainder of the distance quite easily.

Poorly Designed Truss Chord

Ques. In designing a truss chord, the splice in the lower chord is a problem. Is the detail shown in the upper sketch (Fig. 8) satisfactory? The fastenings indicated are 2-1/2-in. ring connectors.

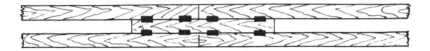

Fig. 8. Truss design. **Unless the splicing scab is at least twice as thick as the combined thickness of the spliced members, this detail should not be used. The fastenings indicated are split-ring connectors (top). If the splicing scabs are the same thickness as that of the outside members, use this detail (bottom).**

Ans. The splice, as sketched, is not satisfactory. These splices should never be used, except when the thickness of the scab, or splicing piece, is at least equal to the combined thicknesses of the pieces that are spliced. If it is necessary to use scabs that are the same thickness as the joined members, the detail shown in the lower sketch (see Fig. 8) is recommended.

A Three-Story Heavy-Timbered Frame

Ques. In building a three-story chicken barn, rough-sawed native timbers are to be used for the frame. How should the joist-bearing girders be framed into the posts? If the posts are made only single-story height, is the pressure too much for side-grained wood. How did the old-time framers fasten these frames together?

Ans. Assuming that mortise-and-tenon framing is to be used, which is practically a lost art, the job can be done, but this type of work requires specialized skills. The tenons and the "relishes" for the mortises were cut with an adze, and sometimes smoothed up and trued with a "slick," which is a 3-in. chisel with a 3-ft. handle. Power boring equipment could probably be rigged up for boring out the mortises.

The sketch (Fig. 9) shows how the girts were framed into the posts by the old-time framers. Note that the weight of the girder, including the imposed joists and floor, was not borne on the side of the tenon alone but was also borne on the edge of the "relish" which was cut into the post approximately 1/2 inch. The pins were usually made from green white oak split from a short block,

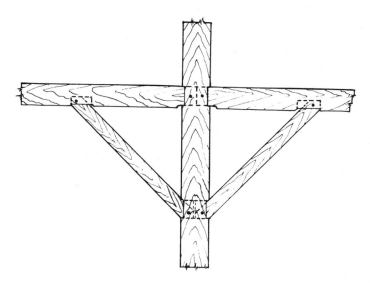

Fig. 9. Demonstrating the method of setting the girders and braces into the posts in the old-time mortised-and-pinned heavy-timber framing.

sharpened, and then chased through a hole in a steel plate by means of a sledge. Most of the pins were 1-in. diameter. The pin holes were bored with approximately 1/8-in. "draw," assuring that the joints would be pulled up tightly. When the sharpened and tough oak pins were sledged through the slightly mismatched holes, they acquired a slight double curve; they could not be removed, except by boring downward to the tenon on both sides. The 3-ft. run, 51-in. length braces were usually 4″ × 4″, or sometimes 3″ × 4″, and they were mortised and pinned at the plates and girts. The braces imparted a stiffness to these frames that has been unattainable by any type of modern framing.

Platform Framing Unsuitable for Brick-Veneered Buildings

Ques. The sills beneath the living room wall of a new brick-veneered home are rising; in some places, the sills are 3/8 inch, or more, above the foundation. What is the cause of this and what can be done about it?

Ans. Apparently, the house has a platform frame, and the joists and other side-grained wood are shrinking. This places the structural loading on the single course of brick on the outside, through the brick ties and the lintels which are fastened to both the wooden frame and the brick wall. The sills should be shimmed tightly to hold them in the raised position; otherwise, a problem may occur around the window and door frames.

The platform type of frame is inexpensive and easy to erect, but it should not be used with brick-veneered or stucco jobs. The studs should run downward beside the joists to the sills; then there is less side-grained, shrinkable wood between the ends of the studs and the foundation wall (see Fig. 10).

The sole plate of the home is undoubtedly well spiked to the joists; otherwise, the floor system would tear loose from the wall

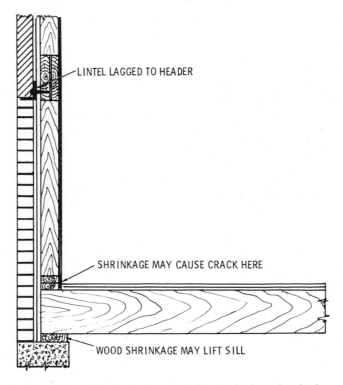

LINTEL LAGGED TO HEADER

SHRINKAGE MAY CAUSE CRACK HERE

WOOD SHRINKAGE MAY LIFT SILL

Fig. 10. Illustrating the effects of shrinkage of framing lumber when brick veneer is used with platform-type framing.

framing at the floor line, permitting the floor to drop and leaving cracks beneath the baseboard. Then it is necessary either to lower the baseboard or to lower the shoe molding to cover the crack. These repairs are commonly required when green or wet framing lumber has been used in a building, and sometimes these repairs may be quite expensive.

Deformed-Shank vs. Plain-Shank Nails

Ques. Some truss framing instructions call for deformed-shank nails. Is there any reason why plain-shank nails are not permitted, if more nails are used?

Ans. There is no valid reason why the same number of plain-shank nails cannot be used, if they are of identical size. Nearly all types of deformed-shank nails possess greater withdrawal resistance than plain-shank nails, but this is of minor importance. Good framing designs do not place nails in withdrawal if it is possible to avoid doing so.

It is slippage, and *not* ultimate strength, that governs the use of nails for fastenings in structural work. Since nailed joints tend to slip and if the nailed joint is to be rigid, only one-tenth to one-sixth of the ultimate strength of the nail can be utilized. Up to at least seven times the allowable working loading, the behavior of the deformed-shank nail and the plain-shank nail is practically identical, when their sizes are the same. Above that point, the deformed-shank nail has the advantage, but the nail usually snaps off suddenly at the point of failure, which is not a desirable characteristic. At lighter loadings, the plain-shanked, unhardened nail begins to bend, and failure is slower. For these and other reasons, the plain-shank nail is fully as acceptable, or more acceptable, than deformed-shank nails in structural nailing where the nails are in shear.

Strength of Notched Joists

Ques. Is the strength of a joist reduced appreciably by notching the ends—for example, notching a $2'' \times 12''$ timber to make a $2'' \times 10''$ timber at the bearing?

Ans. A $2'' \times 12''$ timber reduced to a $2'' \times 10''$ timber by notching at the bearings possesses approximately the same load-carrying capacity as a $2'' \times 10''$ timber, but it is stiffer. Shearing stresses remain at maximum, or equal to the maximum, near the

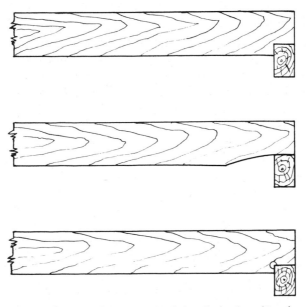

Fig. 11. Illustrating three recommended methods of notching the joists above the girders. The method at the top is the least desirable method.

ends of the joist, and they concentrate at the corner of the notch. The joist tends to split, and the crack begins at the notch. This concentration of stresses may be minimized by making a long, smooth curve, rather than a square notch. Also, it is said that the same results may be obtained by boring a hole at the corner of the notch, but this claim is not substantiated by tests (see Fig. 11). The two recommended methods in the lower portion of the illustration are preferable to the other method of notching the joists.

Trusses too Narrow

Ques. In construction of a 30-ft. building, are the proposed trusses of the design shown in the sketch (Fig. 12), set 2 ft. apart, adequate for support of the flat roof?

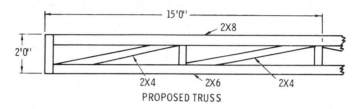

PROPOSED TRUSS

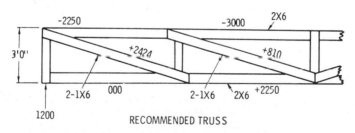

RECOMMENDED TRUSS

Fig. 12. The proposed truss (top) is not deep enough to be practical, since it lacks stiffness. In the recommended design (bottom), the numbers on the various members indicate the forces, in pounds, which are active through those members when they are placed under a uniform roof load of 40 lb. per sq. ft. of roof space, the trusses being set on 24-in. centers.

Ans. The trusses are too narrow for satisfactory stiffness. It is not considered good design if the height of the trusses is less than one-tenth the span—one-sixth the span is better. Since the trusses are not to be heavily loaded, trusses that are 3 ft. (but not 2 ft.) in depth may be used. Make the diagonals from two 1″ × 6″ boards, fastening the joints with three 1/2-in. bolts.

Framing Octagonal Bays

Ques. How can the lengths of the sloping sides of an octagonal bay be determined when the projection is known; or, conversely, how can the length of projection be determined when the lengths of the sloping sides are known? What steel-square miter cuts can be used for the plate and sill?

Ans. To find the length of a sloping side when the length of the projection is known, multiply the projection by 1.414. If the length of a sloping side is known, multiply the side by .707 to find

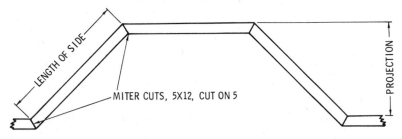

Fig. 13. Plan for an octagonal bay. To find the length of a side, multiply the projection by 1.414. To find the width of the projection, multiply the length of a side by 0.707.

the length of the projection (see Fig. 13). The steel-square cut for the miters is 5 $\times$ 12, cut on 5.

Faulty Structural Steel Connection

Ques. In a recently completed bank building, a situation which the owners consider unsatisfactory has occurred, and they want it corrected. A steel joist-bearing girder is spliced, but the splices are not directly above the columns. The heavier beams at the ends of the run are cantilevered above the columns, and a lighter beam is inserted in the middle span. The splices consist of plates placed on each side of the webs, with six 3/4-inch bolts placed on each side of the splice (see Fig. 14). The lighter beam in the center has dropped downward more than 1/4 inch; apparently, the bolt holes are too large. What can be done to correct the splice satisfactorily?

Ans. It is surprising that a steel-fabricating concern permitted this detail to go to the shop, because the problem described is fairly well known. A lighter beam is often used between two cantilevers, since it permits saving in steel.

It is almost certain that some of the bolts in the splices are overstressed, especially the bolts nearest the ends of the beams. The plates tend to rotate around the centers of gravity of the bolt

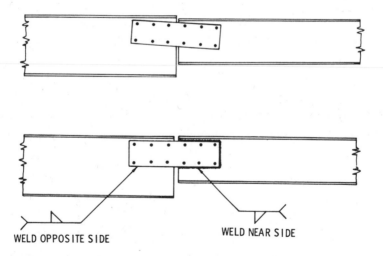

WELD OPPOSITE SIDE   WELD NEAR SIDE

Fig. 14. The upper sketch shows an unsatisfactory splice in a joist-bearing girder. In the lower sketch, measures have been taken to correct the problem. A more satisfactory arrangement is to make the splice plates to a width that fits tightly between the flanges of the lighter beam. Then, welding is unnecessary.

groups; in addition to the direct vertical loading, additional shearing stresses are developed. The beam should be jacked upward to its proper position, slackening the bolts slightly if necessary. Then weld down the edges of one of the plates onto one of the beams, and weld down the edges of the other plate on the opposite side of the beam. Remove the bolts one at a time, and replace them with hardened and fluted Dardelet bolts. Of course, the holes can be reamed and turned bolts used, but 1-inch bolts would be needed. The present holes probably are punched 7/8″ in diameter, which is standard for 3/4″ bolts or rivets.

Roof Joists too Lightweight

Ques. In an uncompleted building that was started by another contractor, the roof joists are found to be 24-ft. long, 2″ × 12″ timbers that are set on 16-in. centers. Are these joists too light in weight to support a plastered ceiling? The roof is to be tar-and-gravel.

Ans. A 2″ × 12″ joist, 1200f grade, 24-ft. span, should safely carry 1194 pounds of distributed load. If the joists are set on 16-in. centers, this is approximately 37 pounds per square foot of roof. The dead loading is approximately:

2″ × 12″ joist, set 16″ centers	3.9 lbs. per sq. ft.
3/4″ wood sheathing	2.2 lbs. per sq. ft.
tar-and-gravel roof cover	6.6 lbs. per sq. ft.
lath-and-plaster ceiling	6.0 lbs. per sq. ft.
total dead loading	18.7 lbs. per sq. ft.

Thus, only (37 − 18.7), or 18.3 lbs. per sq. ft. live load allowance remains, which is not sufficient to meet most codes in the United States. Under *F.H.A.*, the minimum requirement is 20 lbs.

per sq. ft. Also, under the design loading of 37 lbs. per sq. ft., the deflection of the joists would be about 1-1/3 inches; in a short period of time, they would probably develop a noticeable sag. The joists should have been set on 12" centers; and even then they probably could not have carried a plaster ceiling satisfactorily.

Tight Bolts in Trusses

Ques. Is it necessary to periodically tighten the bolts in trusses, if they are built of well-seasoned lumber?

Ans. If the trusses are exposed, the bolts will loosen progressively over a long period of time (probably for a year or more), especially in winter, and this is true although the timbers may have been reasonably well dried when the trusses were built. The bolts should be tightened if they are accessible, because, even with ring connectors, bolts in joints lose a considerable portion of their holding power if they are loose. When the truss joints are not accessible after the building is finished, tighten the bolts immediately before they are covered.

Right-Hand or Left-Hand Doors

Ques. How is the "hand" of doors, locks, and other door hardware determined?

Ans. The "hand" is determined as a person stands in front of a door, and the door opens *toward* him. If the knob is on the person's right-hand side, the door is a right-hand door; if the knob is on the left-hand side, the door is a left-hand door (Fig. 15). Almost all door hardware is reversible, and can be used for either a right-hand or a left-hand door. The "hand" of doors should be specified when there is a possibility that the hardware may not be reversible. Special hardware, such as "antipanic" hardware, may not be reversible.

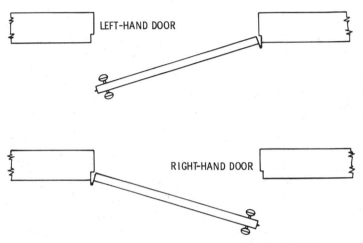

Fig. 15. Illustrating the method for determining the "hand" of doors.

Permanence of Glued Structural Joints

Ques. Although glued structural joints in trusses hold well at first, can they last well? What type of glue is recommended for this type of work?

Ans. Common animal glues deteriorate in the presence of water, or high humidity, but many modern adhesives can withstand boiling. One of the best glues for structural work is resorcinol, but it is difficult to handle and slightly expensive. Nearly all of the laminated timbers that are now produced commercially are casein bonded. This type of glue is cheaper than the synthetics; it is gap-filling, easy to handle, and water-resistant, but under conditions of wetness which would eventually cause the wood to rot, the glue also mildews and decays, unless a preservative is added. Usually phenol, or carbolic acid, is used as a preservative. Most commercial casein glues are fortified with this preservative.

Fortified casein glues are more water-resistant than the glues used in sheathing-grade plywoods, so there should be no apprehension as to the permanence of casein-bonded structural joints in any location where these plywoods can be used safely. Generally speaking, glued structural joints should not be exposed permanently to the weather, but preservatives such as creosote and pentachlorophenol may be used after the joints are made; they preserve the glue in the same manner that they preserve the wood.

An Unusual Type of Trussed-Rafter Roof

Ques. A 30-ft. shed is to be added to the side of an existing building; it is to be used for baled hay storage, and it is desirable that there should be no columns inside the shed. The sketch (Fig. 16) is the proposed type of truss for the rafters. The rafters are

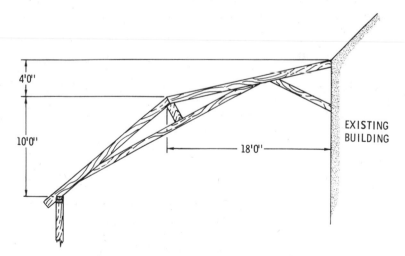

Fig. 16. An unusual type of trussed rafter roof. The design is excellent, if the fastenings are adequate.

2" × 10" timbers, and the bracing consists of 2" × 6" boards. Is this design practical and workable?

Ans. The design appears to be excellent. It does not indicate how the joints are to be made, nor the spacing of the rafters, and suggestions cannot be made without further information. Nail-glued gussets are probably the most economical type of fastenings, and spacing of the trusses is probably governed by the spacing of the studs in the existing building.

Center Joints in Truss Chords

Ques. A small amount of slip has occurred in the bolted joints of the lower chords in the roof trusses. Although the joints appear rigid, the slip has been large enough, in several instances, to break the plaster, and in dry-wall construction the joints have been broken and opened. Are the shear-pin joints (Fig. 17) resistant to slip?

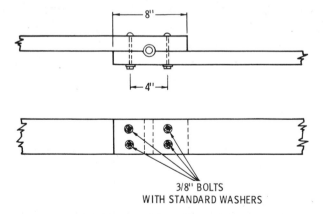

3/8" BOLTS
WITH STANDARD WASHERS

Fig. 17. Bolted joints with 3/4" pipe shear pin, as tested at the Purdue University Wood Laboratory. This is an excellent slip-resistant joint.

Ans. The shear-pin joints (see Fig. 17) have been thoroughly tested in a well-equipped laboratory, and they have proved very resistant to slip, even when the bolts were loosened slightly. In the tests on 2″ × 4″ members, with 3/8″ bolts, these joints showed an average strength of 12,226 pounds when the 3/4″ pipe pin was crushed, and the amount of slip was 1/2 inch. At 2720 pounds, which was considered to be a reasonable working loading, the amount of slip was .01 inch, or nearly negligible.

Shear pins of this type bored into the joints should solve this problem. Slacken the bolts slightly, bore a 1-inch hole in the crack, drive in pins that are made of 3/4″ pipe, and tighten the bolts.

Round Pole-Type Joists

Ques. A client desires to build a summer home in the North woods (Fig. 18). He already possesses several nice straight tamarack poles in nearly all sizes, which he wants to use for joists. They are too small to be sawed into lumber, but a local sawmill can flatten one side. What size of pole is needed to obtain an equivalent to 2″ × 8″ timbers or to 2″ × 10″ timbers for use as joists?

Ans. Since the taper of the poles and the amount of timber that is to be removed in flattening are unknown, a dependable comparison may be obtained by comparing the moment of inertia of the poles at a point one-third the distance from the small end with the moment of inertia of the sawed lumber. The moment of inertia of standard dressed 2″ × 8″ timbers is (57.13 inches)^4, and for 2″ × 10″ timbers, it is (116.10 inches)^4. It is unnecessary to calculate these values, since they are obtainable from a timber handbook.

For circular sections, the formula for determining the moment of inertia is 0.049 d^4, in which d is the diameter of the section. For the circular equivalent of a 2″ × 8″ timber, the calculation is:

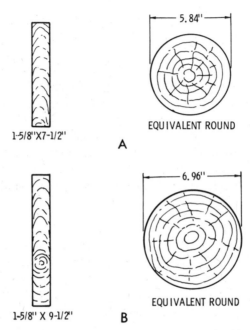

5. 84"

EQUIVALENT ROUND

1-5/8"X7-1/2"

A

6. 96"

EQUIVALENT ROUND

1-5/8" X 9-1/2'

B

Fig. 18. Illustrating the sizes of round logs required to obtain a rigidity equivalent to that of sawed timber joists indicated in (A) 2″ X 8″ dressed timber, and (B) 2″ X 10″ dressed timber.

$$0.094d^4 = 57.13; \quad \text{or } d^4 = \frac{57.13}{0.049}$$

$$d = 5.84 \text{ inches}$$

For the circular equivalent of a $2'' \times 10''$ timber, the calculation is:

$$.049d^4 = 116.10; \quad \text{or } d^4 = \frac{116.10}{0.049}$$

$$d = 6.98 \text{ inches}$$

If a person is unfamiliar with the use of logarithms, he may have difficulty in extracting the fourth root of numbers. It is equal to the square root of the square root; or it can be approximated by the trial-and-error method.

A Queen-Post Truss From Hewed Logs

Ques. A rather large pavilion made of logs is to be built in the North woods. Logs are plentiful, but communication is difficult—except by plane, and sawed lumber is expensive and difficult to obtain. Is there a suggested truss design which can be built from logs, or hand-hewed timbers? Workmen who are skilled with an ax, a broadax, and an adze are available.

Ans. The spans of the trusses are not mentioned, but there is one type of truss available which was built of hewed logs many years ago, and the spans were often 50 feet, or more. The type of truss was often called the "Queen-post" truss (Fig. 19).

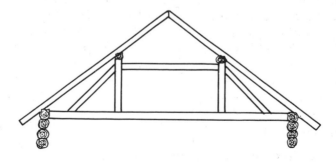

Fig. 19. A Queen-post truss, that is built of hewed logs. This type of truss was known in Europe during the Middle Ages, and it is still a practical design for timber framing.

Many of the members require only partial squaring, and some of them may remain circular. The truss can be fastened together with mortise-and-tenon joints; or simple ironwork and lag screws may be used. Workmen who are skilled with a broadax and an adze can probably do this type of work satisfactorily. Incidentally, that breed of workmen is supposed to have disappeared years ago, but if they are available, they should have little difficulty in framing the trusses.

An Oriental-Style Roof

Ques. An existing roof is to be remodeled into a Chinese pagoda-type roof, with curving eaves and hips. How are these roofs framed; what is the usual pitch of these roofs; and what are the proportions of the overhang? No difficulty with the roof covering is anticipated, since red asphalt shingles which conform to almost any curve are to be used.

Ans. Apparently, there is no preferred pitch for these roofs. At the steepest portion, some of the slopes seem to approach 10 or 12 inches of rise per foot; in other portions, the slopes may be as flat as 6 inches of rise per foot. There also seems to be no standard width for the overhangs, but the overhang is always very wide proportionally and dominates the entire exterior of the building. All these roofs use the double-cantilevered framing shown in Fig. 20. The varying eaves and hip lines are obtained by varying the lengths of the short struts between the cantilevers. The double-cantilever type of construction is widely used in China, Japan, Tibet, and in bridge construction. The architecture in all of these countries is similar.

Shrinkage in Continuous Headers

Ques. It is proposed to use continuous 2″ × 6″ planks, placed on edge for the top plates in homes, instead of the usual doubled

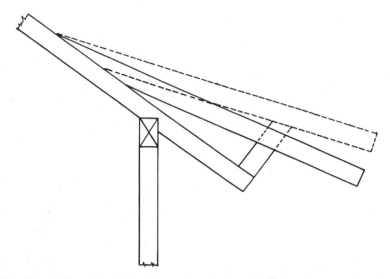

Fig. 20. A type of cantilevered-eaves framing used in China, Japan, and other Oriental countries. The cantilever type of construction is widely used by artisans throughout the Orient.

2″ × 4″ members, thereby eliminating the heavy plank headers above the window and door openings, which have caused considerable difficulties with plaster cracks. By the use of continuous plates, can this problem be eliminated?

Ans. Using the 2″ × 6″ plates, instead of the usual double 2″ × 4″ members, increases the shrinkable wood along the ceiling area by approximately 69 percent, and the probability of the plaster crushing along that line is increased accordingly. If the 2″ × 6″ plates are "green" or wet when the framing is done, there will probably be a problem (Fig. 21). If dried from 28 percent moisture, or a "green" condition, to the 12 percent moisture content that is common in wooden frames of houses in winter, the

SHRINKAGE HERE MAY CRUSH PLASTER

Fig. 21. Illustrating a potential source of trouble when wet or green lumber is used for continuous-header framing.

shrinkage in $2'' \times 6''$ planks may be as much as 5/16 inch. Therefore, if dry lumber cannot be obtained, do not use continuous headers. That is merely trading one type of shrinkage for another. Plaster walls cannot withstand the shrinkage. With dry-wall construction, allowance can be made for possible shrinkage, but this cannot be done with plaster walls. Difficulty with plaster cracks above wide-plank headers may be minimized by the use of dry lumber.

Advantages of Diagonal Sheathing

Ques. When many old houses which had stood for many years have been wrecked, it has been noted that the sheathing was always placed horizontally. Is it necessary to place wall sheathing diagonally?

Ans. The best of the old houses were not wrecked. As long as 50 to 75 years ago, diagonal sheathing was used generally in many parts of the country. By actual test, diagonally sheathed walls are eight times as strong and 4.3 times as stiff as horizontally sheathed walls, and they are more than twice as strong as frames with diagonal braces cut into the studs. If it is nailed properly, and if the framing is sufficiently heavy to hold the nails, the advantage of the diagonal sheathing is probably even greater than indicated.

Diagonal sheathing firmly ties the entire structure to the sills, because each diagonal board serves as a brace as well as a tie-down (Fig. 22); this cannot be done with horizontal sheathing. It is true that there is more waste and that more labor is required in applying

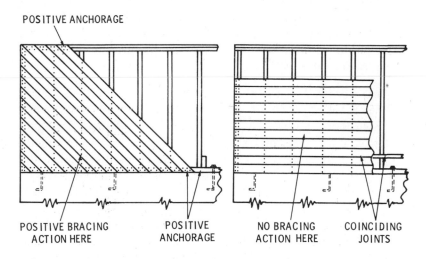

POSITIVE ANCHORAGE

POSITIVE BRACING ACTION HERE   POSITIVE ANCHORAGE   NO BRACING ACTION HERE   COINCIDING JOINTS

Fig. 22. Comparison of the frame having diagonal sheathing (left) with the frame that is sheathed horizontally (right). In addition to the obvious lack of wind-resistance of the horizontally sheathed platform frame, the diagonally sheathed frame possesses eight times the strength of the horizontally sheathed frame if it is not braced in some other manner.

diagonal sheathing. With T&G lumber, the boards cannot be reversed, and some lumber is wasted because of the slanting cuts; however, shiplap lumber is better. Although the diagonal sheathing may cost 10 percent more than the horizontal boards, it is worth the extra cost. In the hurricane regions, horizontal sheathing with platform framing should be prohibited. It is probably the least wind-resistant of any type of framing in common use.

Camber in the Lower Chords of Trusses

Ques. A house with trussed rafters was built recently. A design prepared by an architect was used. Nails were used for fastenings throughout, and the lower chords were given the 1/2-in. camber as specified. The span is 25 ft. and the rise is 5 ft. Now, the roof is completed, and despite a snowfall of more than 12 inches, the 1/2-inch camber remains. The walls are to be plastered, and the interior partitions must be shimmed. Is this problem to be expected when trussed rafters are used?

Ans. For many years, it was customary for architects to specify camber in the lower chords of trusses. In long unobstructed spans, this was thought necessary to counteract the illusion of sagging which is always present when the long lower chords are exactly straight, to allow for some inelastic sagging caused by slip in the joints, and to allow for elastic deflection caused by normal loadings. This habit, or custom, has been carried over to be applied to wood-framed trussed rafters, and it has caused some difficulties.

Calculations of deflection for this type of truss have been made, using a live load of 90 pounds per foot of span, which is more than twice the loading generally specified by codes and far above any actual loading which would conceivably be applied (Fig. 23). Under this design loading, the elastic deflection was found to be .171 in., or slightly less than 3/16 inch. The elastic deflection caused by

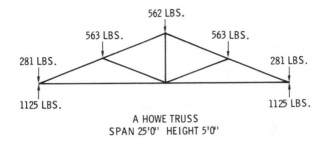

562 LBS.

563 LBS.   563 LBS.

281 LBS.   281 LBS.

1125 LBS.   1125 LBS.

A HOWE TRUSS
SPAN 25'0'' HEIGHT 5'0''

Fig. 23. This is the type of loading that is assumed for the truss considered in the text. The following calculations were obtained: Elastic deflection = 0.171 in. at the center of the span; inelastic deflection, if joints each slip 0.03 in., = 0.237 in. at the center of the span; and total deflection, elastic and inelastic, = 0.408 in.

slipping joints is practically "zero" if the designer uses the usual nailing standards. Eventually, there may be a slight slip after the wood has dried out and seasoned, but this is usually not significant.

It is an excellent practice to build nailed trussed rafters with no camber if the pitch is 4 inches or more per foot. It may be necessary to follow the floor, since some contractors build slab floors slightly higher in the center. If the trusses are nail-glued, always follow the floor, because these joints are unbelievably rigid—even more so than well-nailed joints, and the rigidity is permanent. If the pitch is 3 inches, or less, per foot, some allowance for sagging probably should be made, because these trusses sag far more than those of more reasonable depths.

Oak Timbers for Framing

Ques. Are there any special methods or treatments necessary when native oak lumber is used for framing? The oak lumber is available. The trees were cut last winter, and the lumber has been placed on sticks for nearly six months. It was intended to use this oak lumber for sills and joists, but an advisor has informed us that it is unwise to use oak timbers for sills, because joists that are placed in contact with them rot quickly. Is this true?

Ans. It is fortunate, indeed, that some of our forefathers did not have the advice of your informants available. Some of the colonial homes that are still standing in New England were framed almost entirely of oak lumber, and they have lasted only three hundred years.

It is quite true that oak timber contains acids which are activated when the wood is wet, and it corrodes nails under these conditions, but this action does not occur when the wood is dry. The species of the available oak timbers was not mentioned, but the burr oaks, white oaks, and related species in general are naturally moderately to highly resistant to rot, and they are exceptionally well suited for sills and joists. The red oaks are not as resistant to rot, but the pioneers used them for hand-rived shingles and clapboards. When used for railroad ties, red-oak timber placed in contact with the ground has an expected life of four to five years; white-oak ties last nearly twice as long. Red-oak ties are usually pressure treated with creosote, but the heartwood of white-oak timber does not absorb preservatives well. It is almost impervious to liquids, which is the chief reason that it is used almost exclusively for whiskey barrels.

If the available timber is red oak, black oak, or willow-leaved oak, it is desirable, perhaps, to give the sills a couple of thorough moppings—all they can absorb—of creosote or pentachlorophenol, if they are to be placed near the ground. If they are white-oak timbers, this is of little benefit, except for the sapwood, but good heartwood timbers of this species do not require the treatment.

Bending of Wooden Timbers

Ques. What chemicals may be used for treating wood, so that it can be bent easily, and how are the chemicals used?

Ans. Chemical or other treatment is not needed when bending the relatively thin plies in glue-lam beams and arches, if the lumber is reasonably clear and the slope of the grain is not too great. Either pine or fir lumber is commonly used for this type of work, and it is worked while dry. These timbers do not absorb either steam or chemical treatment well, but nearly all hardwoods may be steamed or boiled in water, and bent more or less readily. Steaming is best accomplished in a simple steam box, under atmsopheric pressure.

The chemical that is commonly used to plasticize wood for bending is urea. This is a common commercial chemical, $CO(NH_2)_2$. It is reasonably inexpensive, and is frequently used as a source of nitrogen in fertilizers. It is obtainable from fertilizer dealers and farm stores in the form of dry crystals which dissolve readily in water. The wood that is to be bent is usually soaked in a hot solution. Urea is not poisonous, but when it is heated it releases ammonia fumes which are unpleasant.

Do not attempt to bend the green wood. Allow it to dry to approximately one-half its green moisture content; then steam, boil, or treat the wood chemically for 1/2 to 1 hour, bend it, and provide a means for holding it in shape until it is dry. After drying, it retains its shape.

Solid Molding on Weather Side of a Door

Ques. Which side of a fir door with solid sticking, solid-rasied panels, and two small panes of figured glass at the top is considered the inside of the door? The glass is not puttied in, but the smooth side is set against the solid moldings. The door is to be exposed to the weather.

Ans. Usually, all types of obscure glass are set with the smooth side to the outside. The glass in doors is usually not bed puttied at the mill, except on special order and at extra cost, but some doors are set with the glass in a plastic adhesive at the mills. If the glazier's union has jurisdiction, it insists on doing this type of work on the job. Pull the stops, remove the glass, and prime the rabbet with lead and oil. When it is dry, place a strip of soft putty or glazing compound in the rabbet and press the glass firmly into it, smooth side to the putty. Press the glass until the putty is squeezed out, assuring that the crack is filled. Then nail the stops in again, turn the door over, and cut off the squeezed-out putty, smoothing it down until flush with the edge of the molding. If the glass has a figure that permits a clean job, some glaziers press a fine line of putty into the crack between the strips and the glass. This assures

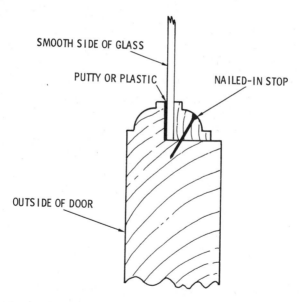

SMOOTH SIDE OF GLASS

PUTTY OR PLASTIC   NAILED-IN STOP

OUTSIDE OF DOOR

Fig. 24. The correct way to place figured glass in outside doors.

that the glass is held firmly. Glazed in this manner, the glass does not leak and the strips do not become soft and rotten, which occurs when they are placed outside in the weather (Fig. 24).

Patterns for Door Sticking

Ques. The terms *ogee, ovolo,* and *pegee* are often applied to door stickings (Fig. 25). What do these terms mean?

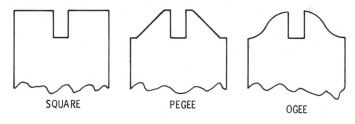

SQUARE   PEGEE   OGEE

OVOLO   COVE AND BEAD   BEAD AND COVE

Fig. 25. Illustrating the different patterns of door sticking. All except the square and pegee stickings are classic moldings.

Ans. Sketches of more-or-less standardized moldings vary slightly among the manufacturers. The "pegee" is sometimes called a "splay." It does not seem to be as well standardized as the other types, and sometimes has a slightly different shape than the design shown.

Steel Connector Plates

Ques. How do the metal connector plates used on trussed rafters by many prefabricating concerns compare with the older, more conventional plywood gussets and solid timber scabs?

Ans. In our opinion, there is only a slight basis for comparison. The glued-on scabs and plywood gussets can be designed to develop nearly the full strength of the timbers they join, but the metal plates can hardly be expected to do that, although they may be entirely adequate for many uses. Also, the glued-on connections may be designed to withstand compression, as well as tension, but the lighter steel plates may buckle under compressive stresses. The effect of drying out of the joined timbers, if they are assembled with high-moisture content, may have a disastrous effect on the steel-plated joints.

At least one dozen types of steel-plate connectors are available, but the greater portion of the market is supplied by approximately six manufacturers and each manufacturer claims special advantages for his products. Only a small number of test results are available and no recommendations other than the claims of the manufacturers can be made. Probably, the principal advantages in the use of the steel plates lie in the speed, ease, and economy of assembly, and not in the actual structural superiority over the fastenings mentioned. These advantages are chiefly for the builder, and they may or may not be passed on to the owner in the form of reduced costs. The owner is concerned only when better methods are available at only slightly increased costs; or equally effective methods are made available at lower costs.

Rotation of Truss Joints

Ques. The trusses for house roofs are being built by a lumberman, using pronged steel-plate joints. Recently, he refused to build a truss design that was obtained from a magazine. The design required a 28-ft. span, using 2″ × 4″ boards for all members. He maintained that some of the members were too light and that they would "rotate" in the joint. This is obviously impossible What did he mean?

Ans. He meant exactly what he said. To *rotate* means to move about an axis, but it does not necessarily mean that the member will *revolve*. When a truss member is too light in weight, it may tend to bend under loadings which are applied in certain ways, and there *is* a tendency for their ends to rotate, usually about the center of gravity of the fastenings. The lumberman evidently fears that this would loosen the pronged plates and destroy the integrity of the joint. He was probably fully justified in refusing to build the trusses.

Air-Dry Lumber

Ques. Several years ago, serious trouble was experienced with framing lumber drying out after the house was built, and now dry lumber is demanded. My lumberman does not object to checking the moisture in the lumber he sells, and he has an electric meter. Recently in a carload of 2″ × 4″ pieces, some of the boards tested 18 percent moisture. The lumber neither appeared nor felt as though it were excessively wet, but isn't 18 percent too high in moisture content for use in a house? The dealer calls it "air dry."

Ans. The species of lumber that was checked was not mentioned, but the moisture content of yellow pine dimensioned lumber that is sold as "air-dry" is limited by the *SPIB* grading rules to a maximum of 19 percent moisture; if sold as "kiln-dried," the limit is 15 percent. In most of the Midwest, the moisture content of the wooden frame of a house during summer is usually approximately 12 percent, or perhaps slightly less, depending on the weather and climatic conditions. The dealer was perfectly honest and ethical in designating lumber with 18 percent moisture as air-dry lumber after a period of years. A slight shrinkage can be expected in framing lumber that is nailed at 18 percent moisture, but the shrinkage should not be serious. If the lumber is dried from 18 percent to 12 percent moisture content, which is about as low as possible, a 1/8 to 3/16-inch shrinkage should be normal in a 2″ × 10″ joist. A moisture content of 18 percent is much less than the 29 or 30 percent moisture that was found in some of the lumber of a few years ago from the West.

CHAPTER 4

Beams

Diagonal Tension in Concrete Beam

Ques. Why are there such complicated arrangements of stirrups and bent-up bars in the ends of concrete beams? An engineer reports that their function is to resist "diagonal tension." What does he mean?

Ans. Properly positioned reinforcements cross the lines of probable failure. Since concrete is strong in compression, reinforcement is seldom necessary along the top or compression surfaces of correctly designed beams, but concrete can resist little or no tension, so the bars are necessary along the lower or tension side.

The actions that cause diagonal tension are too complicated for a simple explanation, but heavily loaded concrete beams often fail because cracks begin at, or near, the bearings, and extend upward and inward, as shown in the sketch (Fig. 1). These cracks are the result of the forces called diagonal tension, and they are common causes of failure. Note that the bent-up bars and stirrups cross the lines of the cracks. None of the bars in the lower portions of the beam (the straight tension reinforcement) can be spared— even though bending forces are lighter near the ends of the beam, so stirrups are used to supplement the bent-up bars. In the past, the stirrups were often slanted; they were thought to be more effective if the lines of stress were crossed more directly, but vertical stirrups have been found to be almost equally effective and easier to assemble. Practically all concrete beams that have been heavily loaded at any time have been cracked near the center of

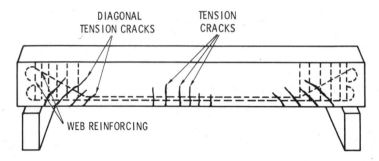

Fig. 1. Illustrating the effects of straight tension and diagonal tension in reinforced concrete beams.

the span by straight tension, as shown in the sketch. Because of the elasticity of steel, the cracks may close up when the loadings are removed, and they may become invisible. These cracks do not appear to impair the strength of the beam.

Brace-Reinforced Wooden Beams

Ques. Built-up wooden beams are often reinforced by nailing two 2″ × 4″ members, rafter-fashion, between two planks. Although this seems to stiffen the beams, the braces are not as effective as they should be. Is there anything wrong with this practice?

Ans. The theory of the arrangement seems to be that the 2″ × 4″ members act as braces, but this is a fallacy. The braces have no support to bear against at the lower ends; the excess tensile forces are exerted on the lower portions of the planks, which are already normally stressed. If the braces are glued in place, or even nailed well, some advantage is gained, because the complete assembly must work as a unit. The neutral axis of the beam is elevated at the center of the span, increasing the tension on the lower side, but the same effect can be obtained, probably more effectively, by nailing a straight $2'' \times 4''$ member to the upper edge.

If the beam is to be braced, add a steel tension rod, as shown in the sketch (Fig. 2). Place large plate washers underneath the nuts at the ends. Do not tighten the nuts too tightly or the beam may be

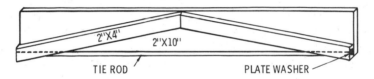

Fig. 2. A braced wooden beam, with the nearer side removed. These arrangements are rarely satisfactory without the addition of the tie rod.

cambered seriously. If one end of the beam can be left exposed until the framing bearing on the beam is finished, the camber can be adjusted almost as desired.

Raising a Heavy I-Beam Lintel

Ques. It is expensive to construct a hoist for elevating a single 18 ft. $\times$ 14 in. I-beam lintel to position above a double garage door. Is there an easier and more simple method?

Ans. These beams can be "walked" upward on a crib made of concrete blocks, but, of course, any kind of cribbing may be used (Fig. 3). Two men can do this easily, although it is a rather slow process. The beam can be skidded into position alongside the open-

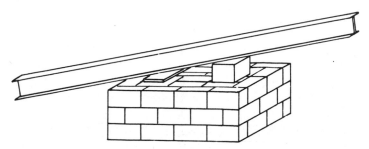

Fig. 3. "Walking" a heavy I-beam lintel upward on a crib consisting of concrete blocks by alternately raising each end and blocking beneath it until another course of blocks can be placed. This method is not difficult, although it is slow.

ing, and then pried upward until the first tier of blocks can be placed under it near the center point. Then, one man can easily raise one end of the beam while the other man places blocks beneath the raised side on the upper side of the blocks. Then the other end of the beam is raised, blocked beneath, and the operations repeated until the succeeding tier of cribbing blocks can be placed. Also, two simple scaffolds of $2'' \times 4''$ boards can be used, and, instead of blocking upward, slats are nailed across the scaffolding, alternating as the beam is tilted. This is a tricky procedure and someone can easily be injured. A 14-in. I-beam that is 18 ft. in length weighs approximately 540 pounds. "Walking up" is the easiest way to raise this type of beam into place inside a home, where there is not enough space for a hoist.

Peripheral Beams on Concrete-Block Walls

Ques. What method is recommended for topping out a concrete-block wall (for wind-resistance) so that a good anchorage for the rafters is provided?

Ans. In those states where windstorms are common, many codes provide that peripheral beams should be used. This is merely a reinforced concrete beam, usually approximately 8 × 8 inches, with not less than two continuous 1/2-inch reinforcing rods. Reinforcement also can be provided by the use of special blocks for the top course. These blocks are "U" shaped, and they are set with the opening placed upward. The rods are positioned and the beams poured in place. Anchor bolts may be hooked to the rods (Fig. 4).

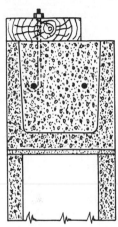

Fig. 4. A peripheral or coping beam poured in special concrete blocks. This satisfies most codes, but the plate anchorage is not adequate in regions where extremely high winds are quite prevalent in some seasons.

Single loading Concentrated at Center of Span

Ques. The owner of an auto repair shop desires to install a beam for a hoist which is to be used for lifting engines out of automobiles. The span is 18 feet, and the loading should not exceed 2 tons. Several good full-sized 8″ × 12″ timbers are available. Are these timbers strong enough for this purpose?

Ans. To determine the loading for beams that have a single load concentrated at the center of the span (if the quality of the timber is equal to, or better than, No. 2 stress-rated yellow pine), the following formula may be used:

$$\text{allowable loading} = \frac{\text{breadth} \times \text{depth}^2 \times 66.7}{\text{length of span}}$$

When the breadth and depth are in inches, and the span is in feet, the calculation is:

$$\text{allowable loading} = \frac{8 \times 144 \times 66.7}{18} = 4269 \text{ pounds}$$

Thus, the 8″ × 12″ timbers are strong enough for the 2-ton concentrated loading, if deflection is not to be a problem. Under a 2-ton loading, it may be necessary to brace them in some manner to prevent their buckling and turning sidewise.

Stiffness of Timbers not Proportional to Depth

Ques. Is it correct to assume that a 4″ × 8″ timber is only twice as stiff as a 4″ × 4″ timber? What is their actual relative stiffness?

Ans. The stiffness of timbers that are the same breadth, span, and have the same intensity and method of loading is not proportional to their depths, but is proportional to the *cube* of their depths (Fig. 5). The relative stiffness of the 4″ × 8″ timber to that of the 4″ × 4″ timber is *not* 8 to 4, but $(8)^3$ to $(4)^3$, or 512 to 64; therefore, the 4″ × 8″ timber is eight times as stiff as the 4″ × 4″ timber. Under the same type of loading, the 4″ × 8″ timber can carry eight times as much loading as the 4″ × 4″ timber with the same deflection. This, of course, assumes that the 4″ × 8″ timber is set with the edge upward.

If the beams are the same depth, but vary in their widths (other factors being equal), their relative stiffness is directly proportional to their breadths. If the 4″ × 8″ timber is set flatwise, its stiffness, relative to that of the 4″ × 4″ timber is 8 to 4; therefore, the

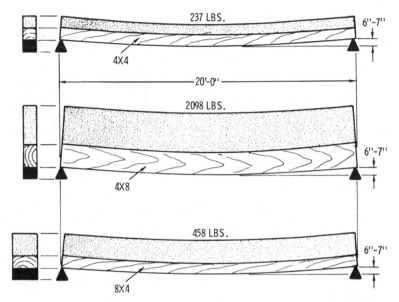

Fig. 5. Illustrating the stiffness of beams of various depths, and how the distributed loads deflect them at 1/360 of their spans. The beams are standard dressed sizes.

$4'' \times 8''$ timber is twice as stiff as the $4'' \times 4''$ timber, in that position.

Strength of Built-up Beams

Ques. Is a built-up beam consisting of seven $2'' \times 12''$ timbers as strong as a standard $12'' \times 12''$ timber, if both timbers are the same in quality?

Ans. For timbers having identical dimensions and quality, there is no difference in strength or stiffness of built-up beams and the solid timbers providing the planks are set on edge and sufficient fastenings, such as bolts or spikes, are used to prevent the lamina-

115

tions from buckling. A built-up beam consisting of seven 2″ × 12″ planks is only slightly smaller in breadth than the standard-dressed 12″ × 12″ planks—probably not enough to provide a significant difference.

If the planks are to be laid flatwise, however, the built-up beam is neither as strong nor as stiff as the solid 12″ × 12″ timber. Mechanical fastenings are not rigid enough to withstand entirely the horizontal shearing forces, or the tendency of the planks to slide on one another when the beam is bent by loading. If the laminations are glued effectively, there is, theoretically, no difference in the two beams.

The laminated beam is usually preferable to the solid timber, because large solid timbers are invariably checked—sometimes seriously. The planks, if they are well dried before the assembly, are usually free from serious checking. If it is possible to do so, a solid timber with serious checks should be placed in service with the checks placed on the top and bottom, to keep the cracks away from the lines of shear.

Calculation of Safe Loadings for Wooden Beams

Ques. Can the following formula be used to calculate the safe loading for wooden beams when the loads are concentrated at the center points of the span? Can it be used for beams with distributed loads—and for cantilevers?

$$P = \frac{f \, b \, d^2}{18 \, L}$$

in which;

> f is allowable fiber stress, pounds per square inch
> b is breadth of beam, inches

d is depth of beam, inches
L is length of span, feet

Ans. The above formula, along with the constant (18), can be used only for freely supported beams that have a single load concentrated at the center point of the span. These formulas may be used for the following calculations:

1. For beams with distributed loadings;

$$W = \frac{f\,b\,d^2}{9L}$$

2. For cantilevers with loading concentrated at the free end;

$$P = \frac{f\,b\,d^2}{72L}$$

3. For cantilevers with distributed loading;

$$W = \frac{f\,b\,d^2}{36L}$$

Actual, not nominal, sizes of timbers should be used in the above calculations for determining the safe loadings for wooden beams.

Flitch-Plates in Plywood Beams

Ques. Plywood beams have been found badly deflected when used in construction. Can they be improved by bolting a metal plate to serve as a web between two thicknesses of plywood (Fig. 6)?

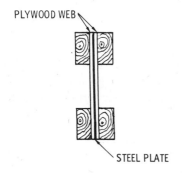

PLYWOOD WEB

STEEL PLATE

Fig. 6. A flitch plate added to the web of a plywood beam is not an economical use of materials.

Ans. The questions of the practicability of this type of beam depends on whether it is a better beam for slightly more money when compared with the more orthodox structural members. It is certain that the proposed beam is not economical. It is true that shearing forces in I-shaped sections are almost entirely concentrated in the webs, and it is also true that the frequent excessive deflections of plywood beams are partially caused by shears. Placing the metal plate in the web would probably correct this deficiency, but the plywood in the web would be almost wholly inactive, which would make the beam expensive. The plywood is much less rigid than the steel, and the two materials do not work together. The steel would have to be stressed nearly to the point of failure before the plywood portion of the beam would be brought into action.

It is impossible to estimate or calculate accurately exactly how the stresses would be distributed. To do this, some of the beams would have to be tested. Some testing has been done on composite beams with steel webs and wooden flanges; the tests' results were promising, but they apparently were not sufficiently attractive to warrant further serious consideration of this type of beam as a structural member.

Roof-Supporting I-Beam as a Heat Conductor

Ques. In a recently built meat market, the ceiling underneath the joist-bearing beam has been wet nearly all winter. This beam is boxed in, it is 18 inches deep, and the joists are $2'' \times 12''$ timbers set on shelf angles. What can be done about this?

Ans. The I-beam is a good heat conductor, and it runs almost continuously from the inside to the outside (Fig. 7). The inside

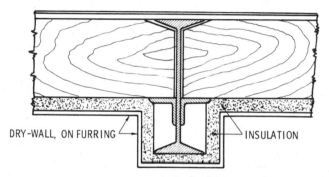

DRY-WALL, ON FURRING   INSULATION

Fig. 7. The I-beam joist bearer is a good heat conductor, and it may become so cold in winter that condensation collects on it. Insulation, as shown in the illustration, with an effective vapor barrier above it should halt this difficulty.

flange becomes cold enough to condense moisture from the air inside the shop, where the relative humidity is normally rather high. It is necessary to insulate the beam, placing a vapor barrier underneath the insulation. It may be wise to insulate the ceiling.

Beams Placed Flatwise or Edgewise

Ques. Old-time framers placed door and window headers flatwise, usually two $2'' \times 4''$ members for most windows and door openings, which seemed to be adequate. Modern builders advise that the timbers should be set on edge. What is the difference, since the overall dimensions of the headers are nearly identical?

Ans. The numerical value of the strength of a beam, considering only its *size* and *shape*, is called its *section modulus*. The length of span and the type of material are not considered in regard to section moduli. Consequently, in beams having identical materials, spans, and methods of loading, the section moduli provide a con-

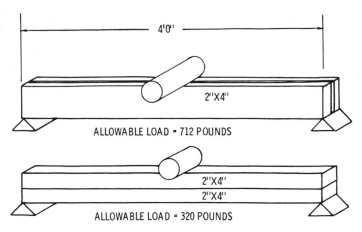

Fig. 8. Allowable concentrated loads on two 2 × 4 members set edge upward (top) and flatwise (bottom).

venient basis for strength comparisons (Fig. 8). In wooden beams having rectangular cross sections, the formula for determining the section modulus is:

$$\text{section modulus} = \frac{b\,d^2}{6}$$

in which;

b is the breadth

d is the depth

For a standard dressed $2'' \times 4''$ member, *set flatwise,* the calculation is:

$$\text{section modulus} = \frac{3\text{-}5/8 \times 1\text{-}5/8 \times 1\text{-}5/8}{6} = (1.60 \text{ inches})^3$$

If an identical $2'' \times 4''$ member is *set on edge,* the calculation is:

$$\text{section modulus} = \frac{1\text{-}5/8 \times 3\text{-}5/8 \times 3\text{-}5/8}{6} = (3.56 \text{ inches})^3$$

These calculations indicate that the strength of the two $2'' \times 4''$ members is slightly more than doubled when they are set on edge, in comparison to setting them flatwise.

Box Beams Often Lack Shearing Resistance

Ques. The glued, clamped, and spiked box beam (Fig. 9) is proposed for a joist bearer for the second floor of a house. How does the strength of this type of beam compare with that of the more conventional types of beams? Is it permissible to use the hollow portion of this type of beam either for a heating duct of a forced-air system or to conceal electric wiring?

Ans. In regard to actual bending strength, this type of box beam is approximately equivalent to that of a beam constructed from four $2'' \times 12''$ timbers, but the uses for nearly all types of wooden box beams are governed by their resistance to horizontal shears, rather than by their bending strength.

The length of the spans and the probable loadings are not mentioned, but the proposed box beam (see Fig. 9) with a span of 14 feet, may safely carry approximately 372 pounds per lineal foot,

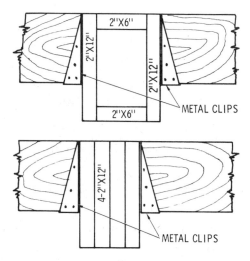

Fig. 9. A proposed six-beam joist bearer (top). The section modulus is equal to (148.12 in.)³. The use of this beam is limited to a loading of approximately 5168 lb. on a 14-ft. span because of horizontal shears. In a beam built up from solid 2″ × 12″ timbers (bottom), the section modulus is equal to (143.28)³. The use of this beam is limited by a deflection of 1/360 of the span of 14 ft. This beam may carry safely a loading of 9964 pounds, with shears of 100 psi and stress in extreme fibers of 1460 lb. per sq. in.

which is near the 120 lbs. per sq. in. shearing stress that is allowable on Southern pine or Douglas fir beams. On the other hand, a beam of identical span built up from four 2″ × 12″ timbers can support safely 712 pounds per lineal foot, with a deflection of 1/360 of the span governing, and with shears well below the allowable 120 lbs. per sq. in.

The hollow beam could be used to enclose electric wiring, but the holes for the outlets, especially if they are located near the ends of the spans, reduce the beam's shearing resistance still more, as do seasoning checks and cracks. The beam cannot be used for a heating duct of any type. These ducts should be made of sheet metal; most codes specify that they shall be covered with not less than 1/2 inch of noncombustible insulating material and that the insulation be located at least 1 inch from any combustible material. This makes the allowable duct so small that it is almost useless, even for forced circulation, and cutting into the beam for outlets or inlets is even more disadvantageous. Unless there are more logical reasons for using the box beam than those that have been mentioned, an orthodox solid timber, or built-up beam, should be used to avoid complications (see Fig. 9).

Comparative Strengths of Timbers

Ques. What are the comparative strengths of the different species of timber that are commonly found in lumberyards?

Ans. Hardwoods are not usually obtainable from lumberyard stocks. Strength is considered to be the actual breaking point. The following are the comparative strengths of commonly used softwoods, in air-dry condition (12 percent moisture). The testing was done at the United States Forest Research Laboratory.

Long-leaf yellow pine	100%
Larch	95%
Short-leaf yellow pine	87%
Douglas fir, coast-type	82%
Tamarack	79%
Cypress	72%
Spruce (except Englemann)	70%
Hemlock, Western	69%
Redwood	68%
Douglas fir, mountain type	65%
Hemlock, Eastern	61%
Red cedar, Western	52%
White cedar, Northern	44%

Sawing Strongest Possible Beam From a Log

Ques. How can the proportions of the strongest possible beam that can be sawed from a log (24-inches diameter, for example) be determined?

Ans. The height to breadth proportions are nearly 7 to 5. If slightly more accuracy is desired, the breadth of the beam is 1.7321 times the *diameter*. For the 14-inch log, the breadth is:

$$\frac{24}{1.7321} = 13.856 \text{ inches, approximately}$$

The height of the beam can be solved by the Pythagorean formula, (diameter)^2 less the (breadth)^2 = (height)^2. This is the calculation:

$$(24)^2 - (13.856)^2 = 384.01,$$

and the height is its square root, or approximately 19.6 inches.

Sawmill men have sometimes solved this problem graphically, using a steel square on the end of the log, as shown in the sketch (Fig. 10). This method is mathematically correct.

Colonial-Style Beamed Ceilings

Ques. It is planned to finish some of the rooms in a new home with authentic 17th century colonial-style trim. What type of beams were used in the early homes, and how were they arranged?

Ans. The beams in the ceilings of these early homes were purely utilitarian. They were used primarily for structural purposes. If any thought was given to their appearance, it was a secondary matter; however, the appearance was attractive (Fig. 11).

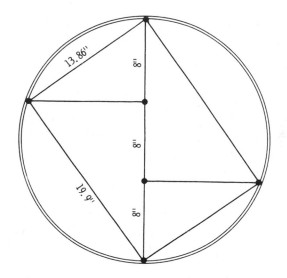

**Fig. 10. A graphic method for determining the strongest beam
that can possibly be sawed from a log.**

The width of these homes was usually too great for a single span of joists, so a very heavy beam, called a "summer beam," was extended longitudinally. This beam was a hewed log, usually 18″ × 18″. Much lighter beams, or joists, were framed into the beam flush with its top, and extended to the walls at right angles. They were spaced at wide intervals (3 or 4 feet), and they carried a heavy floor with the lower side exposed. In 18th century homes, the spaces between the beams were often lathed and plastered.

The elaborate arrangements of imitation beams that were often found in early 20th century American homes were never found in colonial homes. In the colonial home, the beams were placed there for a purpose; the purpose was evident, and the effect was pleasing. Beyond question, this is excellent architecture at its best.

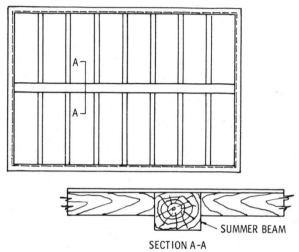

SECTION A-A

Fig. 11. Two views of the common arrangement of "summer" beam and joists in the 17th-century-style houses. One end of the summer beam rests on the chimney masonry.

In a replica of these homes, the summer beam need not be extremely deep, but it should be relatively broad, and the joists should be more narrow and more shallow. A beam, or half-beam, was generally used at the walls. Actually, this was an extension of the timber used as a plate on the one-story-high studs used in the walls.

CHAPTER 5

Ceilings and Walls

Necessity for Building Paper

Ques. Is it necessary to place a layer of building paper, or sheathing paper, over wood sheathing and beneath the siding? Does the paper possess any heat-insulating value?

Ans. Authorities have failed to reach complete agreement on this subject. Since there is some difference of opinion, the necessity for building paper may be questioned. Actually, it possesses no worthwhile heat-insulating value.

Oldtimers used red rosin-sized sheathing paper to "seal the cracks against the wind." Bugs sometimes ate the paper, and it was not waterproof. Modern builders know that the walls of homes *need* ventitalion to the outside air; this seems to contradict the earlier idea. In any instance, *never* seal the outside surfaces of the walls of a home with vapor-barring paper or foil if condensation problems are to be avoided. Present-day practice is to use a tarred-felt sheathing paper beneath the siding. This paper is waterproof, is not a vapor barrier, and is not eaten by bugs. It is well worth its cost if only for the assurance that it provides against leaky siding.

Hollow-Masonry Walls

Ques. Are hollow-masonry walls necessary in a climate such as that in the state of Kansas? How are these walls usually constructed?

Ans. For reasonable satisfaction, it is necessary to use *insulated* hollow-masonry walls in the state of Kansas. Two 4-in. concrete-block walls are sometimes used; or bricks for the outside wall and the hollow blocks for the inside wall may be used (Fig. 1). The

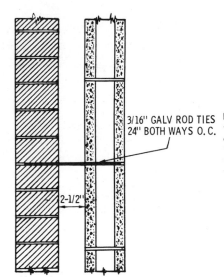

3/16" GALV ROD TIES 24" BOTH WAYS O. C.

2-1/2"

Fig. 1. A conventional cavity wall: 4" face brick; 2-1/2" air space; and 4" concrete blocks. With no insulation, U = 0.35 Btu; cavity filled with vermiculite, U = 0.14 Btu; and with 2" foamed styrene slabs in cavity, U = 0.11 Btu.

hollow blocks are tied together with No. 6 galvanized wire ties placed at 24" intervals in every third block joint. The cavity is usually 2-1/2 inches in width, and the insulation that is used may be poured perlite or vermiculite, but 2" foamed styrene slabs are preferable. Foamed styrene is the more efficient insulation, and it also provides its own vapor barrier.

Plastered Concrete-Block Walls Unsatisfactory for Homes

Ques. In a house with walls constructed of 8″ concrete blocks plastered against the masonry, mildew forms in the corners and beneath the windows. What can be done to halt this trouble?

Ans. The only practical remedy is to furr out the walls and apply insulation. The problem may be partially relieved by keeping the house extremely well ventilated, but this alternative is costly, because it means a large loss of heat, which is expensive. There is no type of noninsulated 8″ masonry wall that is entirely satisfactory for use in residences.

Plastering Over Painted Plasterboard

Ques. In plastering a summer home, is it necessary to remove the painted plasterboard and apply new lath, or should new metal lath be applied over the old plasterboard?

Ans. New plaster can be applied directly over the painted plasterboard surface, if holes are drilled for clinches. It is suggested that 3/4-in. holes located at a distance of 4 in. on centers be drilled. This gives approximately the same area for clinches that is provided in the standard perforated or spaced lath. Then scratch the old painted surface; if the joints are taped and finished, place strips of metal lath over them.

Plate Bracing in One-and-One-Half-Story House

Ques. In one-and-one-half-story houses, are the plate braces shown in the sketch (Fig. 2) really necessary?

Ans. If the walls are constructed of masonry, the bracing is absolutely necessary, and they are advisable in frame houses. Sometimes they are not used, but they may prevent the studs from bending and the walls from pushing outward because of settlement in the roof framing. In addition, they act as tiedowns to resist wind uplift in the room. The braces are usually placed at 4-ft. intervals.

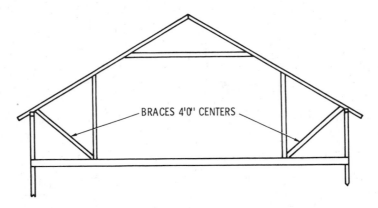

BRACES 4'0' CENTERS

Fig. 2. Plate braces in a one-and-one-half story house. These braces are extremely important if the walls are constructed of masonry.

Nails for Plasterboard

Ques. What types of nails are recommended for applying drywall plasterboard? Can either aluminum or galvanized nails be recommended?

Ans. Laboratory tests have indicated that there is no nail that is more efficient or more economical for applying plasterboard than the standard sharp-pointed, blued plasterboard nail with the medium-large head. It is not necessary to use rust-resistant nails under normal conditions; tests showed no advantage in using either cement-coated nails or nails with deformed shanks—in most instances, the plain plasterboard nails were superior.

Lintels Placed in Masonry Walls

Ques. An opening that is to be cut in a 13-in. brick wall is 16 ft. wide by 7 ft. high. The masonry extends to approximately 16 ft. above the lintel. There are no windows, and there are no joists that bear on the lintel. What size I-beam should be used?

Ans. In instances where the wall extends to a considerable height above the lintel and where there are no openings in the wall, the wall itself forms a kind of pyramid, and the portion of the wall above the pyramid acts as a self-supporting arch (Fig. 3). For brick masonry, the height of the pyramid is usually assumed

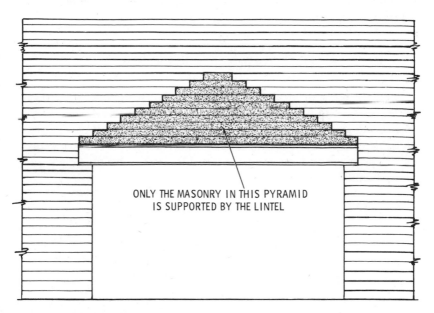

ONLY THE MASONRY IN THIS PYRAMID
IS SUPPORTED BY THE LINTEL

Fig. 3. Diagram showing how a masonry wall with considerable height pyramids above a lintel. In brick masonry, the height of the pyramid is approximately one-third the span; in block masonry, it is approximately one-half the span.

to be one-third the lintel span. Then, at 140 pounds per superficial sq. ft., the load on the lintel is:

$$\frac{140 \times 16 \times 16}{3 \times 2} = 5973 \text{ pounds}$$

The bending moment in beams with pyramidal loading is:

$$\frac{WL}{6} = \frac{5973 \times 16 \times 12}{6} = 191,136 \text{ inch-pounds}$$

Allowing 18,000 lbs. per sq. in. on the steel, the section modulus of the required beam will be:

$$\frac{M}{f} = \frac{191,136}{18,000} = 10.6 \text{ inches}^3$$

From a table of structural shapes, it can be found that either an $8'' \times 3'' \times 18.4\#$ standard I-beam or an $8'' \times 5\text{-}1/4'' \times 17\#$ WF beam may be used. The deflection of the beam beneath the dead weight of the pyramid will be approximately $5/8''$. A cambered beam should be used, if possible, or the beam should be shored until the mortar has set.

Checking of Plaster

Ques. Checking of plaster in the form of irregular cracks is being experienced. The proportions that are being used are 1:3, 1:4, and 1:2 mixes for scratch, brown, and finish coats, respectively. Is the checking due to improper proportioning of the mixes?

Ans. It is improbable that improper proportioning is causing the trouble. According to the Underwriter's Code, the mix is slightly heavy on the sand. The code specifies 1:2 scratch coat and 1:3, or sometimes 1:2, for brown coat; usually, the higher proportion of sand decreases the probability of checking. The checks are probably caused by shrinkage in setting and drying; this form of checking is usually worse when the coats are relatively thick. The checks are undesirable, of course, but they are usually paid little attention, since subsequent coats cover them effectively and they seem to do no damage. The final coat, however, should be a thin coat to prevent checking caused by shrinkage. If wooden lath are not well soaked before the plaster is applied, they may swell, sometimes buckle, and cause checking that is damaging.

"Ghost" Streaks on Ceilings

Ques. What causes the dark, shadowy streaks that often appear on plaster ceilings? In some instances where wooden lath were used, an outline of every lath in the ceiling shows through—as well as every joist above the ceiling.

Ans. The causes of these "ghost" marks are unknown, but a theory stating that it is an electrostatic phenomenon has been advanced. It is believed that airborne dust particles carry the electrical charges and that a surface carrying an opposite charge attracts them. This is the basic principle of electronic air cleaners, or precipitators. It is well known that warm surfaces attract dust particles, as indicated by the dark, dirty streaks found on the walls and ceilings above all types of heat registers, radiators, and electrical fixtures.

Perhaps, temperature influences the intensity of the electrical charge carried by the surface, and the temperature of the portions of the ceiling beneath the joists and lath is different from the temperature of the portions where the clinches in the plaster are exposed to the cooler air temperature above, which may affect the intensity of the electrical charges carried at these points. It may be worthwhile to note that "ghosts" rarely appear on a well-insulated ceiling.

Floors Below Radiant Ceilings Heat Slowly

Ques. Inspection of an office heated by means of a radiant ceiling has revealed that the heating system is apparently operating satisfactorily, but the slab-on-ground floor is too cool for comfort. It is practical to cover the slab with aluminum foil and then install a wooden floor directly above the concrete to overcome this problem?

Ans. There is no practical method of installing a wooden strip floor directly above the concrete, but wood blocks may be installed with adhesive. Aluminum foil is useless for insulation if it is sandwiched between two other surfaces. To be effective, the aluminum foil should face at least a 3/4-inch space, and it may be placed on either the warm side or the cool side of the cavity. If the floor is to be laid on sleepers, the idea is practical. Reflective insulation is especially effective in floors where convection loss is entirely absent. Since the coldest level in the room is always near the floor, conduction loss is a minimum. Heat losses from radiation are especially significant in floors, and reflective foils are used to resist radiation.

The client may not be using the radiant heat to best advantage. Although the radiant ceiling is in a most advantageous position, it is impossible for the floor to become warmed comfortably. If the heat is turned off or turned down during the night, the floor naturally becomes cold; radiation is *not* directly proportional to the temperature of the radiant surface, but to the *fourth power* of the temperature. For example, if the heating system is satisfactory with the ceiling temperature at 90°F., turning the temperature downward to 80°F. reduces the radiation emitted by 37-1/2 percent. If the temperature is reduced at night, most of the next forenoon may be required to return the floor to a comfortable stresses occur at the corners and at points where the cross-sectional temperature. This indicates that in severe weather it is not practical to reduce the heat in a radiant ceiling at night.

Contraction in Concrete Walls

Ques. In a building that is to be constructed with solid concrete walls, the longest wall is 75 ft. in length and 10 ft. in height. Are expansion joints necessary?

Ans. Some expansion may be provided for, but expansion usually is not a serious problem, since concrete is usually poured during warm or hot weather; however, contraction is a serious problem, because concrete can withstand little or no tension. Heavy reinforcement is not entirely effective, because it merely prevents concentrations of stresses and large damaging or unsightly cracks; yet, it allows numerous small, perhaps invisible, cracks which are not so damaging or conspicuous. Heavily concentrated tensile direction, shape, or area changes suddenly.

Many types of commercial joints are available. Some of these joints are metal; some of them consist of a tongue-and-groove or bellows-like arrangement; and some joints are made of rubber or rubber-like materials. In general, the joints should be located at corners, at points where high and low portions abut, at openings—especially large doors—and at intervals of 25 to 50 feet.

Popping of Plaster

Ques. What causes the plaster in a house that was completed some time ago to develop serious pits and blisters?

Ans. Two types of lime are used for plastering. The high-calcium limes are considered more satisfactory, but some high-magnesia limes are also marketed for this purpose. Properly burned and hydrated high-magnesia limes may make good plaster, but they may contain some particles that are not properly slaked. In fact, manufacturer's standards may allow 8 percent, or more, of these imperfectly hydrated particles, and they are known to cause pops and blisters for some length of time, possibly five years. This may be causing the trouble. Probably, the holes can be paddled out with a high-gauge material, but that might be quite difficult.

Nothing can be done to prevent this problem, except to soak the lime for a longer period of time. If the time required to soak the lime thoroughly cannot be spared, another brand of lime should be used.

Control Joints in Concrete-Block Masonry

Ques. Is it absolutely necessary to allow for expansion in concrete-block walls? How are control joints usually spaced? Can joint reinforcement be used to prevent the walls from breaking up?

Ans. Expansion and contraction should be allowed for in walls of concrete-block masonry that are exposed to temperature changes. In general, this type of movement is relatively high in concrete-block masonry—more than twice that occurring in burned-clay masonry; the blocks also swell and shrink slightly as they are wetted and dried. Reinforcement does not prevent expansion and contraction, since steel has about the same expansion coefficient as concrete; but it does prevent the wall from breaking up with unsightly and damaging cracks, and the reinforcement may be used to concentrate the movement at control joints, although it does not prevent such movement.

It is difficult to allow for continual expansion and contraction as the temperature rises or falls, without producing cracks that may range through the entire wall; much dependence is placed on elastic calking compounds and joint fillers of various types. Since most walls are pilastered, control joints are most often placed at

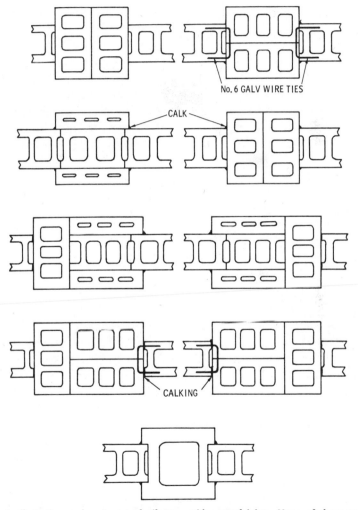

Fig. 4. Illustrating various types of pilasters with control joints. None of these types is ideal, but they are commonly used.

the pilasters, and the pilasters are usually placed at distances of 16 to 20 ft. apart. The accompanying sketches (Fig. 4) show some of the commonly used types of pilasters with control joints. None of these types can be considered ideal, but the ones shown are commonly used types.

Reinforcing, or metal ties, preferably should not run completely through the control joints, but when this is necessary to hold the two portions of wall in alignment (as shown in the illustrations) the projecting ends are greased heavily to prevent bonding with the mortar.

Nailing Plasterboard to Ceilings

Ques. Difficulty has been experienced in nailing plasterboard dry-wall to the ceilings. The plasterboard dimples around the nails and sags away from the supporting joints. If the plasterboard is pressed upward, the dimples disappear. What causes this problem?

Ans. Probably the boards were not held tightly against the joists while they were being nailed, and it was attempted to draw the board upward with the nails. The rounded poll of the hammer has crushed the plaster in the plasterboard, leaving little more than the paper covers to hold up the plasterboard. If the board were held tightly against the framing while it was being nailed, driving the nails up too tightly would have the same effect.

A sheet of plasterboard cannot be drawn up with the nails in the same manner as with plywood or a board. The panel of plasterboard should be held tightly to the joists, and a rounded-poll hammer should be used to drive the nails flush with the surface, without crushing the plaster.

Applying Wallpaper to Plywood

Ques. How should wallpaper be applied over plywood?

Ans. One should not attempt to apply wallpaper over plywood, hardboard, or softboard paneling, because all of these boards shrink and swell with the changes in humidity of the surrounding air. The joints in boards of this type cannot be permanently filled and smoothed because of this action, and they cannot be wallpapered without the joints showing through the paper. It is necessary to panel these walls with batts or metal strips made for the purpose. Only the joints of the gypsum boards may be filled, spackled smooth, and papered over. The gypsum boards do not shrink with changes in temperature or humidity.

Reinforcing a Ceiling in an Old House

Ques. The ceiling in the living room of a very old house is to be reinforced. Originally, the room consisted of several small rooms, but the partitions were removed, making a single living room of approximately 18 × 21 ft. The joists run the long (21-ft.) way, are hand-hewed approximately 3-3/4 × 7 in., are set on 36-in. centers, and they have sagged an inch. The floor consists of rough 1-in. boards. How can the ceiling be reinforced?

Ans. Assuming that the beamed ceiling effect is to be preserved and that the ceiling height is sufficient to permit the beams to be made wider, it is suggested that rough-sawed 2″ × 12″ timbers be placed on each side of the old joists, jacking the sag out and lagging or pinning the new joists to the old beams (Fig. 5). Use a filler strip of correct width to close the bottom.

This provides reasonable strength and stiffness for the old ceiling, if proper support can be provided for the ends of the new joists. The older beams are probably framed into heavy timber plates, as that was the common method in those days. Some of the ironwork may be used; or possibly the walls may be cut into and the new joists notched beneath the joist bearing plates. The

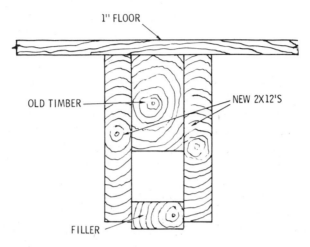

Fig. 5. Illustrating a method for reinforcing an old floor having inadequate timber joists. To preserve the old-fashioned beamed effect, new rough plank joists may be used.

spacing of the joists is slightly too large for a single floor, even though the floor is 1 in. in thickness. Another floor is probably needed above the old floor and it should be laid on thin furring strips; it should be laid across the joists in the same manner as the old floor.

Deflection of Ceilings, and Plaster Cracks

Ques. Difficulty has been experienced with cracks in dry-wall ceilings. They were built according to code requirements with deflection limited to 1/360 of the span under full design loads. One of the most troublesome jobs is a store building. The joists are $2'' \times 12''$ timbers, good-grade hemlock, with a span of 18 feet; the floor above them has never been loaded heavier than the design loading. Assuming that a deflection of less than 1/360 of the span does not cause plaster to crack, there seems to be no reason why the joints in dry-wall construction should do so. The joints have been repaired, filled, and smoothed twice. What could be causing the problem?

Ans. The "1/360 of the span" formula has no magical powers. Tests have proved that lath-and-plaster ceilings on heavily loaded, deep joists sometimes crack under only one-fourth to one-third that deflection; probably dry-wall ceilings are no more resistant than lath and plaster. In fact, they are actually *less* resistant than lath and plaster, because stresses are certain to concentrate at the joints.

It is tension on the lower sides of the joists, and not bending strains, that causes this type of problem. When the joists are stressed by bending, the lower edges are stretched, or elongated, and the plaster or dry-wall material which is firmly fastened to the joists must go along; these materials cannot withstand stretching. If the deflection is the same (1/360 of the span), the elongation is much greater in the deep joists. For example, a distributed loading of 1507 pounds is required to deflect a 2″ × 12″ joist with an 18-ft. span, a distance of .6 inch, which is 1/360 of the span; tension in the lower edge is then 1136 lbs. per sq. in. Approximately 418 pounds loading is required to cause the same amount of deflection in 2″ × 8″ joists, but the extreme fiber stress developed is approximately 741 lbs. per sq. in.; the lower edges are stretched less proportionally, with less probability of cracked plaster although the deflection is the same.

If the ceiling finish, either plaster or dry-wall, is fastened in place by means of flexible clips, or if the finish is plaster on fiberboard lath which will "give" slightly at the nails, this tension is not transferred so readily to the inextensible finish; often, the deflection at the point of failure is much more, often twice as great, as the so-called "allowable" 1/360 of the span.

One contractor who "prestresses" the joists when using dry-wall construction on long-span joists, loads the joists from above until they are brought down slightly more than the "allowable" point; then he nails on and finishes the ceiling panels. Thus, when the loading is subsequently removed, the dry-wall material is slightly in compression. Therefore, it is suggested that if the ceiling is repaired again that the floor above be loaded slightly heavier than normal; then fill and finish the joints. Under the normal, or less, loads, the joints remain in compression.

Piers in Concrete-Block Walls

Ques. A fire station 50 $\times$ 48 ft. with 15-ft. walls is to be built. It is to be roofed the 50-ft. way with long-span open-web steel joists, and the longest unsupported wall is to be 48 ft. long. Also, 12-in. concrete blocks with a reinforced peripheral beam or plate are to be used. Is this an approved type of construction, if no pilasters are used?

Ans. It is not appropriate to build a fire station, of all things, which is not in accordance with the Fire Underwriter's Code. The following is an excerpt from their National Code of 1955, Section 909.7 (b): "Walls of hollow-masonry units shall be supported at right angles to the wall face at intervals not exceeding eighteen times the nominal wall thickness."

According to that provision, two piers, or outside buttresses, are needed in the 48-ft. length, and 12-in. blocks are required for the 15-ft. height. Furthermore, concrete-block walls cannot be built much longer than 20 to 25 ft. without making allowance for expansion and contraction that is caused by temperature changes. This movement is approximately twice as great in concrete-block walls as in brick masonry, and the logical place for the expansion joints is at the piers. A supplier can furnish special pier blocks that are made for this purpose. A concrete-block wall as long as 48 ft. should never be built without control joints, and the top beam is needed to provide adequate bearings and anchorage for the long-span joists. Incidentally, the easiest way to build these beams is to use the special U-shaped blocks that are made for this purpose. The reinforcement should not pass through the control joints.

Moisture Content and Shrinkage in Paneling

Ques. A problem with shrinkage and joints opening in random-width pine paneling has been experienced. Clients apparently prefer the wide boards, but the narrow boards are supposed to have less shrinkage. Is it true that all boards, regardless of their width, have about the same shrinkage if the moisture loss is the same?

Ans. That is incorrect. Shrinkage in 1-inch lumber is almost directly proportional to the width, but flat-sawed boards shrink slightly more than edge-grained boards. Most paneling is flat-sawed.

In the average home that is heated in winter, paneling and other interior woodwork usually dries to 8 to 9 percent moisture content, although 6 percent is by no means unheard of during extremely cold winter weather. All yellow pine paneling which bears the *SPIB* brand is kiln-dried, and the moisture content when it is shipped is guaranteed to be not more than 12 percent in any single piece. With proper care and storage, this moisture content can be maintained until the lumber is used.

Drying from 12 percent moisture content to 8 percent, the shrinkage in 1″ × 4″ boards is approximately 3/64 inch; in 1″ × 6″ boards, 1/16 inch; in 1″ × 8″ boards, 5/64 inch; and in 1″ × 10″ boards, 1/8 inch. If fillet strips are not used, the cracks may be expected to open up at least that distance. If fillet strips are used, the width of the cracks may be reduced by one-half. Fillet strips may be used with either clear or knotty grades (Fig. 6).

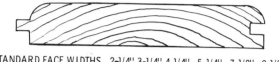

STANDARD FACE WIDTHS, 2-1/4", 3-1/4", 4-1/4", 5-1/4", 7-1/8", 9-1/8,"
3/4-INCH THICK

STANDARD DIMENSIONS, 1-1/4 INCH FACE, 3/4-INCH THICKNESS

Fig. 6. These are standard patterns of yellow-pine paneling and fillet strip, but many other patterns are available with the same dimensions. The use of the fillet strips is not imperative, but it is recommended, as it reduces the width of cracks which may be caused by shrinkage.

If the lumber possesses the moisture content which it normally possesses when it is used, the cracks open in winter when the house is heated and the humidity is low, but they close, at least partially, when the humidity is high in summer. There is no way to prevent this action.

Cracks in Radiant Ceilings

Ques. In a house with radiant ceilings, the hot-water pipes were embedded in the plaster. Now, the locations of the pipes are plainly indicated by dark, dirty streaks, and in many places the plaster has cracked above the pipes. Will covering the ceiling with dry-wall material reduce the efficiency of the heating system? Is there any other method that can be used to repair this ceiling?

Ans. In some instances, damaged ceilings were covered with 3/8" gypsum boards, applied with adhesives, and they gave reasonable satisfaction; however, authorities on the subject, including the gypsum board manufacturers themselves, do not recommend this method, so it cannot be recommended, except possibly as a last resort. In all instances, the ceiling temperature would certainly be lowered, and the water temperature would probably have to be raised to obtain the same heating effect as before. The ceiling operating temperature has probably been too high. Approximately 130°F. maximum temperature is as high as the plaster can withstand without cracking; the ceiling temperature that is commonly recommended is only 100° to 110° F.

A satisfactory method that can be used to repair cracked radiant ceilings is to cover them with one of the enameled fabric wall coverings. They are applied in the same manner as wallpaper, after spackling the plaster to a smooth surface. The coverings are so thin that they do not affect the surface temperature appreciably, and they can be painted.

Fiberboard Cannot Be "Fireproofed" Effectively

Ques. While remodeling a second-floor apartment, the woodwork and fiberboard paneling in a "knock-head" ceiling above a kitchen range were found to be scorched badly—almost charred. The condition is supposed to have resulted from grease fires on the stove, and it is a mystery that a serious fire was avoided. Is there a chemical which can be used to make materials such as wood and fiberboard fireproof?

Ans. Many brush and spray coatings are available which make the surfaces of combustible materials partially resistant to flame spread and other surface characteristics. Some of these coatings bear the Underwriter's label, but this does not imply that surfaces coated with them are given a fire-resistance rating. The rating merely compares the surfaces so treated with a standard surface of red oak for fuel contributed, flame spread, and smoke developed. These attributes are expressed as percentages, with the red-oak surface rated at 100 percent. These are *surface* characteristics only. The combustibility of the material is not affected. Fiberboard and organic-fiber acoustic tile are not rated; unless they are backed with an incombustible surface of some type, such as reinforced concrete or masonry, their coating is not considered.

The kitchen range should be moved from beneath the sloping "knock-head" ceiling; or the ceiling should be covered with a truly fire-resistant material. Plaster on metal lath is suggested. Do not attempt to "fireproof" fiberboard with any type of coating. In reality, no type of construction can truly be termed "fireproof." The term "fire-resistant" has a meaning (and it can be given a numerical value), but fiberboards, regardless of coating, have no rating.

Nail Withdrawal as Lumber Dries

Ques. A finish floor of cork tile was laid on 3/4-inch plywood over 2″ × 4″ sleepers on a concrete slab. The plywood was nailed with 8d screw nails, driven slightly below flush, and the indentations were filled. Six months after the house was occupied, during the first winter, bumps appeared on each tile directly above each of the nailheads. A few of the tile were taken up, and the nails are apparently working out. What is the cause, and what can be done about this problem?

Ans. Nail withdrawal in these instances is the result of a single cause, and one cause only. The nails were driven into wood that was high in moisture content; when the house was heated, the wood shrank, but the nails did not. The nails remained in place, but the wood around them shrank. Despite some advertising claims, deformed nails are no assurance that this condition will be prevented. In fact, well-conducted experiments performed in a recognized testing laboratory for one of the largest prefabricators in the United States showed that deformed nails actually withdrew slightly *more* than plain-shanked nails. Incidentally, cement-coated nails made the poorest showing. The thickness of the nails apparently was not significant, but unless the nails completely pierced the wood into which they were driven, the longer nails withdrew a greater distance.

There is no method known for correcting the job, except to take up the tile, drive the nails down again, and replace the tile. Probably, there will be no more trouble. This problem never occurs in old houses where the subfloors are thoroughly dry. In new work, the trouble can be avoided only by making certain that the materials are dry or by waiting until they become dry. Use the shortest nails that are practical, and, if necessary, use more nails.

Plaster Damage not Caused by Blasting

Ques. My opinion concerning a damage claim has been requested as an experienced, but distinterested, builder. The owner of a two-year-old house claims that the plaster in the house has been damaged by a blasting job which was done in removing some stumps on a road job at least 1000 feet from the house. An inspection of the house revealed that the foundations were in perfect condition with no signs of cracks or movement, but the plaster is unquestionably checked and cracked seriously. My opinion is that the cracks were caused by settlement, and in some of the rooms, the exact spots where the settlement occurred are evident. Having been called in to verify the owner's claim, it is doubtful that the cracks were caused by the blasting job. Is this a reasonable conclusion?

Ans. Being honor bound, your only choice is to state your honest conclusions. It is extremely doubtful whether the damage was caused by the blasting, unless it was near enough and heavy enough to damage the windows. In some instances, heavy blasting has been done much nearer than 1000 feet from houses, with no damaging effects, and light blasting has been done even closer to houses with no damaging effects. It is more likely that the house was built of green lumber that subsequently shrank, cracking the plaster. This was a common occurrence at about the time the house was built. Make another inspection and ascertain whether this is evident. It would be unfair to say that the owner is looking for the most favorable place to collect damages, because he may be perfectly honest, although in error in his supposition. Nothing more can be done than to state your honest opinion, which is probably correct.

Measuring the Thickness of Plaster

Ques. A serious argument has developed with my plastering contractor over a plastering specification which calls for 7/8 in. of lightweight (perlite) plaster on metal lath. My interpretation is that this means "over the face of the lath," while he insists that the thickness of the keys back of the lath is included. Who is correct?

Ans. The Underwriter's Code says measure from the face of the lath, except for metal lath, when it is measured from the *back* of the lath. Most city codes, and the F.H.A. code, are based on this standard, but some codes and some governmental authorities say, measure from the *face* of the lath. In no instance is it permissible to include the thickness of the clinches. A better and more uncontroversial specification would be to specify the depth of the grounds. This, of course, includes the thickness of the lath, whatever that may be; however, if the thickness of the lath is also specified, the thickness of the plaster is assured. In no instance does it include the thickness of the clinches.

CHAPTER 6

Insulation and
Moisture Condensation

Vapor Barriers in Masonry Walls

Ques. Where should a vapor barrier be placed to prevent wet walls in places such as dairies and laundries? Condensation is a problem on most masonry walls in similar locations.

Ans. If plain uninsulated 8-in. masonry walls are used, vapor barriers cannot control the condensation, and they may aggravate the problem. Humidity becomes very high in these rooms, and heat is conducted away readily through all types of relatively thin masonry walls, which causes the inside surfaces of the walls to become very cold during severe winter weather. Almost invariably, the inside wall surfaces reach a temperature lower than the dew point of the humid inside air. Thorough ventilation reduces condensation troubles, but this means an appreciable loss of heat, and only rarely prevents condensation troubles entirely. The walls can be furred and insulated well; this means that the inside surfaces can be kept warmer, and, possibly, condensation on these surfaces can be controlled. An effective vapor barrier on the inside, or warm side, of the wall is then needed to prevent the water vapor from penetrating the inside finish and condensing at some point *within* the wall. If a wall is hollow, venting the cavity to the outside to allow the vapor that penetrates the inside surface to escape is recommended. In exceptionally steamy rooms, such as meat-processing rooms, no serious attempt is made to control condensation; the walls and ceilings are constructed of materials such as glazed tile, which are not damaged by water.

Cores of Blocks Filled With Insulation

Ques. If a house is built of 8-in. cinder blocks, if the cores are filled with insulation materials such as perlite or vermiculite, if it is painted outside with waterproof masonry paint, and if it is plastered on the inside with lightweight insulating plaster applied directly on the masonry, is there a probability of condensation on the walls?

Ans. Calculations indicate that there is only a slight probability of condensation of moisture on the inside surface of the walls; even when the outside temperature is near zero degrees, if the relative humidity of the inside air can be kept below approximately 80 percent. Even though no special effort is made to ventilate the rooms, the relative humidity in the average home may be near 40 to 45 percent in winter; in severe weather it may be about 35 percent. However, the inside portions of a block wall are very porous, and water vapor may pass into the wall readily. Since the outside surface of the wall is to be painted, the paint may provide sufficient resistance to the entrance of vapor; however, moisture may condense underneath the paint, and the insulation may become wet, eventually causing the plaster to become damp and clammy. It is recommended that the *inside* surfaces of the outside walls be sealed effectively. This usually requires about three coats of a good lead-and-oil paint; a coat of aluminum and two color coats is better, and one of the vapor-barring enameled fabric wall coverings is even more satisfactory.

Heat conduction through this type of wall is no less, and may be slightly greater, than that of a standard uninsulated frame wall. This may be satisfactory in the extreme southern parts of the country, but do not expect too much.

Revolving-Head Roof Ventilators

Ques. It seems that some types of "revolving-head" roof ventilators (Fig. 1) are impractical. If they are practical, what is the explanation?

Ans. They are very efficient under favorable conditions, but unfavorable conditions may restrain their operating action, or

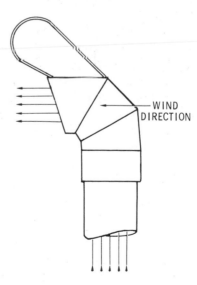

WIND
DIRECTION

Fig. 1. A revolving-head roof ventilator. Many different types of these ventilators are available.

even prevent their operation. They do not operate well if the air inside the building is partially exhausted, as when exhaust fans are placed in operation to dispose of the smoke, dust, or fumes in factories. Even the smaller exhaust fans in the kitchens and bathrooms of homes sometimes cause ventilation difficulties, and many types of heating apparatus that use combustion fuels may exhaust large volumes of air through vents or chimneys. Fireplaces require large quantities of air if they are to work satisfactorily. Remember that air cannot be exhausted from a room without replacing it with air.

Revolving ventilators use vanes to keep the front of the arrangement always facing away from the wind. As the wind rushes around the obstructing ventilator, its velocity is increased; the wind streams are constricted and their pressure is lowered. This is the so-called "Bernoulli Effect" which is an important principle in the design of airplane wings. As a result, the air pressure directly in front of the opening in the ventilator is reduced, and a slight suction effect is developed. If they are not forced to work against negative pressure and if suitable provisions are made for air to enter the room, revolving-head ventilators can operate satisfactorily. They usually work best during the winter months when the exhausted air is warmer than the outside air, because then the ventilators are assisted by natural convection.

Thin Sheets of Asbestos as Inefficient Insulation

Ques. It has been stated that the usual thin sheets of asbestos insulation that are pasted on hot-air furnace pipes are actually detrimental—worse than no insulation. Is this statement true, and if so, why?

Ans. The statement is quite true. Tests have indicated that a single tight layer of sheet asbestos pasted onto bright tin hot-air furnace pipes permitted 37 percent more heat to escape, than the bare tin pipes alone, but three layers of sheet asbestos, loosely wrapped around the pipes, saved about 25 percent of the heat loss that occurred through the bare tin. The emissivity, or ability to cast off heat radiation, of bright tin is very low—it is very high on rough asbestos surfaces. *Dense* asbestos material is poor heat insulation, but *loose* asbestos material, with a large quantity of air contained within its mass, is moderately effective.

Condensation of Water in Chimneys

Ques. What was done incorrectly to cause the chimney of a recently built house to sweat, causing the moisture to damage the inside wall of the house? The dampness can be felt by placing a hand and arm either through the thimble hole or downward from the top. How can this condition be corrected?

Ans. The chimney is too cold to operate efficiently. Chimneys built outside the house often have this problem, as do chimneys that are unnecessarily large. The kind of fuel used was not stated, but gas-burning appliances actually produce large quantities of water-vapor (chemically H_2O) by chemically combining the hydrogen (H) in the gas with the oxygen (O) from the air. If the chimney walls are too cold, vapor condenses on them in the form of water. If wood is burned as a fuel, especially green or wet wood, oils and creosotes are vaporized, condensing in the chimney in the same manner and making a real mess. The velocity of the gases in the flue can be increased, to expel them before they can cause trouble, by reducing the size of the chimney. This is usually done by inserting a metal liner. A sheet-metal worker can make and insert a stainless steel liner; or commercial enameled steel liners are available for this purpose. Neither galvanized nor black iron pipes is suitable for this purpose.

Chicken-Netting as an Insulation Support for a Crawl Space

Ques. Is it a good practice to staple chicken-wire netting beneath the floor joists to support 2-in. rock-wool batts for insulation above a crawl space? Where should the vapor barrier be placed?

Ans. This is an excellent practice (Fig. 2). It provides the extra insulation of a dead-air space, and it holds the insulation in place effectively. Vapor barriers should *always* be placed on the *warm* side of insulations, if it is necessary to use vapor barriers.

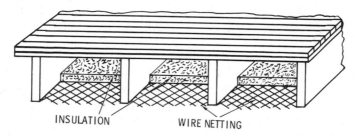

INSULATION   WIRE NETTING

Fig. 2. Wire netting placed beneath crawl-space joists to support insulation batts.

In this instance, the barrier can be placed either just above the insulation or just beneath the floor. Either linoleum or flexible tile on the floor above are effective vapor barriers. A vapor barrier is not necessary if the crawl-space area is dry and well ventilated.

Condensation in a House With Hollow-Concrete Walls

Ques. The walls of a house are constructed of hollow concrete with a 2-1/2″ air space. The first floor is placed on a slab-on-ground, and the second floor is placed on a reinforced slab; hollow tile were used for the roof. The house is heated by means of butane heaters. Condensation on the walls is a very serious problem. What can be done to correct this problem of condensation?

Ans. The house is a very efficient condenser unit. With the information given, calculations are impossible, but heat transmission through this kind of construction is very high. In severe winter weather, the inside surfaces of the walls and roof become very cold—a perfect setup for condensation if the air in the house is permitted to become excessively humid. Large quantities of water, in vapor form, are released inside all normal homes merely by living in them. Bathing, cooking, laundry work, respiration, and transpiration of people and house plants, all contribute to moisture. In addition, butane gas is being burned, and the heaters probably are not vented. Butane gas has a high hydrogen content, which means that about 50 cu. ft. of water vapor is discharged into the home for each 10 cu. ft. of gas consumed. If condensation troubles are to be avoided, this vapor must escape quickly to the outside air, before it has time to condense; or the walls must be insulated and allowed to get very warm, thus keeping their temperature higher than the dew point of the air inside the house.

It is doubtful that the condensation can be controlled without a difficult and expensive job of insulation; eventually, this may be necessary. In the meantime, the heaters can be provided with effective vents to the outside. The house should be kept well ventilated; this is much more important in winter than in summer. Ventilation may not completely prevent condensation, but it should reduce it.

Wet Soil Underneath a House

Ques. After wrecking an open porch on a home, a room is to be built in its place. The soil under the porch is very wet, and it is feared that the joists will rot. What can be done to prevent this?

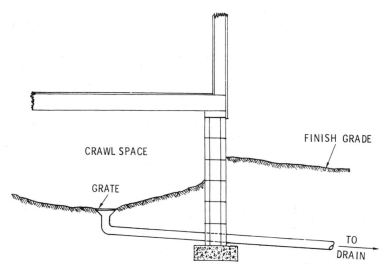

Fig. 3. An approved crawl-space drain. The drain may be connected to a sewer, or it may be emptied into a low place on top of the ground.

Ans. Grade the lawn to drain any water away from the foundation walls, and use foundation ventilators (Fig. 3). There is seldom an excuse for wet ground beneath a house; where this cannot be avoided, the space should be drained by a tile drain connected to an outlet. Usually, with good drainage, the soil beneath a house becomes nearly bone dry. There is little danger of the joists rotting, if they can be placed approximately 1 foot above the ground. If the sills cannot be placed at least 12 inches above the grade, use treated lumber.

Insulating Value of Air Spaces

Ques. Is adequate insulation provided for a workshop if the inside surfaces of the walls are finished with plasterboard? The

NO
INSULATION

2" BATT
INSULATION

CAVITY FILL
INSULATION

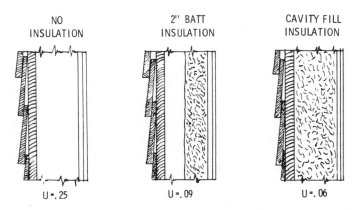

U = .25   U = .09   U = .06

Fig. 4. Illustrating the effect of blanket (left), batt (center), and loose-fill (right) insulations on the standard studded wall, consisting of lap siding, 3/4" wood sheathing, 3-5/8" studs, gypsum lath and plaster.

stud cavities are to be tightly closed, forming dead air spaces (Fig. 4).

Ans. This depends on the definition for "adequate." If the stud cavities are no more than 4 inches deep, they may be termed "dead" air spaces, since convection currents are not significant. The space will have appreciable insulating value, but the wall is not as resistant to heat flow as it could be with some other types of insulation material.

As the wall is described, the "U" value is approximately 0.26. Two inches of rock wool insulation can reduce the "U" value to approximately 0.10; or, if the cavities are filled entirely with insulation, the "U" value may be approximately 0.07. The "U" value of a wall is the amount of heat (in Btu's) which passes through 1 sq. ft. of the wall in one hour of time, if the temperature is 1°F. colder on one side of the wall than on the other side. A wall that is constructed better than the one proposed probably will pay more interest on the investment in the form of increased comfort and reduced heating costs.

Reflective Insulations

Ques. What is the best way to install reflective insulations? Is an air-space necessary on both sides of the foil?

Ans. Two air spaces, each 1 inch in depth, possess twice as much resistance to heat conduction as a single space that is 2 inches deep. However, a single foil facing a space 3/4 inch deep, or more, stops about 95 percent of all incident radiation. There is little or no difference, whether the foil is placed on the warm side or the cold side of the cavity. A foil placed on both sides of the divider, or with the reflective surfaces facing both cavities, is little (if any) more effective than when only one side is made reflective.

Heat transmission by radiation should not be confused with heat transmission by conduction. These are separate and distinct phenomena, and are in no way related.

Water-Insulated Roofs

Ques. In building a flat-roofed auto court, it has been proposed that approximately 4 inches of water be used on the roof as a means of insulation. Winter temperature may be as low as $-20°F$. Is this type of roof recommended?

Ans. The insulating value of a water-covered roof lies almost entirely in its reflectivity—that is, its resistance to the sun's radiation. Consequently, this type of roof is not very effective in winter when the heat flow is in the opposite direction, even though the probability of freezing could be ignored. In winter, additional mass insulation is necessary. It is doubtful that water-covered roofs can be recommended for areas where winter temperatures may drop as low as $-20°F$. In any instance, the roof should be designed to bear the weight of the water; 4 inches of water weighs approximately 20 lbs. per sq. ft. If the water rates are favorable and if the wind drift is not too objectionable, fine sprays for the roof are more effective than a water covering for the roof.

Cavity-Wall Insulation

Ques. A cavity-wall building job is nearly completed, and the owner has decided suddenly that he wants the wall of the cavity insulated. How can this be accomplished at this stage?

Ans. If the usual precautions have been observed to prevent mortar from falling and collecting at the bottom of the cavities, vermiculite insulation probably can be poured in. This type of insulation runs freely, and may fill the cavities satisfactorily. In most instances, it does not settle appreciably. The most difficult portion of the job is to fill beneath the windows, if the sills have been set. Probably, the sills will have to be lifted.

Insulation for Edges of Slab Floors

Ques. In a recently completed house with a slab floor, the lower parts of the walls and the edges of the slab are always damp. In severe weather, frost often gathers. What causes this problem, and what can be done to correct it?

Ans. The described condition is caused by lack of insulation in the edges of the slab. The edges of the slab lose heat rapidly and readily to the cold air on the outside of the house, and the water vapor that is generated inside the house condenses on the cold surfaces. The only thing that can be done is to add insulation on the *outside* of the foundation. The insulation should have been placed *inside* the foundation walls when the house was built, but that is now too late.

Asphalt-impregnated fiberboard or foamed styrene slab insulation approximately 2″ thick is sometimes used. Dig downward along the foundation walls, extending the insulation downward over the wall that is exposed above the grade level (see Fig. 5).

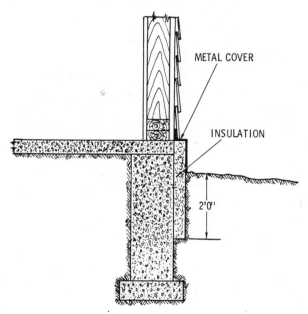

METAL COVER

INSULATION

2'0''

Fig. 5. If insulation of the slab edges is omitted when the house is built, it can be installed later only by placing it outside the walls. Then 2-in. asphalt-impregnated fiberboard is used most commonly.

Damp-Proofing the Cavity of Masonry Walls

Ques. Is it necessary to damp-proof the base of the cavity of masonry walls?

Ans. Damp-proofing may not be absolutely necessary under all conditions, but it is often advisable, and some codes demand it.

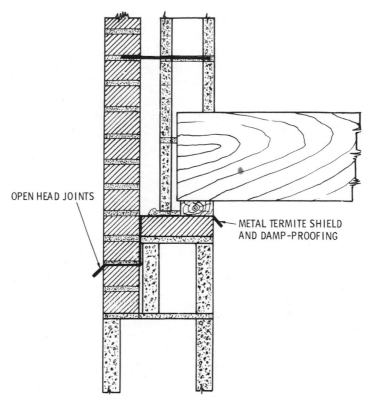

OPEN HEAD JOINTS

METAL TERMITE SHIELD
AND DAMP-PROOFING

Fig. 6. Illustrating how a metal damp-proofing flashing may also serve as a termite shield which is usually required.

The flashing can also serve as a termite shield, and these shields are usually required (Fig. 6).

Controlling Humidity Inside a Home

Ques. Generally, it is believed necessary to place vapor barriers on the inside of exterior walls when insulation has been blown in.

161

Why is it impossible to control the humidity on the inside, thus controlling condensation in the walls?

Ans. It is quite true that controlling the humidity inside a home can *assist* in preventing condensation within the walls, but it is difficult, if not impossible, for the average family to maintain humidity that is low enough to *assure* no problem. Cooking, dishwashing, laundry work, and bathing are contributors to the vapor content of the air inside the home. Extremely effective and continuous ventilation is necessary if the humidity is to be controlled within safe limits. People often forget to ventilate the home, and many persons cannot reconcile themselves to the idea of expelling heated air and replacing it with cold air, which must be heated,

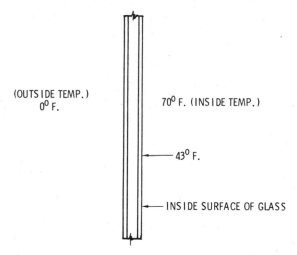

(OUTSIDE TEMP.)
0° F.

70° F. (INSIDE TEMP.)

— 43° F.

◄— INSIDE SURFACE OF GLASS

Fig. 7. Standard double-thickness glass, with 1/4-in. air space. When the outside temperature is 0°F. and the inside temperature is 70°F., the temperature of the inside surface of the glass is approximately 43°F.; when the relative humidity inside the home reaches approximately 41 percent, the glass begins to fog. Condensation on the bars of metal sash, however, begins long before that point is reached.

from outdoors. In addition, many persons are quite conscious of humidity requirements. They believe that high humidity is necessary to health and well-being, although that point is debatable. Due to a combination of factors, the relative humidity in winter in most modern homes located in the Eastern and Midwestern regions of the United States probably averages 40 to 45 percent; in zero weather, it may average 25 to 35 percent, which is much too high to make condensation improbable.

Considering all these factors, vapor barriers should be used in all insulated walls. Then, vapor content can increase without the possibility of condensation ruining the outside paint job. The chief problem is water forming on the windows, which may be present even with double windows. Although the heavy *Thermopane* type of double glass with 1/2-inch air space is used, the glass begins to fog when the relative humidity indoors is 45 percent (and temperature is 70°F. inside; 10°F. outside). Condensation may form on the rails and muntins of metal sash long before these conditions are reached (Fig. 7). Thus, it is necessary to control the humidity inside the home if condensation troubles are to be prevented. This is usually ineffective in colder regions.

Required Area of Vent Openings

Ques. Is there a general rule for determining the correct sizes of ventilators for attics and crawl spaces?

Ans. If the vent openings are all on the same level, as in attics with eaves vents and in crawl spaces with foundation vents, a generally accepted rule is: the free vent opening shall have an area equal to 1/150 of the area of the floor served. For attics, if one-half of the vent area is placed in the roof ridge, or near the ridge, the total free area may be reduced to 1/300 of the area served.

The free area of ventilator openings is reduced by screens or louvers. After the desired free area has been determined, and if the area of the opening is to be restricted by any of the following arrangements, multiply the required area of the vents by a factor given as follows:

hardware cloth, 1/4-inch, multiply by.....................1
wire screen, 8 meshes per inch, multiply by.............1-1/4
insect screen, 16 meshes per inch, multiply by........2
louvers with 1/4-in. screen, multiply by...............2
louvers with 8-mesh screen, multiply by................2-1/4
louvers with 16-mesh screen, multiply by..............3

Sweating Cold-Water Pipes

Ques. Condensation of water is a problem on two copper cold-water pipes recently installed in a meeting hall. During humid weather, or during banquets, water condenses on the pipes and drips down onto the tables. What can be done to correct this problem?

Ans. The pipes should be insulated. Many types of pipe insulation are available, but the common heat insulation is not satisfactory for this purpose, unless a tight vapor barrier is placed over the insulation. Otherwise, the water vapor passes through the insulation, condenses against the cold-water pipes, and dampens or wets the insulation continually.

Placement of Reflective Foils

Ques. Reflective foil is usually placed against the faces of the studs, lathing and plastering directly over it. Should the practice be changed, placing the foil nearer the center of the width of the studs, thereby forming two air spaces?

Ans. The first method is used more often, applying the foil to the faces of the studs. There is little difference in the two methods, so far as the reflective insulating value of the foil is concerned. A single-faced foil that faces a space stops up to 95 percent of incident radiation. The reduction in conductivity that is gained by the use of the two air spaces is not great, as it would reduce the "U" value of the wall only slightly. If the foil is cut between the studs, it is not an effective vapor barrier. If an effective barrier were necessary, it would have to be applied over the faces of the studs, as a foil or film. In all instances, vapor barriers should be placed as near as possible to the warm side of the wall.

Insulating Exposed Ceiling Joists

Ques. A camp cabin which is frequently used in winter has exposed sheathing. Two proposed sketches (Fig. 8) are submitted for insulation of the ceiling, leaving a portion of the rafters exposed. Which of the two designs is preferable?

Ans. Neither of the designs is recommended (see Fig. 8). Condensation above the insulation is almost certain to be a problem. The ceiling may be damaged and the sheathing deteriorated seriously, before the damage becomes evident. Use a continuous and unbroken vapor barrier *underneath* the rafters. The vapor barrier covers on blanket insulations are not effective when the flanges are nailed to the flat sides of the rafters, as indicated in the sketches.

Vapor Barriers for Existing Walls

Ques. In insulating an old house, can a vapor barrier be installed in the existing walls?

Ans. An effective barrier can be developed on the inside of the walls, where it is most effective. A coat of primer and two coats of good-quality oil paint may be fairly effective; or a coat of

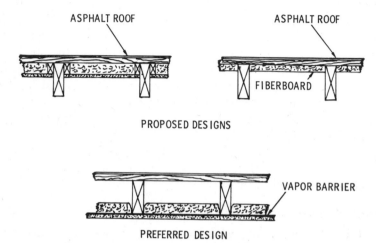

ASPHALT ROOF

ASPHALT ROOF

FIBERBOARD

PROPOSED DESIGNS

VAPOR BARRIER

PREFERRED DESIGN

Fig. 8. Insulating a ceiling with exposed roof sheathing. Neither of the two proposed designs (top) is satisfactory. Condensation underneath the roofing may cause the sheathing to decay, and the ceiling finishes may be damaged by moisture. An unbroken vapor barrier, (bottom) placed as near the warm side as possible, is required to prevent condensation.

aluminum, plus two color coats may be used. Gloss paints are most effective, but most persons prefer the flat finishes. The paint coatings may be effective for a length of time, but they are not permanently effective; one of the enameled-fabric wall coverings is preferable. They are more permanent, can be painted over, and they can be removed readily. Also, there is no risk of piling paint on top of paint, until the heavy coatings flake off. Calcimines and casein paints are not effective vapor barriers.

Dampness in Closets Located on Outside Walls

Ques. In building a 7'0" × 16'0" extension on a bedroom, a closet is located on the outside wall. An adviser has stated that the closet is certain to be damp. Can this be avoided?

Ans. Dampness is not necessarily inevitable, but it is common in closets located on outside walls. These closets are rarely heated directly, and the outside wall often becomes cold in severe weather. Also, the temperature of the wall surface may fall below the dew point of the air inside the house, resulting in condensation, dampness, and mustiness. This often occurs in unheated bedrooms, especially underneath a bed or behind heavy furniture that is placed against the outside walls. Although the room is cool, these walls should always be heavily insulated; then the wall surface may attain a temperature that is high enough to prevent condensation. Excellent air circulation in the closet may prevent these prob-

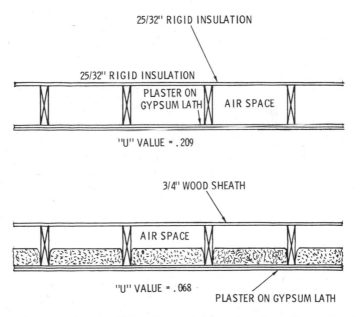

Fig. 9. Illustrating the appreciable reduction in "U" value of a ceiling, achieved by adding 3 inches of insulation.

lems, but that is difficult, if there is no window. Louvered closet doors are often used. It is useless to attempt to seal the closet against vapor infiltrating from the inhabited rooms, unless the closet is vented to the outside.

Do not Overestimate the Heat-Insulation Value of Air Spaces

Ques. Are blanket and batt insulations as effective as a deep air space in actual heat-resisting value for ceiling construction? What are the actual heat-resisting values of the following: (1) plaster on gypsum lath, 7-1/2″ air space, and 25/32″ insulating sheathing; and (2) plaster on gypsum lath, 3″ blanket insulation, and 3/4″ wood sheathing (Fig. 9)?

Ans. The "U" values of the two types of ceiling construction can be calculated as follows:

1. For large air space
   inside surface resistance 0.61
   plaster on gypsum lath 0.42
   7-1/2″ air space 0.91
   insulating sheathing 2.37
   roofing 0.30
   outside surface resistance 0.17
   _____
   Total resistance 4.78

$$\text{``U'' value} = \frac{1}{R} = \frac{1}{4.78} = 0.209 \text{ Btu}$$

2. For blanket insulation
   inside surface resistance 0.61
   plaster on gypsum lath 0.42
   3″ blanket insulation 11.10

4-1/2" air space	0.91
3/4" wood sheathing	0.98
roofing	0.30
outside surface resistance	0.17
Total resistance	14.49

$$\text{``U'' value} = \frac{1}{R} = \frac{1}{14.49} = 0.068 \text{ Btu}$$

The heat loss ("U" value), in Btu, through the blanket-insulated ceiling is only one-third the heat loss through the ceiling with the 7-1/2" air space and the insulating sheathing. Therefore, proper ceiling insulation returns excellent interest on the investment, usually returning its total cost through reduced heating costs in five years.

Insulation of Basement Floors

Ques. A customer wants to insulate a basement floor by means of a perlite concrete slab. What mix should be used? The floor is to be covered with asphalt tile.

Ans. None of the ultra-light insulating concretes, such as perlite or vermiculite, provides exceptional structural strength; to obtain sufficient compressive strength for them to be used for floors, considerable sand and cement must be added, and their insulating value is either gone or reduced to the point where it is no longer significant. At a density of 60 pounds per cubic foot, and requiring eight bags of cement per cubic yard, the strength of perlite concrete may be not more than 150 lbs. per sq. in.; the pressure of a woman's spiked heel easily may be four times that pressure. Thus, it would be practical to pour a conventional floor of sand-gravel concrete above. Conventional sand-gravel concrete (six bags of cement per cubic yard) often tests 5000 pounds per square inch, which is more than 30 times the strength of perlite concrete using eight bags of cement.

Basement floors are usually not insulated, unless it is intended to attempt to control summer condensation on an impervious tile floor or for a similar purpose. Then, insulation may be effective. Even above the grade and with heating elements embedded in the concrete, insulation is not commonly used, except for around the exposed edges of the slabs.

Condensation Between Double-Glass Panes

Ques. Home-built double-glass windows were recently installed in a wall near windows with factory-built double-glass windows. In cold weather, the homemade units frost on the inside of the outer glass, but the factory-built panes do not. How can this be explained?

Ans. The factory-built double panes are sealed airtight along the edges, and the air inside the cavity is very dry. In the homemade units, the moisture-carrying air from inside the inhabited rooms cannot be excluded entirely from the cavity, and condensation occurs on the coolest surface, which is the inside of the outer glass.

There are two solutions: (1) the cavity may be vented to the outside, allowing the humid air to escape freely before it can condense; (2) seal the inside cavity as tightly as possible, excluding at least a portion of the humidity from between the panes. The two methods are often combined.

Effect of Doubling the Thickness of Insulations

Ques. In what proportion does doubling the thickness of insulation increase its efficiency? Is its value doubled?

Ans. Doubling the thickness of insulation doubles the resistance of the insulation to the passage of heat, but this is not the complete story. The necessary calculations are best illustrated by means of an example (Fig. 10).

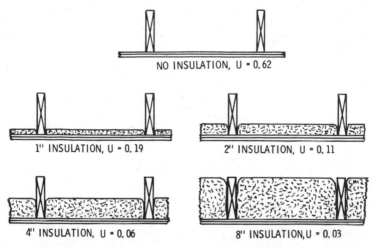

NO INSULATION, U = 0. 62

1" INSULATION, U = 0. 19

2" INSULATION, U = 0. 11

4" INSULATION, U = 0. 06

8" INSULATION, U = 0. 03

Fig. 10. Illustrating the effect of successively doubling the thickness of insulation in a ceiling. The insulation considered is rock wool ("k" value = 0.27). Note that the saving in heat loss achieved by the first inch of insulation is nearly three times the saving attained by the last 7 inches of insulation.

In a simple type of ceiling (plaster on gypsum lath) with an unfloored, unheated attic above, the resistance to the transmission of heat is very low. Expressed in numbers, this is approximately 1.63. The actual heat passage through this type of ceiling per hour, per square foot (for each degree difference in temperature above and below the ceiling) is the reciprocal of the resistance, or

$$\frac{1}{1.63}, \text{ which is 0.62 Btu}$$

171

This number is called the "U" value of the uninsulated ceiling. On many brands of rigid insulation, and on the covers of some batt and blanket insulation, the resistances are marked; these are commonly called the "R" values.

If a 1-in. blanket of rock wool with an "R" value of 3.70 is placed over the uninsulated ceiling, its resistance to heat passage is increased to 1.63 + 3.70, or 5.33, and its "U" value is reduced to

$$\frac{1}{5.33}, \text{ or approximately 0.19 Btu}$$

This is a reduction of approximately 0.43 Btu, which is a reduction of approximately two-thirds the total heat loss through the uninsulated ceiling, which is, of course, worthwhile.

If the thickness of insulation is then doubled, making its total thickness 2 in., the resistance of the ceiling becomes 5.33 + 3.70, or 9.03, and its "U" value becomes

$$\frac{1}{9.03}, \text{ or approximately 0.11 Btu}$$

This is only a slight reduction of approximately 0.08 Btu from the "U" value of the ceiling with 1 inch of insulation, but this is still worthwhile.

Doubling the thickness of the insulation again, to 4 inches, increases the resistance of the ceiling to 9.03 + (2 × 3.70) = 16.43, and reduces it "U" value to

$$\frac{1}{16.43}, \text{ or 0.06 Btu}$$

This reduction is only 0.05 Btu from the "U" value of the ceiling with 2 inches of insulation.

If the thickness of the insulation is then again doubled, to 8 inches total thickness, the resistance of the ceiling is increased to 16.43 + (4 × 3.70) = 31.23, and the "U" value is reduced to

$$\frac{1}{31.23}, \text{ or } 0.03 \text{ Btu}$$

This is a reduction of slightly less than 0.03 Btu from the "U" value with 4 inches of insulation; such a small saving in heat probably would never recover its cost in reduced fuel bills during the life of the building, unless the fuel used is extremely expensive.

Although it is true that the resistance of the insulation in the ceiling is doubled as the thickness is doubled, the heat conserved as the thickness is increased becomes smaller and smaller, until increased insulation is not a paying proposition. This is the well-known "law of diminishing returns." The cost of the insulation must be balanced with the actual savings made in fuel costs. Note that in the above example, the saving in heat loss achieved by the use of the *first inch* of insulation is *nearly three times* as great as the saving attained by the *last seven inches* of insulation.

Vapor Barriers in Laminated Roofs

Ques. A small, rather flat roof is to be laminated with low-grade 2″ × 4″ boards nailed side by side. A 2-in. standard insulation is to be placed over it, and a built-up asphalt-felt cover is to be used. Below, 1″ × 2″ furring strips and dry-wall material are to be used. In the past, some of these roofs have been badly damaged by rot immediately below the roof cover. Is a vapor barrier needed and where should it be placed?

Ans. The vapor barrier is needed, and it should be placed under the furring strips, immediately above the dry-wall material. In all instances, vapor barriers should be placed as near the warm side as possible; otherwise, the barrier itself may become so cold that condensation will occur. The use of a foil, instead of a film, for the barrier will improve the insulating qualities of the roof; this is especially effective in summer, which is very desirable if the room below is to be air conditioned. In any event, to be more effective the barrier should be continuous, and lapped tightly on a furring strip.

Paint Films for Vapor Barriers

Ques. In many situations, it is not practical to remove interior wall treatment to install vapor barriers. Can painting the walls and ceilings of a house provide adequate vapor barriers to prevent condensation?

Ans. Three coats of an oil paint, or one coat of aluminum and two color coats, are a fairly effective vapor barrier, but calcimines, casein paints, and most of the water-mixed paints are not effective. Paint films are not permanently vapor-barring. In time, they check and lose their effectiveness, making it necessary to renew them periodically. It is possible that paint layers piled on may finally result in a flaky coating that is unmanageable. It is more practical to cover the walls with one of the decorative oil-fabric wall coverings. These coverings can be painted at any time, and they are readily removable.

Insulating Values of Sheathing

Ques. What are the insulating values of the various commonly-used sheathing boards?

Ans. For the most part, the insulating values of sheathing boards vary approximately inversely as their densities, i.e., the heaviest boards are the poorest insulators. The insulating values (R value) of the following are:

5/16" plywood 0.30
1/2" gypsum board 0.45
3/4" matched wood boards 0.94
1/2" fiberboard 1.43
3/4" fiberboard 2.14

Condensation on Windows

Ques. Why does condensation sometimes form on windows when the outside temperature is only 50°F., while at other times, when the temperature is near freezing, condensation does not appear?

Ans. Condensation is caused by humidity conditions as well as temperature conditions. At any given temperature, there is a "dew point" humidity; or point at which the air begins to lose a portion of its vapor, which is usually deposited as dew, water, or frost on the coldest surface that it contacts. The accompanying list gives the temperatures of the surfaces corresponding to the various relative humidities of the air inside a home (at the usual winter inside temperature of 70°F.) at which dew begins to form on the surface:

If relative humidity is 20%; dew forms on a surface at 28°F.
If relative humidity is 30%; dew forms on a surface at 37°F.
If relative humidity is 40%; dew forms on a surface at 45°F.
If relative humidity is 50%; dew forms on a surface of 51°F.
If relative humidity is 60%; dew forms on a surface at 56°F.
If relative humidity is 70%; dew forms on a surface at 61°F.
If relative humidity is 80%; dew forms on a surface at 64°F.

Insulation Space Around Chimneys

Ques. Is it true that no insulation in a 2-in. space between the wood framing and the chimney is actually safer than packing this space with mineral wool? This does not seem logical. Can you explain?

Ans. Insulation does not stop heat flow. Insulation may retard heat flow, but if the heat cannot escape readily, it may build up, and the insulation may become so hot that it becomes a fire hazard. If there is a free-air space located between the hot chimney and combustible wood, it is probable that the heat can escape through cracks between the baseboard and the wall or between the shoe molding and the floor, or through similar vents that can be provided purposely (Fig. 11). Natural convection assures some air movement if the cavity is void, but if the cavity is packed with insulation, air movement is prevented, and a heat build-up is likely.

It is well recognized, however, that a 2-in. air space between a hot chimney and wood framing is not automatically a safeguard against fire. If the winter is cold and firing is intense and continuous, a 4-in. air space is recommended.

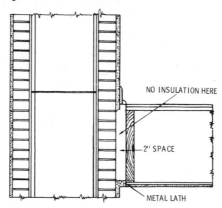

NO INSULATION HERE

2" SPACE

METAL LATH

Fig. 11. It is recommended that a 2″ air space between the chimney and combustible framing be left *void* of insulation of any type, which itself may become so hot that it becomes a fire hazard.

Wood ignites when it is exposed to a temperature of 600°F. for only a short time. Wood can withstand exposure to temperatures up to 300°F. for long periods of time, but, unquestionably, this is a dangerous practice. A practical rule is as follows: *If a wooden surface is heated so highly that the bare hand cannot be held comfortably against it, the conditions are unsafe.*

Insulation of Brick-Veneered Walls

Ques. A lumberman advises that it is not necessary to insulate the walls of a brick-veneered house that is being built. Is this advice valid?

Ans. It is definitely *not* true. Heat transmission through a standard uninsulated frame wall, with lap siding, wood sheathing, $2'' \times 4''$ studs, lath and plaster inside, is approximately 0.25 Btu per hour for each square foot of surface per degree of temperature difference between outside and inside. This is called the "U" value of the wall. The same wall, with brick-veneer siding replacing the lap siding, possesses a slightly higher "U" value, of approximately 0.27 Btu. Neither of these walls should be built without insulation, because of excessive fuel costs. The cost of the insulation may be returned in the form of reduced fuel bills within approximately five years.

Clearances for Furnaces

Ques. The top portion of a hot-air furnace is approximately 12 inches from the lower side of the basement ceiling, and the ceiling becomes so hot that the pitch fries out of the pine boards. Is this considered dangerous? How much clearance is usually necessary, and how can the ceiling be fireproofed? Should it be covered with sheet metal?

Ans. The installation is definitely a serious fire hazard. Although residential warm-air furnaces are generally classified as "low-heat" devices, a minimum of 18-inches clearance from combustible walls or ceilings is recommended. Less than the recommended clearance requires some type of fire-stopping material.

Sheet metal, *Transite,* or gypsum plaster on gypsum or metal lath can be used, but these materials should not be placed tightly against a wooden ceiling. A space between the fire-stopping material and the combustible surface should be provided to allow air circulation to carry away the heat; otherwise, the fire-stopping material itself may become hot enough to become a fire hazard. Probably, the old wooden ceiling should be removed, and the fire-stopping material applied directly to the lower side of the joists.

Chimney That Overheats

Ques. An inside chimney in a three-story house becomes very hot during severe winter weather when the oil burner is working hard. The plaster on the chimney becomes so hot that a hand cannot be held against it. Is this high temperature dangerous, and what can be done about it?

Ans. This type of problem is unusual, arising only when the chimney is extremely high and, perhaps, slightly undersized. Usually, it is the shorter chimneys that are a problem. If the chimney is relatively short and oversized, it may not become hot enough to operate efficiently, and tars, water, oils, and creosotes may condense from the smoke and chimney gases, making a mess. If the chimney is relatively tall and has excessive draft, as in this instance, the draft may be so strong that unburned, but vaporized oil is drawn into the chimney and the combustion process completed there. This action probably does not occur, but if it does occur, the chimney is a real fire hazard, and it is very wasteful of fuel.

To correct the condition, a balanced damper, sometimes called a barometric damper, should be installed in the smoke pipe near the chimney inlet. These devices are inexpensive, and they are fully automatic and effective in their action. When the fire begins in the burner and the chimney is cool, the draft is low and the damper remains closed. As the chimney is heated up and the draft is increased, the damper opens; the draft is held down and cooled by the introduction of cool air. A manually controlled damper cannot replace the barometric damper. In most instances, barometric dampers are not necessary, but some codes require their installation with oil-burning equipment. Although the use of the barometric damper is generally discouraged by heating engineers, it is extremely useful in some installations.

Condensation Problems in Attic

Ques. Condensation troubles have developed in the attic of a one-story ell attached to a house (Fig. 12). This new addition was well insulated when it was built, with loose-fill insulation placed above the fiberboard ceiling finish, but frost forms against the roof sheathing in winter, despite the ventilators in the gable. Aluminum foil was placed above the joists, but water collected underneath · the foil and the foil has to be removed. What can be done to halt this problem?

Ans. The water vapor is being generated in the room below the attic. The vapor passes readily through the fiberboard ceiling, through the insulation, and enters the attic. Since the roof covering itself is more or less an effective vapor barrier, water condenses against the roof covering. If the roof temperature is below 32°F., the condensation is in the form of frost or ice. Note that this condition is actually aggravated by the ceiling insulation, because it prevents the heat from below passing upward to warm the attic.

179

The idea in which a vapor barrier was placed above the ceiling was excellent, but it was placed in the wrong position. When placed above the insulation, the foil becomes cold in the same manner as the lower side of the roof covering, because it is insulated from the heat below; and when the temperature of the foil drops below the dew point of the humid air from below, water is formed. Vapor barriers are useful in their proper place, but they must be kept *warm*. This means that they *must* be placed on the *lower* or *warm* side of the insulation.

It is slightly more difficult to install an effective vapor barrier now. It should have been placed directly beneath the ceiling joists, immediately above the fiberboard finish and under the insulation when the room was built. It is hardly worthwhile to remove the insulation now and cut in the vapor barrier between the joists.

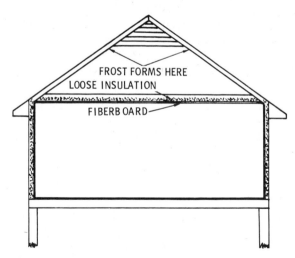

Fig. 12. Despite the gable louvers, condensation on the roof boards is a problem in this room. The condensation can be prevented only by using a vapor barrier on the warm side of the ceiling.

These jobs are not often satisfactory. The barrier cannot be made continuous beneath the joists, and it cannot be made vaportight. This identical problem has been solved by removing an old wall-board ceiling, with loose insulation lying directly on it. The old wallboard was placed above the top edges of the joists, and the insulation placed above it. Then, a vapor barrier with a reflective aluminum face was placed beneath the joists, and a new dry-wall ceiling applied. This was an extremely messy job, but it has been entirely satisfacory.

As an alternative, the ceiling may be covered with one of the vapor-barring oiled or enameled fabric wall coverings. They are applied in the same manner as wallpaper, they are decorative, they can be painted when it is desired to do so, and they can be removed readily. This type of covering keeps the vapor out of the attic, and the barrier never becomes cold enough to condense the moisture. However, a vapor build-up in the room below may occur, and increased ventilation in the room may be required.

Condensation in Chimneys

Ques. A two-story chimney is built on the outside, but it is exposed on the inside of the house and plastered against the brick. Formerly, coal and wood were used for fuels, but three winters ago the fuel was changed to gas. Now, brown stains have appeared on the plaster of the chimney inside the house, and the chimney itself is becoming stained on the outside of the house. What can be done about this problem?

Ans. Probably, the brown stains result from the residue from the fuels that were formerly used, especially the wood. Brown creosotes condense readily from wood smoke, and they are water soluble. Gas fires leave no residue, except for water which may condense if the chimney operates at a temperature that is too low.

Water from the gas fire is probably dissolving the residues from the former fuels to make the brown stains.

The chimney should be lined with a stainless pipe or one of the commercial chimney liners that are available. They are inserted at the top, coupling on additional sections as the pipe is lowered. An expert sheet-metal man can do this job. The pipe reduces the size of the chimney, the liner operates at a hotter temperature, and the velocity of the flue gases is increased. The gases and vapors are exhausted to the open air before they can be cooled and condensed. Do not attempt to use ordinary black or galvanized smoke pipe for this purpose; it does not last long enough to pay for the labor in installing it.

Condensation on a Basement Floor

Ques. Approximately 2-1/2 years ago, during rather cool fall weather, the basement floor was poured in an unfinished house, completing the pouring operation after nightfall. The finisher remained on the job nearly all night, but left toward morning, leaving approximately one-half the floor darbied, but still very wet. On returning early the next morning, the remaining portion of the floor was slightly too hard to trowel, so it was made wet again, sprinkled lightly with neat cement, which was floated and troweled in. This portion of the floor is in excellent shape; it is very smooth and hard, but the portion troweled the night before is rather rough and probably porous, since it was troweled while it was too wet.

Now, when the weather is humid, water collects on the smoother portion. During a humid period last summer, this portion was slippery wet, although at the time there was a protracted dry spell. In the rough, porous portion, there was no sign of water. The floor is poured on a well-compacted gravel fill, and during cold winter weather, it is all quite dry. Can the floor be covered with asphalt tile this winter, to avoid condensation troubles later?

Ans. The following illustrates what is actually occurring. Normally, the outside air has a temperature of 80°F., with a relative humidity of 78 percent. These conditions are very common in summer. The dew point of air at that relative humidity is approximately 72° to 73°F. If the air contacts a surface with a temperature that is lower than its dew point, condensation is deposited on the surface. The temperature of the basement air is approximately five degrees cooler than the outside air, for example, 75°F., and since the floor slab is in direct contact with the cool earth, it is constantly losing heat to the earth. Perhaps it is not losing a great amount of heat, because a gravel fill, if it is dry, possesses appreciable insulating value. However, the surface of the floor slab needs to be only three or four degrees cooler than the basement air to begin condensation. Note that it is entirely possible to insulate the floor from the gravel, halting the heat flow and thereby allowing the slab surface to attain nearly the temperature of the basement air. This would prevent condensation, because condensation is impossible when a surface has a temperature that is the same as that of the surrounding air. Although that type of insulation is often thought unnecessary in basement floors, it can be very effective in preventing condensation.

The temperatures of the rough and smooth portions of the floor are approximately the same, but the rough portion is highly porous and the vapor in the air either passes through before it has time to cool and condense or, if there is slight condensation, passes downward and is lost in the relatively dry gravel and earth. The hard-troweled portion has a dense and vapor-resisting surface; this is probably not an exceptionally efficient barrier, but it is fairly effective. At least the vapor movement is retarded at that surface, and water is condensed. The water cannot pass downward to the ground; or, at least, it cannot get away fast enough, and the wet, slippery floor results.

A floor covering of asphalt tile only aggravates this condition, because the tile is an extremely efficient vapor barrier and has no insulating value. The tile floor possibly will be more of a problem in summer, because it will be a good setup for condensation, without any way to reduce the probability. Rugs that are left on these floors during summer often mildew and rot before the condition is observed, because the floor beneath them is actually colder than if there were no rugs at all. Under these conditions, the advice is to ventilate properly. Water does not condense readily out of fast-moving air, but condensation still may be troublesome. Forced ventilation is often called for.

Comparative Values of Roof Insulations

Ques. What thickness of poured vermiculite concrete is required to equal the insulating value of standard 1-inch impregnated fiberboard roof insulation?

Ans. Most impregnated fiberboards have a "k value" of approximately 0.38, and their resistance or "R value" per inch of thickness is

$$\frac{1}{0.36}, \text{ or } 2.63$$

The insulating value of lightweight concretes is nearly directly proportional to their weights, and reputable roofing concerns do not mop on a roof on a deck of excessively lightweight concrete. Approximately 40 lbs. per cu. ft. should be near the minimum density, which requires 6 to 7 bags of cement per cu. yd. of the concrete. The "k value" of this type of concrete is approximately 1.15, or R = 0.87 per inch of thickness. To equal the insulating value of 1 inch of impregnated fiberboard, then, requires 2.63/0.87,

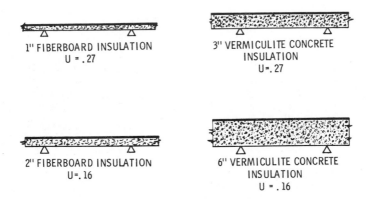

Fig. 13. Illustrating the comparative values of roof insulations.

or nearly 3 inches of vermiculite concrete with a density of 40 lbs. per cubic foot (Fig. 13).

Heated and Unheated Crawl Spaces

Ques. Houses are now being built with concrete-block foundation walls, 4-ft. crawl spaces with gas-fired furnaces in the crawl spaces, and with under-the-floor ductwork. The building inspector is demanding that 2-in. insulation be used on the foundation walls. This will add at least one hundred dollars to the cost of a house. The uninsulated crawl spaces have been trouble-free so far. They are dry and warm, with no indications of condensation. Is the insulation necessary?

Ans. Probably your code requires that warm crawl spaces be insulated, and the inspector is only doing his duty in enforcing it. Also, the code probably allows the use of either warm crawl spaces or cold crawl spaces, but a crawl space cannot be both warm and cold at the same time. Apparently, it is desirable to consider the crawl space warm, with the furnaces and ducts beneath the floor; but an attempt is being made to consider it a cold crawl space, by eliminating the insulation. Probably, the code permits insulation of the furnaces and ducts effectively, and some type of under-the-floor insulation is required. Then, it can be considered a cold crawl space and the walls require no insulation. If only the initial cost of the installation is of concern, it is cheaper to insulate the foundation walls and allow the crawl space to warm up. In other words, either one alternative or the other must be selected.

Vapor Barriers for Floors

Ques. My house has a slab floor with 6 inches of pea-gravel underneath it, but no vapor barrier. One portion is carpeted over asphalt tile. On this area in summer, so much moisture is formed that the carpet must be taken up. A 4-in. drain tile line has already been installed around the foundation, but it is ineffective. It is now too late to install a vapor barrier beneath the floor. Can anything else be done?

Ans. It may be fortunate that there is no vapor barrier beneath the slab, because all the floors might be wet. Some years ago, popular hysteria demanded that vapor barriers be placed wherever possible, and, in some instances, the results were disastrous. Vapor barriers are absolutely necessary in many instances, but they must be used with discretion. With 6 inches of well-drained pea gravel beneath a slab floor, vapor barriers are necessary only when the ground-water level is near. At present, enlightened codes require them only in special instances, when the subbase cannot be kept dry.

The problem is condensation, and this instance is typical. The slab is cool, even cooler than the air inside the house, and, in summer, the air inside the house is usually several degrees cooler than the air outside the house. Carpets and rugs are good insulators, and they keep the slab cooler than if there were no covering over it. A perfect setup for condensation occurs when the slab has a vapor-barring cover beneath the carpet, such as the asphalt tile. On the remainder of the floor, with no vapor barrier above it, the water vapor passes through the porous slab more or less readily and is lost in the ground before it can condense. A possible exception occurs when the surface is troweled to an extremely dense and smooth surface, especially if it is machine troweled. This is sometimes a vapor barrier that is sufficiently impermeable to stop, or at least retard, the passage of vapor, allowing some condensation to form. When a vapor barrier is placed beneath the slab, the same action takes place, and the entire slab may become saturated.

It is regretful, but there is no solution for the problem, except to keep the rooms extremely well ventilated; even then, some dampness may form in corners and around the edges of the floor where the air movement is slight. Moisture does not condense readily from moving air. In winter, when the normal outside air may be carrying only 1/50 (or perhaps even less) of the moisture that it carries during humid weather in summer, there should be no problem, even with carpets on the floor.

Heat-Conduction Through Electrical Outlet Boxes

Ques. A room with a slab floor extends 4 feet below grade; it is used as a meeting place for various organizations. The walls are made of concrete blocks, waterproofed on the outside, and furred, insulated, lathed, and plastered on the inside. The electrical wires run through the cores of the blocks. Moisture gathers around the electrical outlets which are placed in the portions of the walls below the grade. The plaster around them sometimes becomes wetted, and some electrical shorts have occurred. Condensation is probably causing the trouble. Should the steel electrical boxes be replaced with plastic boxes? Perhaps plastic has a lower dew point than metal. Or could it be possible that cold is traveling in over the electrical wires?

Ans. Materials such as metals and plastics do not have "dew points." The term is applicable only to air. When air at a given relative humidity is cooled to a certain temperature, it begins to lose a portion of its moisture. That temperature is its dew point. If the surface temperature of a material drops below the dew point of the air surrounding it, moisture collects on that surface. This moisture around the electrical boxes is condensation.

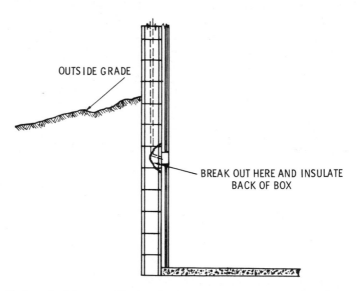

OUTSIDE GRADE

BREAK OUT HERE AND INSULATE
BACK OF BOX

Fig. 14. A method for controlling condensation around electrical outlet boxes which are set on a concrete-block wall against the ground.

Coldness does not "travel." Coldness is a negative term, which means that an object or substance is not hot. Heat does travel; it can be retained in a given place only with difficulty. Heat always moves from a warmer to a cooler substance, and when enough heat has escaped from the substance, it is said to be *cold*.

Probably sufficient heat is not escaping through the wires to cause the trouble, although this may be contributing to the problem. Copper is one of the best heat conductors known to man, but the cross-sectional area of the wires is relatively small. It is more likely that the rear surfaces of the outlet boxes are in direct contact with the concrete blocks, since the total thickness of the 1-5/8" furring, lath, and plaster permits such a contact, and the blocks lose heat rapidly to the cooler ground. This condition is correctible without difficulty, but it is not satisfactory to merely break the contact between the boxes and the concrete. They should be insulated as follows: (1) Take out the boxes and break a hole through into the block cavities; (2) Pack the hole full of glass or rock wool, making the hole large enough that a good thickness of insulation can be placed between the boxes and the concrete, and then replace the boxes (Fig. 14). This is not difficult, and the wetness problem should be halted.

Shredded Redwood-Bark Insulation

Ques. When inspecting an old house with the idea of buying it, the house was found to be insulated with shredded bark of some type, probably redwood or red cedar, judging from the slight odor. Is this material a fire hazard, and is it liable to become infested with vermin?

Ans. It is probably redwood bark, which is a by-product of the redwood lumbering operations. Since the supply is rather limited, it is not advertised extensively. The material possesses excellent insulating value, similar to other loose fiber fill-type insulations, and it is usually treated with chemicals to increase its fire-resistant properties. Since the origin of the insulation in the house is unknown, that cannot be checked.

Some brands of shredded redwood bark insulations are marketed bearing the Underwriter's label, but the label does not indicate that they will not burn. Regardless of the treatment, they are still combustible, but they are no more of a fire hazard than the other chemically-treated organic fill-type insulations. All types will burn, but they do not contribute extensively toward feeding a fire. For redwood bark, and other organic fill-type insulations, the Underwriter's states: "Under conditions favorable for such action, this product will continue to glow and smoulder progressively."

The processors claim that shredded redwood bark is naturally vermin-repellant, that it does not settle and pack, and that it does not absorb moisture from the air. The last statement may be questioned slightly, because wood and most wood products are highly hygroscopic. Redwood bark insulation is approved entirely by all known codes, and there should be no apprehensions concerning its use.

Insulating of Plaster on Radiant Ceilings

Ques. A house is to be plastered with gypsum-board lath, and the cables for radiant heating are in place on the ceiling. The joists are only 2″ × 6″ boards, set on 16-in. centers, and the spans are 14 ft. To save weight, lightweight plaster was proposed, but the heating contractor absolutely refuses to allow it. What is the reason for his refusal?

Ans. The 2″ × 6″ joists, set on 16-in. centers, and with 14-ft. spans, are too light for *any* plaster ceiling, and lightweight plasters are not acceptable for use on *any* radiant ceiling. To operate properly, it is necessary that radiant ceilings are *warm,* and lightweight plasters possess some insulating value, thus defeating the intended purpose of the ceiling.

The radiation emitted by a radiant ceiling is proportional to the fourth power of its temperature; thus, only a few degrees drop in temperature causes a tremendous difference in its efficiency. A ceiling with a surface temperature of 85°F. is actually emitting nearly 27 percent more heat than when it is operating at a surface temperature of 80°F. With only a small amount of insulation over the cables, to bring the ceiling temperature to what it would be with no insulation, or less insulation, requires that the ceiling heating cables be operated at higher temperatures, requiring more electrical energy and greater expense.

Molds and Mildews on Walls

Ques. In a three-year-old house with plastered walls, a problem has been experienced with large dark spots or blotches on the walls in a bedroom and in a closet on the outside wall; evidently, the spots or blotches have come through the paint. If it is mold or mildew, and since the walls must be redecorated, what can be done to prevent its happening again?

Ans. The spots are probably caused by a mold or mildew. Molds and mildews are living organisms, the lowest order of plant life, and are called fungi, or funguses. All of them require water or dampness to live and grow, which infers that the walls are damp, at least at intervals. To prevent a recurrence of the trouble, the cause should be removed. Dampness of outside walls that is caused by condensation of moisture in winter is quite common in unheated or intermittently heated closets and bedrooms. Either heating the rooms or ventilating them well controls the problem, and well-insulated walls make this easier.

If it is necessary only to kill the molds, dissolve six one-half gram tablets of bichloride of mercury in one quart of hot water and paint the walls with the solution. After it has dried, the solution can be painted over. This kills the molds, but it does not prevent the dampness. The bichloride solution also may be used to inhibit mildews and mosses on outside siding and shingles. Be careful in using it, because it is a virulent poison.

Effect of Dampness on Casein Glues

Ques. Three years ago, nine lockers were built and placed in a building at our high-school athletic field. For the most part, they were made from edge-jointed and glued boards, using casein glue. The outside was primed, but no other finish was used. Although the lockers are still usable, it has been found that nearly every glue joint has let go—not *through* the glue line, but *beside* it. The building is constructed of concrete blocks, is cold and damp, and is heated only occasionally. What can be the possible cause of this type of joint failure?

Ans. Chemists have called this problem the effect of hydrolysis, a chemical phenomenon resulting from the reaction of the highly alkaline glue in the presence of dampness which breaks down some of the constituents of the wood. In any situation, casein glue joints should not be subjected to excessive dampness for long periods of time, although they can resist water effectively for short periods, and they can withstand a moderate amount of weathering. Most commercial caseins are "fortified" (usually with phenol or carbolic acid), and they are somewhat decay-resistant, but the plain casein rots if it is allowed to remain damp for long periods of time. All caseins are highly alkaline.

CHAPTER 7

Acoustics and Noise Transmission

Sound Insulation for Apartments

Ques. Is it necessary to soundproof the walls and ceilings between apartments in an apartment building that is being constructed? How should this be done?

Ans. Sound-insulation is absolutely necessary between apartments. If there are upper-story apartments, a double-framed floor system should be used, with no connection (not even a wire or a cleat) between the floor and the ceiling. For the walls, a staggered-stud partition (Fig. 1) is usually satisfactory. Effective spring-suspension systems are available from plaster manufacturing concerns (see a plaster products supplier). Do not attempt to "sound condition" the walls and floors with wool or fiberboard heat-insulation materials. The results are usually unsatisfactory, and acoustic tile is worthless for resistance to transmitted noises.

Isolate Noises to Avoid Sound Insulation

Ques. In a wooden-framed school building that was originally intended for use as a music room, the school board has added a

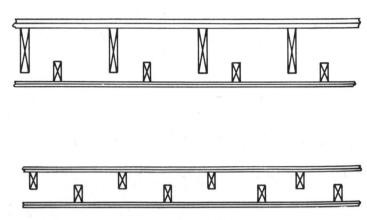

Fig. 1. Methods of providing sound insulation for apartments. The conventional double-framed ceiling (top) is designed to resist sound transmission. Average sound reduction is approximately 50 decibels. Gypsum lath and sanded plaster are used below, with a double floor above. A conventional staggered-stud sound-resistant wall (bottom) provides average sound reduction of approximately 40 decibels. Gypsum lath and sanded plaster are used on both sides.

woodworking shop at one end. Only a concrete-block wall separates the two rooms. The music students have a problem when the woodworking machinery is running, and the boys in the woodworking shop are distracted when the band is playing. Can anything be done?

Ans. Nothing can be done. It is useless to reduce noise transmission through the wall, because the high-intensity vibrations that are generated in both rooms cause nearly all parts of a light-framed building to vibrate in unison, which cannot be avoided. The two sources of noise should never have been placed in proximity. It is a fundamental principle in all noise-abatement projects that the noise-generator should be isolated as well as possible when the intensity of the noise cannot be controlled by any other means.

Walls that are constructed of good heavyweight concrete blocks possess a good noise-resistance rating (not less than 30 decibels, and often 40 decibels or more), depending on how they are installed. Much of the noise may be transmitted indirectly between the two rooms. In other words, the noise *goes around* the partition. Perhaps some noise is transmitted to the outside air and then into the adjoining room. It seems that the only satisfactory solution is to move one of the noisy rooms to an isolated part of the campus. Even then, the room should be built of heavy masonry or be of concrete construction.

Noise Transmission Through Partitions

Ques. In a recently completed motor court for tourists, noise-transmission problems through the partitions have arisen. The partition walls are plaster placed on wooden studs, the floor is made of concrete, and the ceilings are acoustical tile placed on plasterboard. Is there any inexpensive and effective method of dealing with this problem?

Ans. There is no method that is both cheap and effective, but most of the problems can be eliminated. Do not disturb the existing partitions, but erect another wall on one side, using either $2'' \times 2''$ studs or $2'' \times 3''$ studs, placed flatwise. Leave a $3/4''$ space between the studs and the existing wall, and cover with either lath and plaster or $5/8''$ plasterboard. Leave nothing in the cavities—not even a block or a nail between the two partitions.

Probably, at least a portion of the noise is transmitted through the ceilings to the space above the ceiling, crosses *over* the partitions, and is again transmitted downward through the adjoining ceilings. The cavities above the partitions should be blocked solidly and tightly, extending to the roof above each partition. This is also an elementary precaution to prevent spread of fire. Acoustic tile is almost useless for resisting transmission of noise.

Sound-Resistant Partitions for Motels

Ques. Which of the three types of partitions (see Fig. 2) is most satisfactory for reduction of noise between motel units?

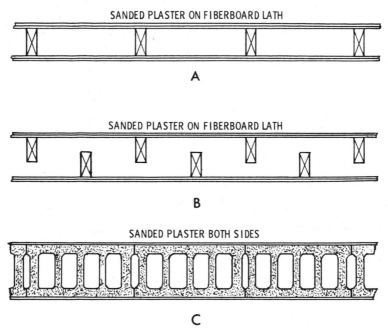

Fig. 2. Showing three types of partitions proposed for use in a motel: (A) Noise reduction, 41 decibels; (B) Noise reduction, 54 decibels; and (C) Noise reduction, 52 decibels. Partitions with a noise reduction of less than 45 decibels are unsuitable for use in motels.

Ans. Actual tests have been made to determine the noise-resistant capability of three types of partitions that have been proposed for use in motels (see Fig. 2). The results of actual tests made on partition areas are as follows:

1. Standard studded wall, 2″ × 4″ set 16″ on centers, 1/2″ fiberboard lath, and 1/2″ sanded gypsum plaster both sides. Noise reduction, 41 decibels.
2. Staggered 2″ × 4″ studs, 8″ on centers; 2″ × 6″ plates; 1/2″-fiberboard lath; and 1/2″ sanded gypsum plaster both sides. Noise reduction, 54 decibels.
3. 8″ standard lightweight concrete blocks, plastered both sides with sanded gypsum plaster. Noise reduction, 52 decibels.

Partitions with less than 45 decibels reduction in noise are not considered satisfactory for use between motel units. Partition *A* is not acceptable, but partitions *A* and *B* should prove satisfactory (see Fig. 2).

Extend the noise-resisting partitions upward against the roof, making them *tight*. Any type of ceiling may be constructed *between* the partitions. The so-called "acoustic" ceilings are practically worthless for resistance to transmitted noise. Sounds may be transmitted readily through acoustic ceilings to the air in the cavity above, cross over the partition, and again be transmitted into the adjoining rooms. The best sound-resistant partitions are ineffective under those conditions. In addition, if there is an attic, the partitions that are continued upward to the roof serve as effective fire stops.

Soundproofing Doors

Ques. A local doctor wants to soundproof the doors in his office. Conversations in the consulting room can be heard and understood in the waiting room. After looking at the job, most of the sound seems to be passing through cracks around the door. Is this theory correct and what can be done to correct this situation?

Ans. The theory may be partially correct, but an ordinary panel or hollow-core door is only slightly sound-resistant at best. Normally, cracks around doors afford approximately 15 decibels of noise reduction, which is insufficient for reasonable privacy. Sealing the cracks may help the situation. An effective and readily available arrangement is to use common spring-brass weather stripping, well fitted around the door. If it is used at the bottom of the door, a threshold is required. If there is carpeting through the doorway, drop-bar sealers are available. Soft-rubber, or hollow-rubber gasketing strips are available for application to the stops. Felt strips are not recommended; they are too porous to be effective. In any instance, the effectiveness of the sealing demands that the door be closed *firmly* against the sealing strips, which requires a conscious effort.

To make the soundproofing effective, two doors are required. They should be well sealed around the edges, with a "sound lock" space between them. The sound lock is most effective when the space between the doors is at least 24 inches, but the doors are often hung on the same jamb. This provides at least 35 decibels of noise reduction, and loud conversation is, for the most part, unintelligible through the two doors. Only one of the doors requires closing unless extreme privacy is demanded (see Fig. 3).

A Sound-Resistant Floor

Ques. In finishing an unfinished upper story in a house where the floor has not been laid, the joists are only $2'' \times 6''$ timbers, which are inadequate to carry a floor; therefore, it is necessary to "jump in" new and heavier joists between them. The owner desires that the floor be sound-resistant. What method should be used for this purpose?

Ans. The job could be done by blocking up the new joists on the supporting plates, thereby making the floor and ceiling fram-

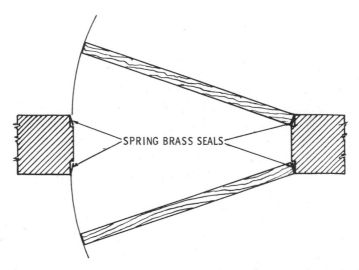

Fig. 3. Two doors hung on a single jamb are effective in reducing sound transmission. For best results, the doors should be spaced not less than 24 in.—even a shallow space is effective.

ing systems independent of each other. There should be no connection between the two sets of joists. This type of framing has excellent sound-resistance qualities, but often cannot be done so easily.

Noise-Transmission Problem Through Ventilating Ducts

Ques. The owner of a three-apartment building has requested that a noise-transmission problem between bathrooms be corrected. The noise may be traveling through the water pipes, but it is more likely that it is passing through the ventilating duct, which has openings on all three floors, and into all three baths. Is it likely that a fan can be installed to correct the problem; or, if not, what can be done to correct this trouble?

Ans. It is unlikely that installation of a fan can solve the problem, except that sounds from the bathrooms may be covered partially by the "background noise" of the fan. The sounds may travel readily *against* the blast, since the speed of sound is approximately 1100 feet per second, which is far faster than the air speed attainable in the duct.

Matters may be helped by removing the grilles and placing a sound-absorbent lining in the duct, as far as the arm can reach. A thin glass-wool blanket is excellent for this purpose; or special acoustic lining materials can be obtained. This may solve the problem; but if the result is not satisfactory, new duct work, with "silencers" between the baths may be the only solution. Many types of commercial silencers for the ducts are available, because noise transmission through the duct work is relatively common. A sheet-metal contractor may be contacted for advice.

A Sound-Resistant Floating Floor

Ques. It is desired to soundproof the floor of a children's playroom which is upstairs. A single floor consisting of 1" × 6" D&M boards is involved, and the ceiling below consists of lath and plaster. Can an acoustic tile ceiling placed below the room solve the problem; or is it necessary to install a "floating" floor to do the job. How are these floors built?

Ans. An acoustic tile cover on the ceiling below cannot be of any appreciable help, since they are not intended for that purpose. The tile can control reverberation and lower the noise level in the lower room by a few decibels, but they are practically nonresistant to transmitted sounds.

To build the floating floor (Fig. 4), remove the base and shoe, and cover the floor with 1-inch pliable glass-wool insulation, butting the joints and extending it upward on the walls for 2

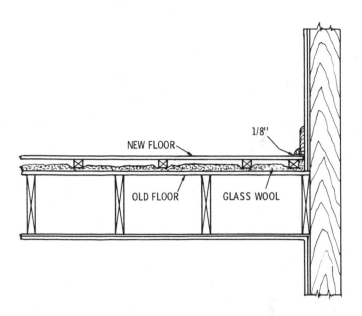

Fig. 4. A floating-raft type of floor. This floor possesses excellent sound-resistant qualities. It should provide 40 to 45 decibels reduction in noise, and with good carpeting and padding, provide excellent resistance to impact sounds.

inches. Use no nails. On the blanket insulation, place 2″ × 3″ sleepers (flatwise), running them parallel to, and midway between, the joists. Cut the sleepers approximately 1/2 inch short of the walls at the ends, and temporarily nail strips to hold them in place. Then, lay standard 25/32″ flooring directly on the sleepers. When the floor is completed, the glass wool is compressed to about 3/8″ below the sleepers. Replace the base and shoe, but leave approximately 1/8″ between them and the floating floor. Slide the blade of a steel square underneath the shoe molding as it is nailed, nailing it into the base, rather than into the floor. This is one of the most resilient floors that can be built, possesses excellent resistance to sound transmission, and it should be entirely satisfactory.

Acoustical Problem in Doctor's Offices

Ques. Several rooms were recently converted into a doctor's office, consultation, and examination rooms, as shown in the sketch (Fig. 5). The result has been highly unsatisfactory. Conversation

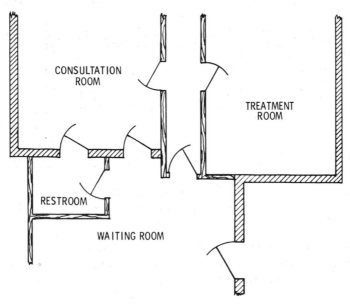

Fig. 5. Illustrating an unsatisfactory arrangement for a doctor's offices and treatment rooms. Without extensive and expensive alterations, the sound-transmission problems in these rooms can be expected to continue.

in the consultation room may be plainly heard, and reasonably well understood, in the waiting room. The walls are all plywood placed on wood studs, except for the old masonry walls, and in the consultation room, the walls are acoustical tile downward 3 feet from the ceiling. All the ceilings are acoustical tile, all the floors are vinyl tile over a concrete slab, and all doors are the hollow-core slab type. The sounds may be traveling through the rest-room. What can be done to remedy this situation?

Ans. Please pardon the criticism, but the entire layout possesses such exceptionally poor sound-resisting properties that, without extensive changes, it seems impossible to make it suitable for a doctor's use, because a high degree of privacy is not only desirable, but absolutely demanded. To begin with, walls of plywood placed on wooden studs are the *least* resistant to transmitted sound of any type of partition that is in general use. Sheets of 1/4-inch plywood placed on $2'' \times 4''$ studs have a noise transmission loss of approximately 31.3 decibels; the old-fashioned walls of plaster placed on wood lath on both sides provides a reduction of 35.7 decibels, and with gypsum lath under the plaster the loss is 41 to 48 decibels. None of these walls, with the possible exception of heavy-sanded plaster on gypsum lath, could possibly be satisfactory for doctor's consulting rooms, or even for bathrooms in private residences. A conversation in ordinary tones of voice can be carried through a partition with 35 decibels reduction, or less. A single hollow-core flush door with the usual clearance cracks around its edges provides approximately 15 decibels reduction, and even if the cracks are closed tightly with rubber gasketing, approximately 20 decibels of reduction is provided.

In any arrangement where a rest-room with two doors, one opening into a public waiting room and the other into a highly private doctor's office, is about the most incongruous design possible. However, it is probable that most of the annoying sound is not passing through the rest-room, but through the single door, or even more likely, through the acoustic ceiling, above the partitions, and through the joists cavities, attic, or other continuous space above, to be retransmitted to the adjoining rooms. This is a very common problem. Acoustic ceilings have practically no resistance to transmitted sounds, and cannot be expected to reduce sound transmission; acoustic tile was never intended for that purpose. If acoustic tile ceilings are used, separating partitions should be built first, extending them upward tightly against the roof, upper floor, or other tight surface. Then, the acoustic ceilings may be placed *between* the sound-resisting walls. At least, no harm can be done. Acoustic ceilings *may* reduce the noise level slightly *in the room where they are exposed,* but that is all that can be expected.

Controlling Noise Through Ceilings

Ques. It is desired to soundproof a basement ceiling to control annoying noise from above. The owner suggests that the ceiling be covered with acoustic tile, but prior experience indicates that the tile are ineffective for this purpose. Is there an alternative type of ceiling which is effective?

Ans. Probably the most effective treatment available is to place a spring-suspended ceiling below the joists (see a dealer in gypsum products). Most of the manufacturers of these products can furnish the spring clips and other fittings for this type of work. The ceiling is dropped only 2 inches, or slightly less, depending on the type of ceiling finish to be used. Either 1/2" or 5/8" gypsum board or sanded gypsum plaster on rock lath is recommended. These ceilings provide sound reduction of 30 to 40 decibels, which should be satisfactory.

If it can be arranged properly, almost any type of wooden board or plywood ceiling, with paper and 2 to 3 inches of dry sand on the top surface provides 20 to 30 decibels of sound transmission resistance. In addition to the resistance furnished by the weight of the sand, dry sand also possesses excellent sound *absorbent* qualities. It weighs approximately 10 pounds per square foot per inch of thickness. Acoustic tile may be used as a finish above the boards. They lower the noise level in the room where they are exposed approximately 3 to 5 decibels, but they are practically nonresistant to transmitted sounds.

Building a Noise-Resistant Second-Story Floor

Ques. A second story is being built on an existing house. The present structure has 2" × 6" ceiling joists on 16" centers, and it is proposed to place new 2" × 10" floor joists between them, blocking up the bearings to prevent contact with the present ceiling. Will noise transmission be reduced if some type of resilient bearings are placed beneath the ends of the new joists?

Ans. If the walls were heavy masonry, the ceiling would probably be fairly satisfactory without the resilent bearings, but with wood-framed walls, vibrations, especially impact sounds or footsteps on the floor above, may be transmitted along the joists, thence to the wood-framed walls, and from there to the ceiling or walls below, and retransmitted as noise. This is called *indirect* or *flanking transmission,* and it is sometimes very annoying and difficult to control. An attempt to control this type of noise by the means proposed may prove satisfactory, but the more orthodox "floating floor" is known to be effective. There must, of course, be no continuity through the resilient pads beneath the joists. The joists must not be nailed through pads, which means that they must float free (Fig. 6). The pads should be rather hard and rigid; or, if soft rubber is used, they must be thick to allow for compression. It is unlikely that fiberboard would prove suitable, since it loses its resiliency in time. Overall, the idea is excellent.

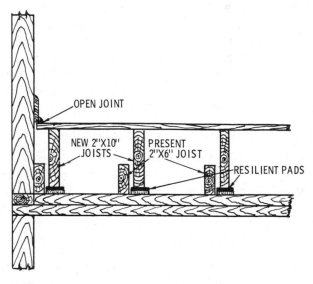

Fig. 6. A floor that is floated on resilient bearings, designed for sound-transmission resistance on a remodeling job. This type of construction should be satisfactory, even though the bearing walls are framed with lightweight wood.

Do not nail the baseboard and shoe molding to the floor. Place the blade of a steel square beneath the molding as it is nailed into the baseboard.

Alternation of Staggered-Stud Walls

Ques. Is noise transmission through a staggered-stud wall resisted, if the cavity is filled with rock-wool pellets? What type of construction can be used to improve resistance to noise transmission?

Ans. Sounds do not pass through the walls unless there are holes in the walls. Sound waves carry energy. Not much energy is carried, of course, but energy is carried in definite, measurable quantities. When a sound wave strikes a tight wall, the wall is caused to vibrate at the same frequency as that of the sound wave, and the vibration is retransmitted on the opposite side of the wall as audible sound. The value of the staggered stud wall in reduction of noise transmission lies in the fact that there is no connection between the two sides of the wall, so that the opposite side does not vibrate in sympathy with the side that receives the impulses.

Another type of sound-resistant construction is to make the wall so heavy that the energy in the sound waves cannot vibrate the wall at all. In these instances, the inertia of the wall enables it to resist sound impulses.

When a fill of any type is placed in the cavity of staggered-stud walls, the discontinuity is destroyed. The two walls then vibrate more or less in unison, and sound-insulating value is lost. On the other hand, added weight makes the wall more resistant to vibration. Although an increase in resistance to vibration has been gained, the gain is very slight if heat insulation is used for the fill, because these insulations are very light. In many instances, the loss in destruction of the discontinuity is not compensated for by the increase in weight, and usually the fills are actually detrimental to the sound-resistance quality of the wall. All heat insulations have extremely poor resistance to transmitted sound. Ordinarily, they are porous, and sound *does* pass readily through holes in the walls.

Double Walls for Sound Control

Ques. How can the noise resistance of a wall between bedrooms in an apartment house be increased? The existing wall is lathed and plastered, and it is proposed to strip it with $1'' \times 2''$ pieces of wood and apply plasterboard or fiberboard. Is there a better way to do this?

Ans. There is a better method (see Fig. 7). The partition that is proposed will improve the situation, especially if it is covered with heavy plasterboard. However, it will be even more improved if either 2″ × 2″ or 2″ × 3″ studs are set flatwise, leaving a space between the studs and the old wall. Cover with 1/2″ (or preferably 5/8″) plasterboard. The resulting partition should be satisfactory under nearly all conditions. Some noise may be indirectly transmitted above or beneath the partition, if the joists in the ceiling or floor are continuous throughout, but it is doubtful that this will be serious. Carpeted floors are also quite helpful in controlling noise.

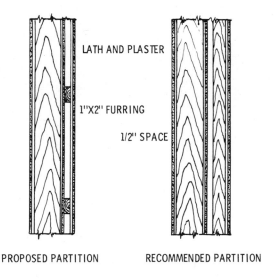

LATH AND PLASTER

1″X2″ FURRING

1/2″ SPACE

PROPOSED PARTITION   RECOMMENDED PARTITION

Fig. 7. The recommended partition (right) possesses excellent sound-resistant qualities; probably there is no more effective way to do the job more economically.

Heavy Partitions for Sound Resistance

Ques. It is desired to make a 10'0" × 12'0" room, where a saw and other light, noisy machines are operated, more noise resistant. The present walls are 2" × 6" studs, 3/4" D&M boards on both sides, and the cavities are filled with vermiculite. This is very unsatisfactory. What can be done to the wall to make it more acceptable?

Ans. Weight can be added to the walls. Including the vermiculite fill, the wall weighs only approximately 10 pounds per square foot. If the supporting joists or floor can withstand the weight, remove the vermiculite and fill the cavities with dry sand. This makes the walls weigh approximately 49 lbs. per sq. ft., which increases their noise resistance by 69 percent.

Other problems may be encountered. The noise can be transmitted *under* the partitions by the floor or joists. If this occurs, it may be necessary to isolate the machines from the floor. If there is a thin door through the partition, it may be necessary to use *two* doors, with a space between them, and gasketed cracks may be necessary. If the noise is passing over the partition through an open attic, or through the joist cavities, it may be necessary to extend the partitions tightly against the roof or floor.

How Sounds Pass Through Frame Walls

Ques. What is the general theory as to how sounds are able to pass through frame walls?

Ans. The following general information is from excellent authority, and it is usually applicable. In the usual single-studded wall, two relatively rigid diaphragms are attached to opposite sides of the studs. A noise on one side of the wall causes the diaphragm on that side—the plaster, or other covering—to vibrate. Vibrations are transmitted across the space, for the most part by the studs, and the surfacing on the opposite side vibrates in unison, retransmitting the vibrations as noise. Only a small percentage of the energy is transmitted through the air in the cavity, but a much larger percentage is passed through the fastenings of the studs at the top and bottom, and the energy may be retransmitted by the floor or ceiling. Unless the walls themselves are exceptionally light, lightweight fillers, such as heat insulations, are of no value in reducing the sound transmission; in some instances, they are actually detrimental. The empty air space is usually better for reducing sound transmission.

It is worthwhile to note that there is little value in erecting partitions with a noise resistance of 40 decibels, and then installing a door in the wall that has a resistance of only 10 to 15 decibels. The actual noise-resistant quality of the complete installation, regardless of the noise-resistant quality of the wall, will probably total only 10 to 15 decibels more than of the door; and for the usual hollow-core door, with both sides faced with 1/8" hardboard, and with the usual cracks around it, the resistance is normally 10 to 15 decibels or less. By gasketing the cracks tightly, this may be increased to 20 or 25 decibels. In many instances, doors and windows could be made noise resistant, rather than increasing the resistance of the walls.

Sound Transmission Underneath Partitions

Ques. In a recently completed motel, a spring-suspended ceiling was placed beneath the second floor. Noise transmission from the second floor to the rooms below is not serious, but there have been complaints about noises being transmitted from room to room in the upper story. Double dividing walls were used, and the noise seems to be passing underneath the partitions. Is this possible? The joist cavities are continuous underneath the partitions.

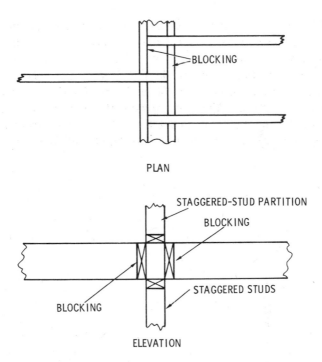

PLAN

ELEVATION

Fig. 8. Two views of an extremely effective method of blocking between joists to prevent noise transmission underneath partitions. This type of blocking also serves as an effective fire stop.

Ans. This is called "indirect" sound transmission, and it is quite common, especially if the floors on both sides of the partitions are not carpeted. This type of noise transmission may be objectionable, even though the floors have semirigid coverings, such as asphalt, vinyl tiling, or linoleum. The joist cavities should always be tightly blocked; this is an elementary precaution against the spread of fire, and the blocking is also effective in preventing the transmission of noises. An effective method of blocking is illustrated in Fig. 8, with the joists offset. In this type of framing, two barriers are used to stop the transmission of noises; the joists have full-width bearing on the plate below, and, in addition to their other functions, the blocking supports the edges of the ceiling below and the flooring above. If the blocking is used with the double partitions, the transmission of noises underneath the partitions should be prevented effectively. Heavy carpeting and padding is demanded in all first-class hotel and motel rooms.

CHAPTER 8

Masonry

Mortar for Fireplace Linings

Ques. About a year ago, a fireplace was built, laying the firebrick lining in cement mortar; now the bricks are loosening. What kind of mortar is recommended for this purpose?

Ans. It is advisable to use one of the specially prepared commercial refractory mortars for laying fireplace linings. A materials dealer can supply them. The cost is nominal, because mortar joints should be very thin—about 1/8 inch. Common fire-clay mortars are not suitable for fireplace linings. These mortars are hardened by fusing at temperatures higher than 2000 degrees. Since fireplace linings never reach that temperature, except in high-temperature furnaces, fire-clay mortars are not entirely satisfactory. Common cement mortars will calcine and powder at high temperatures.

Number of Bricks Required to Build a Chimney

Ques. What is the common method of estimating the number of bricks that are required to build a chimney?

Ans. The actual number of bricks required to build a chimney depends on the size of the bricks and on the thickness of the mor-

CONSTRUCTION METHODS	SIZE OF OPENING	NUMBER OF BRICKS PER COURSE	NUMBER OF BRICKS PER FOOT OF HEIGHT
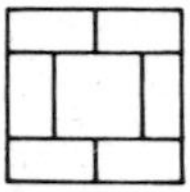	8"X8"	6	27
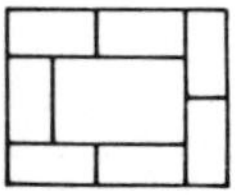	8"X12"	7	31-1/2
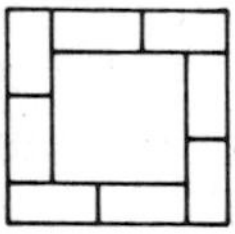	12"X12"	8	36
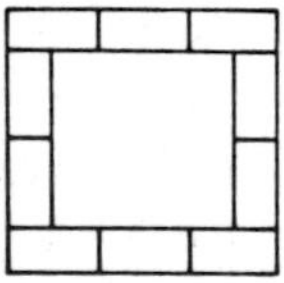	16"X16"	10	45
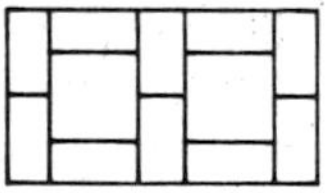	8"X8" 8"X8"	10	45
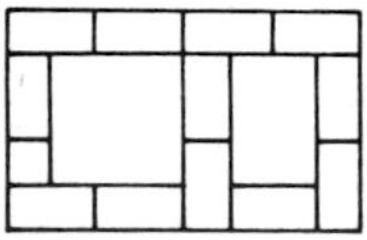	8"X12" 12"X12"	12-1/2	56-1/4

Fig. 1. Calculating the number of bricks required for a chimney.

tar joints. The standard size of a common brick is 2-1/2" $\times$ 3-3/4" $\times$ 8", but hard-burned face bricks may vary slightly from these dimensions. Many contractors estimate 4-1/2 courses of bricks per foot of wall height. If the bricks are standard size, mortar joints may be approximately 4/10 inch in thickness. Some contractors estimate four courses of brick in 11 inches of wall height, which allows for 1/2-inch mortar joints. The chart (Fig. 1) indicates that 4-1/2 courses per foot of wall height are used in building the chimney.

Lime-Cement Mortar

Ques. Why is lime used in cement mortar? Why do dry bricks float in the mortar? Is this because the cement is too old to be suitable for mortar?

Ans. Lime makes the mortar tougher and more workable, and also it probably makes a stronger bond with the bricks. Bricks do *not* float on *any* type of mortar if they are not wet or frozen; or if they are not of a type that is burned so hard that they become vitrified and can absorb little or no moisture. Dry, soft bricks do not float on any type of mortar under good working conditions. Never use exceptionally old masonry cement, because it may absorb so much moisture from the air that it may lose its setting qualities.

Quantity of Mortar Required for Brick and Tile Masonry

Ques. What quantity of mortar is required in laying a hollow-tile wall, as compared with the quantity required in laying a brick wall?

Ans. The quantity of mortar (per 1000 bricks with 1/2-inch joints) that is required to lay a brick wall can be calculated as follows:

flat stretcher courses ....11.7 cu. ft.
shiners, edge-up .... 7.9 cu. ft.
headers ....14.9 cu. ft.
row locks ....14.9 cu. ft.
soldiers ....11.7 cu. ft.

The quantity of mortar (per 1000 tile) required to lay a hollow-tile wall can be calculated as follows:

3-3/4″ × 5″ × 12″ tile, on side.............................16 cu. ft.
8″ × 5″ × 12″ tile, on side.............................31 cu. ft.
8″ × 8″ × 8″ tile, on side.............................25 cu. ft.
8″ × 12″ × 12″ tile, on side......................... 11.34 cu. ft.
8″ × 12″ × 12″ tile, on end.............................31 cu. ft.
3-3/4″ × 12″ × 12″ tile, on side.............................20 cu. ft.
3-3/4″ × 12″ × 12″ tile, on end.............................20 cu. ft.
12″ × 12″ × 12″ tile, on side.............................50 cu. ft.
12″ × 12″ × 12″ tile, on side.............................35 cu. ft.

Removing Smoke Stains From Stonework

Ques. A fireplace that was built of native stone is stained heavily by smoke. Is there any recommended method of removing these smoke stains from the stone?

Ans. Possibly not, but an attempt is worthwhile. Try scrubbing the smoke stains with a stiff brush, soap and water, and powdered pumice. If the stains are embedded deeply, dissolve 2 lbs. of tri-sodium phosphate in a gallon of water; then make a paste of 12 ozs. chlorinated lime in water, and mix the two compounds together in a stoneware jar, adding enough water to make 2 gallons. Let the lime settle, and then use the clear liquid to wet some heavy cloth pads. Repeat the treatment as often as necessary.

Removing Mortar From Cinder Blocks

Ques. After using lime mortar for cinder blocks that were laid for interior walls, the walls are badly spattered with the mortar. How can these walls be cleaned?

Ans. The walls should have been washed and cleaned before the mortar was dry; or, even better, care should have been taken to keep the mortar off the face of the blocks. If the "spatters" are only thin smears, the mortar may have "died" before it hardened, and may be washed off with plain water and a wire brush. If that does not do the job, a weak muriatic acid solution of approximately 1 pint of acid in 1 gallon of water may dissolve the lime slowly, but it also attacks the concrete. The muriatic acid should be washed off almost immediately with plain water. With care, the muriatic acid may do the job, if the walls are painted later.

Building Brick Pavements

Ques. A terrace and sidewalks are to be made of brick. Is it more desirable to lay the bricks in concrete; or is a plain bed of sand satisfactory?

Ans. If there is wheel traffic, if the subgrade is doubtful or lacks uniform quality, and if it is important that unequal settlement does not cause the surface to become uneven, brick pavements may sometimes be laid above a concrete slab; that is, if 1/2 to 1 inch of sand is placed over the slab. For porch floors, patio floors, and similar floors where only relatively light foot traffic occurs, and where there is a good solid subsoil, the concrete slab is not needed. It is important that the subgrade is well drained in order to control frost heaving, but good drainage can usually be provided by a 4- to 6-in. bed of gravel, compacted and tamped smoothly and solidly with an inch or more of sand placed on top.

The sand is necessary, because hard-burned bricks that are suitable for paving often vary considerably in thickness.

The joints are usually filled with sand; spread the sand over the surface, sweep it into the joints with a broom, and wash down with plenty of water until the joints are tightly filled. The bricks may be laid in any one of many patterns (Fig. 2).

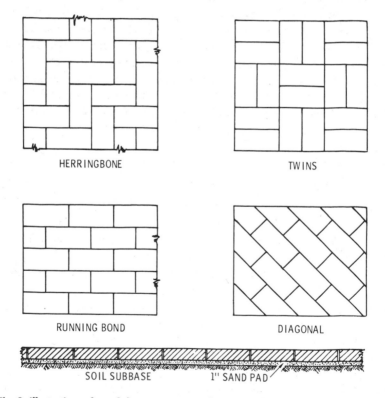

HERRINGBONE

TWINS

RUNNING BOND

DIAGONAL

SOIL SUBBASE   1" SAND PAD

Fig. 2. Illustrating a few of the many patterns that are used in laying brick pavements. Under normal conditions, a concrete subbase is unnecessary.

Removing Soot From Brickwork

Ques. How can soot be removed from the brickwork above a fireplace? Soap and water were tried with unsatisfactory results.

Ans. Try the soap and water again, using a soap or soap powder that contains grit. A hand soap that contains pumice of the type used by mechanics should give satisfactory results. If the bricks are of the smooth dry-pressed type, the stains may be ground off with either a carborundum brick or a piece of coarse grinding wheel and water. This treatment leaves a new surface, but after it has dried, the color can be returned with linseed oil. The bricks are darkened slightly, but they are more easily cleaned the succeeding time.

Incinerator Chimney Robbed of Air

Ques. A fireplace chimney works perfectly, but an $8'' \times 8''$ chimney for a trash burner opens into the same room, and it does not draw well (Fig. 3). This chimney is clean, dry, and extends 3 feet above the roof. What is the probable cause of the trouble?

Ans. The fireplace is probably stealing the available air from the trash burner. When operating properly, fireplaces use tremendous amounts of air, perhaps as much as 100 cu. ft. per minute. The air in the room must be replaced from the outside; it enters by the path of least resistance, which may be downward through the other chimney. To test this possibility, try putting out the fire in the fireplace, closing the damper tightly, and then igniting the incinerator fire. If the incinerator chimney works satisfactorily, the room needs more ventilation.

Efflorescence on Brick Walls

Ques. What is the name of the unsightly powdery, white substance that collects on brick walls? What can be done to prevent formation of this substance?

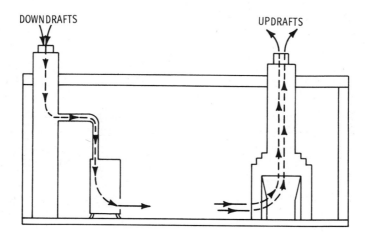

Fig. 3. Illustrating how an efficient fireplace may exhaust the air in a room sufficiently to cause a downdraft in another chimney in the same room.

Ans. The substance is called *efflorescence;* it consists of water-soluble salts which were originally contained within the bricks and the mortar. It probably consists chiefly of salts of magnesium. When the bricks are wetted, the salts are dissolved; then they are leached to the surface and become dry, leaving the whitish deposit. The deposit can be washed off easily with a weak solution of muriatic acid in water (approximately 1 pint of the acid in 4 gallons of water), but the deposit appears again and again. After a period of several years, the problem usually disappears, all the salts having been leached away.

Mortar for Concrete Blocks

Ques. What is a recommended mortar mix for concrete blocks —a mortar having adequate strength and plastic enough to work easily?

Ans. For cinder blocks and other lightweight blocks of all types, used only indoors, a recommended plastic mortar is: 1 part of Portland cement; up to 1-1/4 parts of hydrated lime; and 5 to 6 parts of sand. If desired, cement masonry mortar consisting of 1 part of masonry cement and 2-1/4 to 3 parts sand can be used. The first formula may be a slightly tougher and easier-working mortar, but both mortars are Type B mortars.

For high-strength, sand-gravel concrete blocks that are exposed to the weather, a Type A mortar should be used. This mortar consists of: 1 part of masonry cement; 1 part of Portland cement; and 4-1/2 to 6 parts of sand. This is an extra-strong mortar, but it may not be tough enough for some masons. Lime should not be added, however, because it weakens the mortar.

Antifreeze in Mortar

Ques. Can automobile radiator alcohol or other antifreeze preparations be used in brick mortar to prevent freezing when laying bricks in cold weather?

Ans. Alcohol, salt, or other chemicals should not be used to lower the freezing point of mortar. Calcium chloride may sometimes be used, but it is an accelerator—not an antifreeze—and the mortar must be used immediately after mixing, which is a decided disadvantage. Heating the mortar may cause it to set before it can freeze, if the temperature is only slightly below freezing, but extensive bricklaying usually is not done in severe weather, unless warmed enclosures are used.

Mortars for Masonry

Ques. Is it necessary to add Portland cement to masonry cement when the masonry is to be exposed to extremely severe weather conditions?

Ans. Neither Type A-1 nor Type A-2 mortar can be produced from straight masonry cement and sand. The often used mortar, 1 part Type-II masonry cement and 2-1/4 to 3 parts sand, is Type-B mortar. Most architects do not permit the use of Type-B mortar in brick veneers, footings, or foundations built of hollow-masonry units, heavily-loaded bearing walls of all kinds, or where there is a probability of recurring cycles of wetting, freezing, and thawing. For most types of construction, Type-B mortar is satisfactory. The architect should be consulted if a question arises.

Firebrick Linings for Incinerators

Ques. In maintaining a large incinerator which is used extensively, the firebrick linings seldom last longer than one year. How can the linings be made more permanent; supposedly, they should last at least five years. Is fire-clay mortar recommended?

Ans. Straight fire-clay mortars are not recommended for these purposes. A temperature of approximately 2000°F. is required to set and fuse fire clays properly. Since incinerators usually do not get that hot, fire-clay mortar merely crumbles and sloughs away. It is better to use one of the air-setting specially prepared refractory mortars. They are more satisfactory for low-heat linings. They set in the air, as does concrete, and they are especially adapted for low-heat linings; they are not recommended for extremely high temperatures, such as are present in metal-melting furnaces (see a materials dealer; or contact a firebrick manufacturer).

If the incinerator is extremely large, some provision should be made for expansion and contraction, because firebrick linings contract and expand extensively under temperature changes, which wrecks the linings. An open expansion joint should be used wherever this type of movement can do damage, but they should be placed not more than 10 feet apart. Squeeze the mortar joints to not more than 1/8″ in thickness. Some installers merely dip the bricks in liquid mortar; then they rub the brick down, leaving only a small mortar joint. Where an expansion joint is to be provided, cut pieces of corrugated strawboard to the correct size and lay them in the head joints. They burn out, leaving an open expansion joint after the furnace is fired the first time.

If a furnace is fired and operated continuously, a lining *might* last five years, but if it is operated intermittently, that is practically impossible. The linings expand and contract with each heating cycle; therefore, the best brickwork cannot last indefinitely.

Brick Bonds

Ques. Can you provide illustrations showing how the commonly-used types of brick-bonded walls are laid up?

Ans. The sketches shown in Fig. 4 illustrate four generally-used types of bonding for brick walls. The *common bond* is used

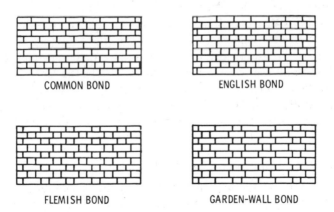

COMMON BOND   ENGLISH BOND

FLEMISH BOND   GARDEN-WALL BOND

Fig. 4. Illustrating the patterns of stretchers and headers in some of the most commonly used brick-bonded walls. Innumerable patterns, ornamental or otherwise, are obtained by using bricks of different colors or textures.

in most work in the United States. A given number of simple stretchers, which may be the five shown in the illustration, or seven or nine (depending on the importance of the work), and then a continuous course of headers may be used. The *English bond* is characterized by alternate courses of headers and stretchers; the *Dutch-cross bond* and the *English-cross bond* are laid in the same way, the cross patterns being obtained by using two different types of brick.

The *Flemish bond* is laid with alternate headers and stretchers in every course; or, if it is desired, "cross" patterns may be produced by using two contrasting colors of brick. Sometimes, instead of straight header courses in common bond, the courses are laid with Flemish headers (alternate headers and stretchers). *Garden-wall bond* is laid similar to the Flemish bond, but with three stretchers and a header in each course.

Walls in common bond are generally preferred, not because of their appearance, which certainly is not exceptional, but because the face-brick stretcher courses can all be laid up for the entire distance between headers, and then backed up; and only one type of brick is used at any one time. This makes erection quicker and easier. With all the other types of bonds, except the English bond, the bricklayer must select the bricks in every course, as face and backing walls must be carried upward simultaneously, and even the tender's work becomes complicated in building walls of this type.

Hardening of Lime-Type Building Mortars

Ques. What is the explanation for the fact that lime does not set when it is not exposed to the air? In an old lime pit that was recently dug into, lime putty which had been slaked years ago (possibly thirty years or more) was found, and it seemed to be still in usable condition.

Ans. The setting or hardening action of lime mortars is, of course, the result of a chemical reaction. Building lime is made up of limestone, which is an impure form of calcium carbonate ($CaCO_3$) along with other substances, such as magnesium carbonate, alumina, silica, iron oxide, and similar substances. When the limestone is burned, the carbon dioxide (CO_2) is driven off and the Ca CO_3 becomes CaO, or quicklime. To prepare the quicklime for the builder's purpose, it is slaked by adding water. It becomes very hot, and combines with the water (H_2O) to form calcium hydroxide, or $Ca(OH)_2$.

The builder mixes the calcium hydroxide, or lime putty, with sand to extend its volume and to keep it from shrinking too much as it hardens, slowly absorbing carbon dioxide from the air and changing back again into the more stable calcium carbonate ($CaCO_3$), which is chemically the original limestone.

Actually, the chemical changes in limes are not quite so simple as they have been outlined. The pure calcium limes do not make especially good mortars. Some types of mason's limes carry as much as 45 percent of magnesium, and they are usually much better for the brickmason's use, although low-magnesium limes are sometimes preferable for plastering. If the slaked lime is kept from the air, it cannot absorb the carbon dioxide necessary to make it harden, and if it is kept wet, it remains as a putty for an indefinite number of years. The magnesium content slakes very slowly, possibly for years, if it is kept wet; and it is possible that the lime putty that was dug up may make an even better mortar than it would have made thirty years, or more, ago.

If the quicklime is exposed to the air for some time without adding water, it absorbs both water and carbon dioxide from the air, and small quantities of both calcium hydroxide and calcium carbonate are formed. This is called air-slaking, and air-slaked lime is valueless in making any type of mortar.

CHAPTER 9

Concrete

Reinforcing Concrete Slabs Laid on the Ground

Ques. Usually, concrete slabs are grooved where the cracks are least objectionable, but they usually break at points other than the grooves. Can this cracking action be avoided, and can reinforcing prevent this problem?

Ans. Reinforcement of concrete slabs that are laid on the ground does not greatly influence their load-carrying ability, but it does control unsightly shrinkage cracks to a large extent. In addition to the shrinkage that is caused by the setting action when the concrete is poured, concrete also shrinks, or contracts, because of temperature drops and, conversely, it expands from rises in temperature. Since concrete is usually poured in summer, contraction is usually of more significance than expansion. In the Midwest, the temperature change from summer to winter is at least 100°; therefore, a 50-ft. concrete slab may contract, or shorten as much as 1/3 to 1/2 inch. The concrete, of course, cannot be dragged over the ground, so the tension that is produced pulls it into two pieces. The cracks that are produced are usually large and unsightly, and the edges of the cracks are often out of alignment. When reinforcement is used, the number of cracks may be greater, but they are smaller and better distributed. During warm weather, the cracks may be entirely invisible, or at least inconspicuous, because the edges of the breaks are held in position by the reinforcement. Stresses always concentrate in the angles of T-, L-, or U-shaped slabs, and at other points where their cross-sectional area or shape changes suddenly. Control joints are necessary at these points, and the reinforcements should not pass through the control joints. Changes in dimension are inevitable in well-reinforced concrete, because the steel reinforcement contracts and expands in practically the same amount as concrete under similar changes.

Prevention of Pitting Action on a Concrete Floor

Ques. In a creamery, the concrete floor, which should be kept in an attractive condition, is pitting badly, probably because of the fatty acids contained in spilled milk. Is there any surface treatment that can stop, or prevent, this problem?

Ans. It is doubtful that any type of surface treatment can restore a concrete floor satisfactorily under the conditions described; probably, it would be just as well to allow it to deteriorate further without spending money, and then replace it with a more practical floor. For best results, the floors used in places such as creameries, dairies, and meat-preparation plants, are either hard-burned paving brick or quarry tile, but the following treatment is effective where the damaging conditions are moderate.

Warm and stir until the mixture is uniform, at a temperature of not more than 150°F.: 4 parts paraffin, 1 part turpentine, and 16 parts toluol. Pour the mixture into cans and cool. Spread the mixture thickly on the floor, allowing it to penetrate for 24 hours; then drive the residue into the concrete with a hot iron. Do not use a flame. After treatment, finish the floor with heavy coats of good floor wax. The floor may be polished, but this seems unnecessary on a wet creamery floor. Take care in using the mixture, because it is flammable.

Making a Concrete Tank Watertight

Ques. How can a concrete tank be made watertight? If a percentage of hydrated lime in a mix can make the concrete water-resistant, what percentage of lime should be used?

Ans. A number of commercial sealers and mixes are available; any of these may serve the purpose. Hydrated lime in the mix helps and, in limited quantity, it does not appreciably weaken the concrete. Lime makes the concrete more dense, more tough, and inhibits separating and honeycombing of the coarse and fine particles. The formula used is as follows: $L = 6$ (S minus $1/2$ lb.); in which L represents the pounds of hydrated lime per bag of cement, and S represents the number of parts of sand in the mix. For example, if the mix is 1:3:5, then $L = 6$ (3 minus $1/2$ = 15 pounds. A gallon of loose hydrated lime weighs about 5 pounds.

Cement (Either Dry or Wet) Poured Into Water-Filled Forms

Ques. Why cannot dry-mixed cement be shoveled directly into forms that are full of water? Why does concrete that is too wet, or under water, fail to set properly?

Ans. Concrete can be made too wet. If the dry-mix cement is shoveled directly into the water, the cement that coats the sand and gravel particles is washed off and imperfect bonding results. Pump the water out of the forms, or, if that is impossible, use a tremie. A tremie is a pipe that is usually, but not necessarily, round in shape with a large funnel at the top. The tremie is lowered into the water, filled with *wet* concrete, and then raised slowly, allowing the concrete to run out and spread; the tremie should not be allowed to become empty, because the water can run in. Tremies are also used in places where concrete is dropped from a considerable height, such as in deep forms for columns. When concrete is dropped from a height, the coarse and fine particles tend to separate, causing "honeycombing" — even when water is not present.

Pouring Concrete Directly Against the Ground

Ques. Why do contractors not follow the practice of pouring concrete foundation walls against the dirt? In many instances, it seems that the job would be as good, or better, thus eliminating much form work.

Ans. When the soil is of a type that can stand vertically, contractors often pour the concrete against the dirt, and savings of hundreds of dollars may be made. If the wall is formed on only one side, however, and if the walls are of appreciable height, the forms may be difficult to hold. For underground conduits, it is often entirely satisfactory to pour the concrete against the soil; then there is no problem with settlement of a back-fill.

The method shown in the sketch (Fig. 1) is often used. After the ground has been graded and leveled, $2'' \times 4''$, or $2'' \times 6''$ boards are laid on the ground; they are then leveled, lined, and staked before the excavating is begun. The planks serve first as guides, and then as forms. Of course, this method is satisfactory only in a good stable soil.

Dusting Concrete Floors

Ques. What causes the concrete floor in a recently built house to dust badly when it is swept? How can this be corrected?

Ans. The floor was probably troweled too wet; or it may have dried too fast and was "burned out." Try treating the floor with

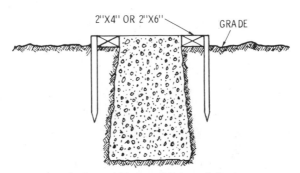

Fig. 1. Illustrating a method in which foundations and footings are poured against the ground to save form work.

a solution of 1 part of water glass (sodium silicate) with 4 parts of water. Allow the application to dry, then soak the floor with the solution again after a few days. Another recommended solution is 3 pounds of zinc sulfate in 1 gallon of water. This solution darkens the concrete slightly.

Effect of Coloring Materials on Strength of Concrete

Ques. Does the use of coloring materials in concrete affect either its strength or its resistance to water?

Ans. The use of lampblack is not approved, but most concrete coloring materials are of mineral origin, and, unless they are used in excess quantities, they should have little or no effect on the concrete, except for the color.

Markers Made of Concrete

Ques. In building concrete markers, it is desired to weatherproof them and to make them as white as possible. Should lime be used in the mix?

Ans. Use white aggregates, crushed marble or white limestone and silica sand, but use no lime. White cement is available and best results can be obtained by using air-entraining cement to increase weather resistance.

Damp-Curing of Concrete

Ques. To what extent does damp-curing affect the strength of concrete?

Ans. Firm figures cannot be given, because air temperature, heat, humidity, etc., vary greatly, and records of actual tests are not available, but the usual 28-day strength of concrete may be reduced by as much as 50 percent if the concrete is not cured properly with adequate moisture. The newer types of sealers may retard the loss of water to permit dispensing with wetting and covering the concrete, but records of actual testing are not available. Vapor-barring paper is an effective covering, and under some conditions, sprinkling may be unnecessary.

Gravity-Type Retaining Wall

Ques. A concrete retaining wall with dimensions of 140 feet long, 3-1/2 feet high at one end, 4-1/2 feet high at the other, is to be built to retain a lawn; there is to be no terrace. The wall is to be sloped on the exposed or street side. How should the wall be proportioned? The wall should be attractive, permanent, and troublefree.

Ans. Retaining walls usually fail from one of two causes; they may slide onto the ground, or they may overturn. Usually, if they are safe from overturning, they do not slide. Most retaining walls are of the "gravity" type; they are held in position only by their weight, and their broad bases provide stability. Many theories relative to the pressure of the fills behind retaining walls have been derived, but the U.S. Army Engineer Corps sometimes uses a logical rule-of-thumb method that is usually safe. It states that at any point in the height of the wall, the thickness of the wall should be 4/9 of the remaining height of the wall above that point.

The footings for such walls should extend below the frost line; but if the soil is well drained, it has been found, in many instances, that this is unnecessary. If excavation is necessary to reach a good bearing soil, it is preferable to pour the footings directly against the dirt. At the lower end of the wall, the footings should have a width of 4/9 of 3-1/2 ft., or approximately 19 inches; at the higher end, the width should be 4/9 of 4-1/2, or approximately 24 inches. Keyways should be placed in the footing to prevent sliding.

As mentioned, the wall should be sloped on the exposed side of the wall. If the wall were constructed vertical on that side, it would be unstable. Place a tongued contraction joint at intervals of 20 to 24 feet in the entire length of the wall. If the concrete is poured in summer, expansion is usually no problem.

Pour the Base of a Retaining Wall Separately

Ques. In building retaining walls, why is it not recommended that the broad base or footing be poured, and the wall set on it, thus saving much cross-sectional area?

Ans. That type of construction is entirely possible and practical, but the footing should be reinforced well and the wall should be tied firmly to the base with reinforcing (Fig. 2). A wall that is set directly on a footing has little, if any, more stability than when the wall is set directly on the ground, because the wall does not bond tightly with the footing. Reinforced retaining walls require a different designing technique from that of common gravity-type walls; the common gravity-type wall is usually more economical when the walls are low to medium in height.

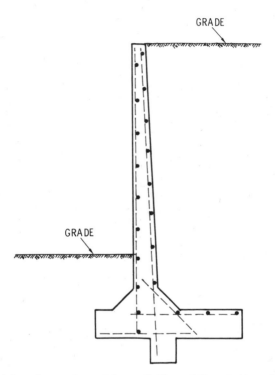

Fig. 2. A reinforced concrete retaining wall. The stability of this wall is obtained chiefly from the weight of the fill on the rear extension of the footing. Since this wall is lacking in weight, the projection underneath the footing is required to prevent sliding.

Pressure in Forms for a Column

Ques. Is there a method that can be used to determine the correct spacing of clamps for concrete columns?

Ans. No method is completely accurate. If the most extreme conditions are considered, the pressure in the column forms should be considered to be fluid pressure (the fluid weighs 150 lbs. per cu. ft.). If the concrete is extremely plastic and if vibrators are used, that assumption may be nearly correct. Assuming a column to be 12 ft. in height and $18'' \times 18''$ square, the pressure at the column base against any side is (12 ft. $\times$ 150 lbs.), or 1800 lbs. per sq. ft. The pressure at the extreme top, of course, is zero. The total pressure against a side is:

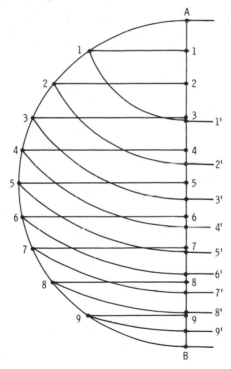

Fig. 3. Showing a method of determining the spacing of clamps for concrete columns. The exact spacing of the clamps is not important if one clamp is placed in each space.

$$\frac{1\text{-}1/2 \text{ ft.} \times 12 \text{ ft.} \times 1800 \text{ lbs.}}{2} = 16,200 \text{ lbs.}$$

If the capacity of each clamp is 1600 lbs., a total of 11 clamps is required; or 9 clamps, plus the clamps at the top and bottom. The spacing required for a loading of 1600 lbs. placed on each clamp can be obtained from the graph in Fig. 3.

To construct the graph, draw line *AB* to scale. Make line *AB* equal 12 ft., dividing it into 10 equal parts. Draw a semicircle against the line, and extend points 1 to 9 horizontally to intercept the semicircle. Using point *A* as a center point, draw the circular arcs 1-1′, 2-2′, 3-3′, etc. The points where the circular arcs intercept line *AB* indicate the approximate positions for the clamps, placing approximately 1600 lbs. of stress on each clamp. If one clamp is placed in each space, the exact spacing of the clamps may not be important.

A Reinforced Concrete-Block Retaining Wall

Ques. In the design for a retaining wall made of concrete blocks and reinforced by filling the cores with concrete as the blocks are laid (Fig. 4), it is proposed to place a 4″ layer of coarse gravel beneath the footing and behind the wall to assure free draining. Is this design structurally sound?

Ans. The wall, as designed, is unstable, but it can be made to be satisfactory. The tendency of this type of wall to overturn is resisted by the weight of the wall and by the weight of the fill which is directly above the extension of the footing at the rear. According to calculations, the weight of the wall, plus the weight of the earth, is about 725 pounds per foot of wall, and the vertical gravity axis is located at a distance of approximately 1 inch behind the blocks.

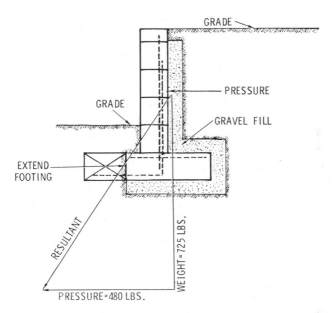

GRADE

PRESSURE

GRADE

GRAVEL FILL

EXTEND FOOTING

RESULTANT

WEIGHT=725 LBS.

PRESSURE=480 LBS.

Fig. 4. A retaining wall made of reinforced concrete blocks. Although this design is not entirely satisfactory, the basic design is practical.

Calculations indicate that the pressure behind the wall, if the fill remains dry, is at least 480 pounds per lineal foot of the wall. For calculation purposes, it may be assumed that this pressure is applied at a point one-third the height of the wall above the low point of the grade level.

To diagram the stresses, extend the gravity axis downward from the point of the load, apply a distance equal to 725 units, using a convenient scale, and extend a line from the lower end to the left-hand side a distance equal to 480 units. These lines, respec-tively, represent the total weight of the wall and fill, and the over-turning force. The resultant of these lines is the line of force resulting from a combination of the two forces. Note that the resultant line of force falls outside the footing (see Fig. 4). This indicates that, as designed, the wall will overturn. Thus, it is necessary either to extend the footing forward, as indicated in the sketch, or to extend it to the rear to increase the weight of the soil, which increases the stabilizing weight and moves the axis of gravity farther to the rear. For best results, the resultant line of force should extend through the *middle one-third* of the footing to insure positive pressure under the entire footing. If the resultant line of force extends through the outer one-third of the footing, as in this instance, even with the 12″ extension in front of the footing, there is no pressure beneath the rear edge of the footing, resulting in a slight tendency to lift upward. Under the circumstances, the wall may be satisfactory; however, the design is not ideal.

Effect of Heat for Drying a Radiantly Heated Floor Slab

Ques. After pouring a concrete floor with embedded heating pipes, how soon can the heat be turned on?

Ans. Don't turn on the heat until the concrete is thoroughly set and dry. This may require three weeks to a month; then the water temperature should not be permitted to rise above approximately 90°F. for a few days.

Surface Curing for Concrete Slabs and Floors

Ques. On a recent construction job, chloride flakes were scattered over the surface of a floor slab. Why was this done and is it necessary?

Ans. This is called "surface curing" and it is done by allowing the concrete to wet-cure overnight; then, instead of sprinkling and covering the slab, approximately 1-1/2 pounds of calcium chloride is scattered uniformly over each square yard of surface. The chloride absorbs moisture from the air, which keeps the surface wetted. This is actually a type of wet-curing. Test figures are not available as to the effect of this type of curing, but it is believed to be superior to nearly all other methods of wet curing; in addition, the surface attains exceedingly high strength and resistance to abrasion.

Calcium Chloride in Concrete

Ques. A two-percent solution of calcium chloride in the concrete on a large paving job is requested. How should the chloride be used?

Ans. Two methods are used: (1) the chloride may be dissolved in water and used as a liquid; or (2) the dry flakes may be added to the concrete in the mixer drum.

To make the standard solution, slowly add two 100-pound bags of the chloride flakes to approximately 35 gallons of water in a 50-gallon barrel, stirring until the flakes are dissolved; then add enough water to make 50 gallons of solution. To use as a two-percent solution, replace two quarts of mixing water with two quarts of the prepared solution for each bag of cement that is used in the mix.

Probably, most contractors add the dry flakes to the concrete in the mixer. The chloride accelerates the setting appreciably, but if there is assurance that the concrete can be used within one hour, the chloride may be added to the concrete in a transit mixer at the central plant; otherwise, it should be added to the concrete in the mixer at the job, allowing the mixer to run for a minute or two before dumping. A pint of the flakes weighs about 1 pound. For the two-percent solution, add two pints of the flakes for each bag of cement used in the mix.

Salt Damage on Concrete Pavements

Ques. Is it true that salting sidewalks and driveways to remove ice and snow may damage the surface? This has been done for years on one sidewalk with no apparent damage, but a neighbor has a badly roughened sidewalk, which he thinks is due to use of salt for removal of ice and snow.

Ans. It is true that salt may damage concrete surfaces. State road authorities have known this for many years, but they think that the desirability of the effects achieved outweigh the damage done, so they continue to use it. It has been found that rich, dense concrete is not usually damaged by the reasonable use of salt, but lean mixes are sometimes badly damaged. If air-entraining cement is used, concrete is more salt-resistant; this type of cement is generally used where there is a probability that salt may be used.

Sawdust-Type Concrete

Ques. Does concrete made of sawdust make a satisfactory floor for barns? How is it mixed, and what are its advantages?

Ans. Sawdust concrete is usually mixed at a proportion of approximately 1 part Portland cement to 3 parts soaked sawdust. It is used primarily for its heat-insulating qualities, and in common with other ultra-light insulating concretes, it has little or no structural value. Ths type of concrete cannot withstand wheel traffic or abrasion, and is not recommended for barn floors. The resistance of 1 : 3 sawdust concrete to the transmission of heat is comparable with vermiculite or perlite concrete with the same proportion of cement in the mix.

Calculating the Weight of Reinforcing Bars

Ques. In a construction job, fifty No. 4 reinforcing bars, 16 feet long are required. How can their weight be calculated?

Ans. The size number of a reinforcing bar indicates its diameter in eighths of an inch. The weight of round bars can be determined by the formula:

$$\text{weight (in pounds)} = \text{size number}^2 \times 0.0417 \times \text{length}$$

In the example, the combined lengths of the bars is equal to (50×16), or 800 feet; then, substituting in the formula:

$$\text{weight} = 4 \times 4 \times 0.0417 \times 800 = 534 \text{ pounds}$$

Corner Reinforcing in Two-Way Reinforced Slabs

Ques. A supporting structure was built recently for a large air tank, $11'0'' \times 11'0''$, with 8-in. brick walls and a 5-1/2-in. slab above. No. 4 bars spaced 6 inches both ways at the center, with the spacing increased to 9 inches at the walls, were used. The slab has cracked across all four corners. What was the cause of this problem?

Ans. Contraction of the concrete due to drops in temperature was not provided for. Concrete expands and contracts considerably more (approximately three times) than brickwork under the same temperature changes. The concrete was, of course, poured during warm weather, and was allowed to bond with the brickwork. When the weather became cooler during the winter, the concrete contracted, the brickwork contracted much less, and the corners were torn off by the tension.

Generally, it is not advisable to allow the concrete slab to bond tightly to the walls. Sheet metal can be used to cover the walls; or strips of roofing can probably be used just as effectively. In addition, double reinforcing material should be used at the corners, running diagonally across the corners in the top of the slab and at right angles to the diagonal rods in the bottom of the slab (Fig. 5). Each band of reinforcement is the same as the main reinforce-

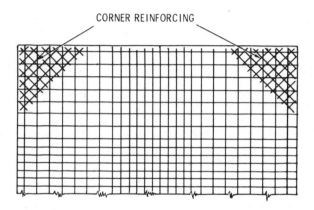

CORNER REINFORCING

Fig. 5. Showing corner reinforcement for two-way reinforced concrete slabs. Without corner reinforcement, the corners are often torn off by the tension caused by temperature drops.

ment in the center of the slab (No. 4 bars on 6-in. centers). The corner reinforcement extends approximately one-quarter the edge length in each direction (see Fig. 5).

Frost Heaving of Concrete Steps

Ques. The foundation of a three-car garage extends below the frost line to good solid clay, but the walls have cracked, as shown in the sketch (Fig. 6). In winter, these cracks open 3/4 inch, or more, and are nearly closed during summer. Is this caused by frost action? How can this be controlled in future construction projects?

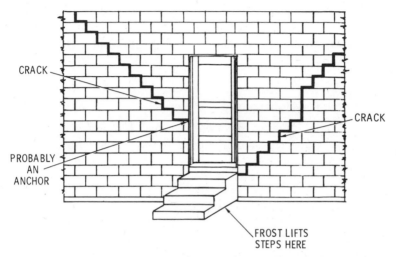

CRACK

CRACK

PROBABLY
AN
ANCHOR

FROST LIFTS
STEPS HERE

Fig. 6. An unusual example of damage done by frost heaving. The steps are bonded firmly to the block wall, and the foundations of the building extend downward to below the frost line.

Ans. The trouble is caused by frost lifting the steps which are firmly tied to the wall either by adhesion or by a mechanical bond of some type, such as metal ties. If the steps heave, the portions of the structure which are tied to them move also (Fig. 6). On the right-hand side of the door, the sill, the frame, and the masonry which is tied to them, has lifted; on the left-hand side, the frame has slipped in the masonry upward to approximately midheight, where a strong anchor may be located, and the crack begins at that point. From that point upward, the wall is hanging on the anchor.

The lifting action caused by frost is tremendous. It cannot be stopped; a lift of 3/4 inch is not uncommon if the soil is tight and poorly drained. Lift can be controlled to some extent by placing a well-drained gravel fill beneath the concrete. In these instances, the steps or other abutting concrete work should not be allowed to bond firmly with a wall or structure where lifting action can cause damage. If water is allowed to run into a crack and freeze, the steps may be pushed away from the wall; therefore, the joint should be calked, or hot asphalt should be poured into the crack.

Aggregates for Lightweight Concrete

Ques. When building specifications call for lightweight concrete, what aggregates should be used? How do the costs compare with sand-gravel concrete?

Ans. To have any real meaning, specifications should be more specific than to require that lightweight concrete is to be used. There are five basic types of lightweight aggregates in common use, and the concretes obtained from them vary widely in physical properties, as well as in cost. Current costs for comparative purposes can be obtained locally. The most commonly used lightweight aggregates are:

1. *Expanded shales, clays, or shales.* The natural products are crushed and burned at approximately 2000°F., when they swell into hollow pellets that are several times their original bulk. The concrete made from these aggregates is strong enough for some structural purposes. With six bags of cement per cubic yard, the compressive strength is 3000 to 5000 lbs. per sq. in., and weighs 70 to 100 lbs. per cu. ft. of concrete.
2. *Expanded slags.* These aggregates are by-products of the iron-smelting blast furnaces; they are made by spraying water on the molten slag. These aggregates are sharper, rougher, and harsher than the expanded shales, slates, and clays. The concrete produced is not quite as strong, but it

is cheaper. With six bags of cement per cubic yard, the compressive strength is 1500 to 2500 lbs. per sq. in., and it weighs 70 to 110 lbs. per cu. ft. These types of concrete are used chiefly for insulation and fire protection, but they have some structural value.

3. *Pumice.* This is a natural volcanic product, and pumice-type concrete is used mostly for insulating purposes where high strength is not necessary. With six bags of cement per cubic yard, the compressive strength is 1500 to 2500 lbs. per sq. in., and it weighs 60 to 83 lbs. per cu. ft.

4. *Perlite.* Perlite, like pumice, is a volcanic product, but it has been burned and expanded into pearly, foam-like pellets. Perlite concrete is a valuable insulating material, but it does not possess enough strength for structural uses. With six bags of cement per cubic yard, the compressive strength is 150 to 500 lbs. per sq. in., and the concrete weighs 25 to 40 lbs. per cu. ft.

5. *Vermiculite.* This is expanded mica. The uses of vermiculite concrete are similar to those of the perlite concretes and, like perlite concrete, it is not strong enough for structural uses. With six bags of cement per cubic yard, the compressive strength is 200 to 300 lbs. per sq. in., and it weighs 25 to 35 lbs. per cu. ft.

In comparison with concretes made from the lightweight and ultra-lightweight aggregates, concrete that is made with the standard proportions of sand and gravel weighs 133 to 143 pounds per cubic foot, and the compressive strength is 4000 to 5000 lbs. per sq. in. The strength of the lightweight concretes, of course, can be increased by adding sand and cement, but their insulating properties are reduced and their weights are increased by the addition of more sand and cement.

Water : Cement Ratio for Concrete

Ques. For a job of reinforced concrete work that is small but rather important, excellent-quality, clean, river-bank gravel is available. Is it possible to use this bank-run aggregate; or should it be screened and graded? The concrete must test 2500 lbs. per sq. in. at 28 days. The aggregates would probably have to be screened and graded by hand, which would be rather expensive concrete.

Ans. It may be economical to screen and grade the aggregates, especially if the gravel carries an excessive amount of sand, as in most bank-run gravels. However, a fairly uniform strength may be obtained by holding carefully to a specified water:cement ratio. This method is fairly safe if there are no previous tests to be used as a guide, and most engineers allow its use, providing only that the ungraded aggregates contain enough sand. An excessive quantity of sand requires more cement, but it does not seem to appreciably weaken the concrete. The check can be made as follows: Place 7-1/2 gallons of water in the mixing drum with each bag of cement, and add measured quantities of the ungraded aggregates until a plastic and workable mix is obtained. For reinforced concrete work, the concrete should be slightly on the wet side, but never sloppy. Make subsequent mixes in the same proportions, taking care that the plasticity is uniform, *but never adding water*. The concrete should test 2500 lbs., or more, at 28 days. Use the vibrator freely; it is doubtful that concrete can be over-vibrated before it has begun to set.

Burned-Out Concrete

Ques. A floor was poured in a cold basement in midwinter, using heated concrete, but no chloride. The resulting floor surface is now soft and powdery. The concrete did not freeze, because a fuel-oil heater was kept going. The basement was closed up tightly after the floor was finished. Is it possible that the heater might have exhausted the oxygen from the air so that the concrete could not set properly? Should some other type of heat have been used?

Ans. There is no remote possibility that this has caused the problem. To begin with, if the oxygen had been exhausted, the heater would have gone out; secondly, concrete does not need oxygen from the air—it sets as readily inside a steel pipe as in the atmosphere. Probably, the concrete was burned out either by heating it to too high a temperature or by allowing it to dry too quickly. There is no "other type of heat." Heat is always the same, but it may have been used unwisely. It is not uncommon to burn out a patch of concrete that is near an oil-fired salamander.

Repair of a Failing Retaining Wall

Ques. A 10-in. concrete retaining wall that is approximately 75 ft. long and 4 to 7 ft. high is to be repaired or reinforced. There is a footing, but it is placed nearly on top of the ground. It is proposed to drill the old wall and extend hand-ties back to concrete deadmen, dig down behind the wall, and attempt to straighten it up by tightening the nuts on the rods. If this fails, a new wall may have to be poured, but the footing will be placed down where they belong. Are there any criticisms of the sketched design (Fig. 7)?

Ans. Hand-ties extending back to "deadmen" are often used when a retaining wall begins to show signs of failure. If the wall is badly tilted, it is doubtful whether it can be pulled back straight as was proposed but this may be worth an attempt. Probably, a new wall will eventually have to be poured.

Do not place the new wall at a distance from the old wall, as was proposed. Place it tightly against the old wall, permitting the concrete to run inward beneath the old footing (see Fig. 7). If

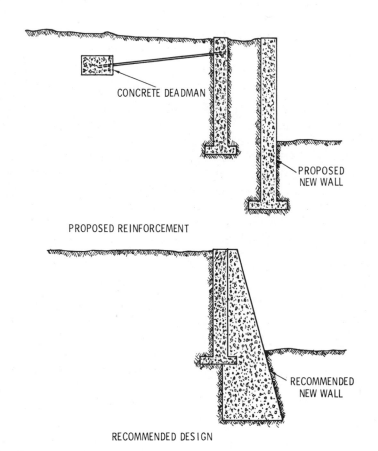

CONCRETE DEADMAN

PROPOSED
NEW WALL

PROPOSED REINFORCEMENT

RECOMMENDED
NEW WALL

RECOMMENDED DESIGN

Fig. 7. A proposed reinforcement for an existing retaining wall (top), and a preferable design (bottom).

the old wall is cleaned thoroughly, the new wall may bond with it; at least the new wall cannot tilt without lifting the old wall. Excellent stability should be attained in this manner, and the wall should never require repairs again.

A Consistency Check for Concrete

Ques. The concrete obtained from a local ready-mix concern, despite my protests, varies widely in consistency and flowability. Is there any way to check the actual quantity of water that they are using?

Ans. There is no known method for checking the actual quantity of water in a batch of concrete, but the consistency can be easily checked. This can be done with a standard "slump cone," which can be made easily. This is a galvanized steel cone, or frustum of a cone, 12″ high, 4″ in diameter at the small end, and 8″ in diameter at the bottom with suitable handles riveted on each side at midheight (see Fig. 8).

The cone is set on a level surface and filled in three layers of approximately 4 inches, after the load is completely dumped. Each

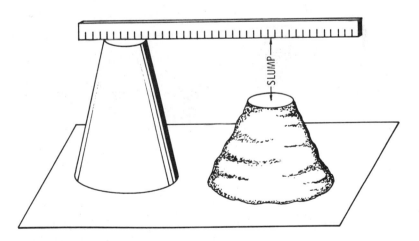

Fig. 8. Illustrating the use of the "slump cone" method for checking the consistency of concrete.

layer is "rodded" by 25 strokes of a bullet-nosed 5/8″ rod, distributing the strokes evenly and each stroke pentrating into the last layer placed. Care must be taken to hold the cone down as it is being tamped. The top should be struck level with a trowel, and the cone should be carefully lifted off and placed beside the pile. A straightedge is laid across the top of the cone, extending over the pile, so that the slump can be measured with a rule. If a vibrator is used on heavy footings and walls, concrete with 1 to 3 inches slump can be used. For thin reinforced walls, columns, and beams, the slump may range from 2 to 6 inches. Use no more water than is necessary, because excessive quantities of water reduce the strength of the concrete.

Schokbeton Concrete

Ques. A new type of concrete has been called to our attention. It is called *Schokbeton,* and it is supposed to be much denser and stronger than ordinary concrete. What is this type of concrete, and is it practical for small concrete contractors?

Ans. The *Schokbeton* process originated in Holland, and was introduced into the United States about 1959. Some firms were licensed to use it, but it is not considered practical for the small contractor.

Basically, the process is not complicated. A very stiff mix is used. Using the standard slump cone check, the slump is zero to 1/2 inch. The concrete is placed in the forms, and it is compacted by sharp blows at a rate of approximately 250 per minute. The result is a tightly compaced concrete with extremely high strength and with a dense and water-resistant surface. At 28 days, strength is usually specified as 6000 lbs. per sq. in., but it is claimed that 12,000 lbs. per sq. in. can be obtained. Despite the stiff mix, *Schokbeton* seems to be extremely applicable to reinforced concrete work, and practical reinforced sections as thin as 2 inches have been produced. Eventually, *Schokbeton* may be used widely, but, as yet, it is barely out of the development stage.

Air-Entrained Concrete

Ques. A contract for sidewalks and paving for a church has been obtained, and the use of air-entrained concrete has been requested. Since it is my understanding that air-entrained concrete is not quite as strong as that made with standard cement, the wisdom of this request may be questionable.

Ans. It is entirely correct that air-entrained concrete is slightly lower in ultimate strength than standard concrete. When it is made by adding air-entraining agents to normal concrete, a slight overdose may result in a strength reduction of 15 percent, or even more. Despite this fact, the advantages gained by the use of air-entrained concretes for outside work greatly outweigh the loss of strength, in most instances. There is no danger of overdosing the concrete when the factory-prepared cement is used.

With ordinary concrete, excess water is required to make the mix workable. During curing and drying, much of the water evaporates, leaving voids which form more or less connected channels through which water may again penetrate the mass. During repeated cycles of freezing and thawing, spalled surfaces may result, especially in outside paving.

Air-entrained concrete requires less water. The tendency of the aggregates to separate, or segregate, is reduced and the concrete is more plastic and workable than standard concrete. Billions and billions of tiny air bubbles, only 1/100 to 1/1000 inch in diameter, and making up 3 to 6 percent of the total volume, are trapped within the mass. The durability of air-entrained concrete in pavements seems to contradict the generally held theory that the most desirable concrete is the densest, and to some extent this is true; however, if salt or chloride is used to remove snow and ice in winter, the solution does not readily penetrate pavements made of air-entrained concrete, and less damage is done, because the tiny bubbles are not connected, forming channels, but remaining separate and individual. It has long been known that dense concrete pavements are less subject to damage by salt, chloride, and repeated cycles of freezing and thawing, than are the leaner, more porous concretes, and air entrainment builds up even greater resistance.

Proportions of Aggregates and Cement in Concrete

Ques. How can the exact quantities of sand, gravel, and cement required for concrete be estimated, knowing only the proportions, such as 1:2:4 or 1:3:5?

Ans. This old-time method of specifying concrete mixes by proportions is not often used these days. On important jobs, a tested crushing strength is more generally specified, and it is up to the contractor to supply it, or else, and he can do nearly as he pleases with the proportions. On less important jobs, it may be specified that a certain water:cement ratio be maintained; the proportions are still the responsibility of the contractor, providing only that the mix shall be plastic and workable. If too little sand is used, the concrete is not workable and plastic; and if there is slightly too much sand, it does not damage the concrete to a greater extent, but the contractor loses money, because the quantity of concrete produced is reduced. Thus, proportioning by volume is not so important as it formerly was.

If the concrete must be proportioned by volume, such as 1:2:4 or 1:3:5, the quantities of each can be estimated by the following formulas:

$$C = \frac{11}{c + s + g}$$

$$S = 0.14 \, Cs,$$

$$G = 0.14 \, Cg$$

In the above formulas:

c is the number of parts of cement
s is the number of parts of sand
g is the number of parts of gravel
C is the number of barrels of cement per cubic yard of concrete
S is the number of cubic yards of sand per cubic yard
G is the number of cubic yards of gravel

CHAPTER 10

Painting and Finishing

Removing Dried Paint From Masonry Walls

Ques. How can dried paint be removed from a masonry wall?

Ans. Any commercial paint remover, especially the "wash-off" types, can do the job satisfactorily, or 1-1/2 pounds of caustic soda can be mixed in a gallon of hot water and the solution applied freely. Wash away the softened paint with a hose stream.

Pastel Colors on Plywood

Ques. How can plywood be finished in pastel colors so that the grain still shows? The desired paste finishes are similar to the blonde finishes, except that they are tinted with various colors.

Ans. The following finish may be used:

1. One coat consisting of a white undercoating, 3 parts; turpentine, 3-1/2 parts; and linseed oil, 1/2 pint. Sand lightly with fine sandpaper.
2. One coat of white shellac. Rub down with No. 1 steel wool.
3. One coat of the desired color in a blending oil. Apply thinly and wipe or dry-brush to the desired tint.

4. One coat of flat varnish. For best appearance, rub this coat thoroughly.

Oxalic Acid Bleach for Wood

Ques. What solutions are recommended for an oxalic acid wood bleach, and how should they be applied?

Ans. The following solutions are recommended:

1. Dissolve 3 ounces of oxalic acid crystals in sufficient hot water to dissolve them.
2. Dissolve 3 ounces of sodium hyposulfite in 1 quart of hot water.
3. Dissolve 1 ounce of borax in 1 quart of hot water.

Allow the solutions to cool. The first two solutions are the bleaching agents; the borax solution is a neutralizer.

Apply the oxalic acid solution with a sponge or brush. When it is nearly dry, apply the second solution. Apply the two solutions repeatedly until the shade is light enough; then allow to dry thoroughly. Apply the borax solution, and let dry overnight. Then the wood may be sanded and finished as desired.

These solutions should not be used on the very dark woods, such as walnut or mahogany. The oxalic acid solution is not strong, but it is a poison. It will irritate the skin, so use rubber gloves when handling the solution.

Paint Peeling Problems

Ques. After a house has been painted four times—the last time was three years ago—the paint has loosened from the wood. What causes the paint to peel off in large pieces?

Ans. Perhaps the coats of paint have been piled on top of one another until the thick coating flakes off; however, the problem is typical of water condensation problems. If the problem is water condensation, and if the walls are reasonably well insulated, a vapor barrier is needed inside the walls to prevent water vapor from passing into the walls and condensing beneath the paint film. If the walls are not insulated, they should be vented to the outside by means of either plug ventilators which can be inserted into auger holes, by wedging the siding laps apart to break the paint seals, or by a similar method.

The water usually condenses in the wood just behind the paint film. Paint cannot stick to wet wood; the better the paint job, the greater the probability of its peeling. Leaky siding also causes the paint to peel, but the sources of that kind of trouble can usually be readily seen.

A vapor barrier inside the walls can usually be formed by applying two or three coats of a lead-and-oil paint, but one of the vapor-barring enameled-fabric wall coverings is preferable. Unfortunately, paint peeling is more of a problem when the walls are well insulated.

Paint Peeling From Porch Columns

Ques. What can be done to prevent peeling of paint from hollow porch columns?

Ans. In most instances, paint peels because of the presence of moisture beneath the layer of paint. If the porch columns are set on concrete, water may move upward through the concrete by means of capillary action; this condition is usually very much evident. Make sure that the columns do not leak through the caps at the top of the columns; place a sheet of copper material beneath the bases of the columns, and saw several small inconspicuous notches in the upper and lower portions of the columns to provide drainage and ventilation.

Painting Aluminum

Ques. What is a recommended treatment for aluminum before it is painted? What types of paints are recommended?

Ans. It is not considered to be especially difficult to paint aluminum. If the surface is unusually shiny, permit it to weather until the high gloss is removed; or roughen the surface slightly with steel wool. Clean off all oil or grease, prime with a zinc chromate primer, and finish with two coats of any good outside paint. Use either a lead-and-oil paint or one of the alkyd paints.

Whitewash Formula

Ques. What formula is recommended for whitewash that can be used both on the inside and outside of buildings?

Ans. The U. S. Government formula for lighthouse whitewash is:

> 62 pounds of lime in 12 gallons of hot water
> 12 pounds of salt in 6 gallons of hot water
> 6 pounds of Portland cement

Mix the ingredients together. The whitewash lasts approximately one season when used outside. When used on the inside of a building, it is an agreeable glareless coating that is slightly fire-resistant.

Portland Cement Paints

Ques. In painting the concrete walls of a basement playroom with Portland cement paint, how can the recommended dampness for applying these paints be avoided? Can they be used on dry surfaces? Is there another type of paint that is satisfactory for this purpose?

Ans. Cement-based paints *must* be applied to surfaces that are quite damp, and they must be kept wet until the cement has set, otherwise they will powder and dust off. If the moisture is objectionable, use another type of paint. Nearly all of the synthetic resin paints, including the alkyds, are suitable for applying over concrete. These paints have proved satisfactory in many instances.

Heat-Resistant Paints

Ques. Is there a formula for heat-resisting paint that is satisfactory for use on registers, boilers, and hot-water and steam pipes?

Ans. For boiler fronts, hot water pipes, and radiators, practically any good-quality interior paint is satisfactory. For higher temperatures, up to 500°F., metal stack paints are available. The following formula has proved to be satisfactory for low-heat surfaces:

1/5 lb. boiled linseed oil
1/5 lb. japan drier
2/3 lb. turpentine
1-1/3 oz. lampblack
1-1/2 oz. powdered graphite
3/8 oz. powdered manganese oxide

Keep the mixture stirred well, and apply immediately, because the mixture dries quickly. The surface may be relatively hot when the paint is applied.

Dilution of Shellac

Ques. Most shellac is purchased as either 4-lb. cut shellac or 5-lb. cut shellac. How much alcohol should be added to these shellacs to produce 1-, 2-, and 3-lb. cut shellac?

Ans. Shellac can be thinned by adding alcohol as follows:

1. To thin 4-lb. cut shellac;
     for 3-lb. cut, add 1 quart of alcohol per gallon of shellac.
     for 2-1/2-lb. cut, add 3-1/2 pints of alcohol per gallon of shellac.
     for 2-lb. cut, add 3/4 gallon of alcohol per gallon of shellac.
2. To thin 5-lb. cut shellac;
     for 3-lb. cut, add 3-1/2 pints of alcohol per gallon of shellac.
     for 2-1/2 lb. cut, add 2/3 gallon of alcohol per gallon of shellac.
     for 2-lb. cut, add 1 gallon of alcohol per gallon of shellac.
     for 1-lb. cut, add 2-2/3 gallons of alcohol per gallon of shellac.

Bugs in Fresh Paint

Ques. Can anything be added to exterior paint to keep off gnats and bugs?

Ans. Supposedly, 2 teaspoonfuls of oil of citronella per gallon of paint will keep insects away. This may be doubtful, because the bugs probably do not fly into the paint because they particularly like it in the first place. The bugs and gnats are probably an "occupational hazard" that painters must get along with. Incidentally, they usually cause only a slight problem when the quick-drying water-mix coatings are used.

Natural Finishes for Exterior Redwood

Ques. It is desired to finish a house with redwood siding in the natural red color. The siding has been stained, but while the effect was excellent at first, it has become an unsightly mottled gray after only two years. Are there any finishes of this type that are more permanent?

Ans. It is believed that no exterior stains compare with good coatings of paint, so far as lasting ability and appearance are concerned, but unlike paints, most of the stains contain wood preservatives which remain in the wood long after their appearance has deteriorated. Most of the paint manufacturers can provide stains, but one cannot expect too much from stains as they just cannot do the job permanently. The following formula is recommended for a homemade stain. The quantities given make 5 gallons of stain:

```
Raw linseed oil..............................................3 gallons
Turpentine or mineral spirits.....................1 gallon
Burnt sienna, color-in-oil...........................1/2 pint
Raw umber, color-in-oil..............................1/2 pint
Red iron oxide, color-in-oil........................1 pint
Paraffin wax...................................................1 pound
Zinc stearate..................................................2 ounces
Pentachlorophenol concentrate 10............1/2 gallon
```

Mix the paraffin and zinc stearate and melt over a slow fire, then take them outdoors and pour them into the turpentine, stirring vigorously. Be extremely careful about fire. Turpentine flashes readily when it is warmed. Let the solution cool; then add the pentachlorophenol, the linseed oil, and the colors in that order. This produces a dark redwood finish.

Paint Peeling Problems

Ques. A house was built and sold, the owner moving into it in March. The last coat of outside paint was applied in May, after the house was occupied. The best available materials, a standard brand of paint, and excellent workmanship were used, but the paint is peeling off (in less than a year) in large pieces, some of them are as large as a man's hand, while the paint film is still tough and elastic. What is the cause of this type of paint failure?

Ans. This type of paint failure is typical of failures caused by condensation of moisture underneath the paint film; the source of the water vapor is inside the house. If there is no vapor barrier near the inside (warm side) of the wall, the water vapor, or water in gaseous form, passes more or less readily through most of the materials commonly used in walls, such as plaster, masonry, dry-wall boards, and wood. The vapor is actually under a slight pressure from the inside, the pressure being equal to the difference in the vapor pressure inside and outside the walls. Inside a home, vapor pressure is normally rather high; outside the home, especially in cold winter weather, vapor pressure is relatively low. If, on its way to the outside of the home, the water vapor encounters no barrier (or a partial barrier), and the temperature is below the dew point, the vapor probably will pass on through the wall, being lost to the outside. Three coats of good-quality oil paint, however, constitute an exceedingly efficient vapor barrier. The movement of the water vapor is halted, and since the paint film is exposed to the outside air, it may become very cold. Condensation begins just underneath the paint layer; the wood siding is saturated, and paint does not stick firmly to the wet wood. The water may freeze, the wood may swell, and the paint may be pushed off. Unfortunately, the higher the quality of the paint job and the more complete the coverage, the greater the probability that the paint will peel.

The remedy, or preventive, is an effective vapor barrier placed near the inside surface of the wall to prevent the vapor-laden air from entering the cavities of the walls. Also, the outside wall surfaces, with its vapor-barring paint, may be ventilated to the outside to allow the vapor to escape freely. In serious instances, both the inside vapor barrier and the outside vents may be required.

Textured Wall Finishes

Ques. How are textured finishes made for dry-wall construction, and what materials are used?

Ans. Many commercial materials are available for this purpose, ready mixed in white and the various colors. Some of these finishes are heavily sanded, and a nearly perfect imitation of sand-finished plaster may be produced. Some of these materials are smooth, but very heavy; by using a rather stiff brush and plenty of the material, the brush marks are left and a very rough texture is obtained. Usually, the finish remains in "swirls," depending on how the brush was handled. One ingenious painter was able to obtain an unusual finish by rolling corncobs in the fresh paint. These types of surfaces may be "highlighted" by allowing the surface to dry thoroughly, and then brushing lightly across the surface with another color (gold or bronze lacquer may be used) in a very dry brush, hitting only the high places. An unskilled workman may make a mess, but a skilled workman can produce a truly artistic finish, and the possibilities are numberless. If it is desired to mix the materials, the following mixture is recommended for a dry-wall surface:

White lead, heavy paste	100 pounds
Dry whiting	22 pounds
Flatting oil	1/4 pint
Drier	1-1/2 gallons

These quantities of materials produce approximately 5-1/4 gallons of finish which should cover approximately 350 square feet of surface, depending on how the work is done. If the dry-wall surface has not been painted previously, it is necessary to prime it before using these types of finishes.

Aluminum Paint as a Sealer

Ques. A house has been painted a deep red, probably with Venetian red and oil, and now it is to be painted white. Is it true that an aluminum undercoat is necessary to seal down the red color?

Ans. Aluminum primers are considered excellent for such purposes. If the present paint is truly Venetian red, it probably has become chalky if it is old, but the aluminum undercoat should seal it satisfactorily. The aluminum undercoat is not transparent as are the lead-and-oil primers, and it can be covered easily with almost any white paint. Aluminum paint may shine through a single coat of lead-and-oil primer, but the titanium whites have excellent covering qualities.

Economical Paint Remover

Ques. Since commercial paint removers are rather expensive, can another preparation which is cheaper be used on unimportant work?

Ans. If the work can withstand wetting, the following preparation does an excellent job: Dissolve 1 cupful of trisodium phosphate in 1 quart of hot water. Mop this on the work; after the paint has softened, wipe off and wash with clean water. Of course, the work must be allowed to dry thoroughly before refinishing is attempted.

Modern Paints

Ques. It seems that the results are no better, if as good, from the so-called "modern" paints, than from the old fashioned lead-and-oil paints. What, if any, advantages are to be gained by using the newer coatings?

Ans. Your partiality for linseed-oil-and-lead paints is fully understandable. There are many things to be said in their favor. When fresh, they possess a sheen and gloss which is rarely found in coatings of other types. In the humid regions of the country, they can bear certain pigments, such as zinc oxide, which inhibit molds and mildews. Although their life is perhaps five years or less, they fail by chalking away, leaving the surface nearly bare and in excellent condition to receive another coating. However, these paints dry slowly, which does not fit into modern high-speed construction methods. They are highly vapor-barring, and blister and peel if proper precautions are not taken to control water vapor condensation behind them. In general, however, the following claims for modern paint coatings are valid:

1. Paints are available which last nearly twice as long on the outside, if they are applied correctly. Of course, it is up to the painter to do the work correctly, which leaves a subject for wide controversy.
2. The newer outside whites are whiter, cover better, and do not become yellowed under certain conditions, which sometimes results when lead-and-oil paints are used.

3. Some paints dry into porous films which are not vapor-barring; therefore, these paints resist peeling that results from condensation and wetting of the wood behind them.
4. Modern paints possess a permanence in colors which was unheard of only fifteen years ago; this is especially true of the pink and yellow colors.
5. Some of the newer paints dry so quickly that a second coat may be applied in less than one hour.
6. Cleanup is a minor problem with some of the newer paints; before they are completely dry, they can be washed away with plain water.

The high cost of labor for painters is, of course, a major deterrent to good painting. Many people feel that they cannot afford to allow enough time to do a thorough paint job and to allow the coatings to dry properly. The total cost of a good paint job often includes 85 percent for labor; the resistance of the labor unions to the use of sprays and rollers does not improve the situation. Eventually, a substitute for paints and on-the-job painting may be necessary.

Painting Plastered Walls

Ques. How much time should be allowed for newly plastered walls to cure before attempting to paint them?

Ans. That depends on the type of paint that is used. When the old-fashioned oil paints are used, most painters prefer to permit white-coated plaster walls to cure for at least six months, or preferably a year. Many owners live in a house until the walls become soiled before decorating them. Fresh lime plaster is highly alkaline, but many modern sealers and wall paints are alkali-resistant, and may be used soon after the plaster sets.

The water-mixed alkyd paints are highly recommended for applying over fresh plaster. They are alkali-resistant, have excellent covering power, work exceptionally well, and do not show laps when either a brush or a roller is used. The finish is rather flat, waterproof, and washable. These paints are thinned only with water. Oil, turpentine, and the common paint thinners cannot be used. Water-mixed alkyd paint can be purchased in many different tints, and in white. All of the colors may be made lighter in color by adding white, but they can be darkened only by adding special pigments. These paints cannot be mixed with colors-in-oil.

Coatings for Blackboards

Ques. Is there any type of coating that makes a wall usable as a blackboard?

Ans. Excellent coatings of this nature are available from a paint dealer. A homemade coating can be used, as follows:

2 ounces lampblack
8 ounces finely-ground whiting
16 ounces boiled linseed oil
enough turpentine to make 2 quarts of solution

If this coating is used over plywood or hardboard, shellac it first. Sand lightly between coats. Several coats may be required to obtain a satisfactory surface.

Paint Vehicles

Ques. What components of paints are called "vehicles," and what do they consist of?

Ans. The fluid components of paints are called the vehicles; many different liquids are used, the most common being the following, which are all oils of organic origin:

1. Linseed oil, extracted from flax seed, and used either raw or boiled.
2. Tung oil, extracted from the nuts of a tropical tree.
3. Soybean oil, extracted from soybeans, a common farm product.
4. Fish oil, mostly from menhaden, a small Atlantic fish.
5. Oiticica oil, from the seeds of a South American tree.
6. Perilla oil, from the seeds of an Asiatic shrub.

All of these oils take oxygen from the air into chemical combination, forming tough, nearly colorless films; the color and covering power are supplied by various pigments that are added to the oils.

The following oils dry without leaving a residue; they are used in paints chiefly to modify oxidizing oils, providing greater penetration and improving spreading qualities:

1. Turpentine, obtained from the yellow pine tree.
2. Mineral spirits, from petroleum distillation.

The following vehicles are used in various types of paints, as noted:

1. Glycerol phthalate, a compound made by cooking together phthalic anhydride, soybean oil, and glycerine. This is the vehicle that is used in alkyd paints.
2. Cellulose nitrate or ethyl cellulose. Used as a vehicle in lacquer-type coatings, such as *Duco*.
3. Silicates, or organosilicates, used as a vehicle in some zinc-dust and other metallic paints.
4. Modified asphalts, used as a vehicle in some aluminum paint.

5. Water, used as a vehicle in the acrylics, latex or styrene-butadiene coatings, and with the protein solutions, such as casein paints. The film formed by these coatings is produced by a chemical change in the pigments called polymerization —not by oxidation or drying of the vehicle.

CHAPTER 11

Roofing

Buckling Asphalt Shingles

Ques. What causes asphalt shingles to buckle and to curl? Can this be caused by sheathing that is wet or "green" when it is installed?

Ans. If the sheathing boards are wide and also wet or "green," they shrink as they dry out; this causes asphalt shingles to buckle. If the sheathing boards are a width that requires two or more courses of shingles to be nailed to the same board, and if the board subsequently shrinks, the shingles are certain to buckle, and the butts of the exposed course of shingles above are lifted. It is not at all uncommon for a $1'' \times 6''$ board to shrink 1/4 inch as it loses moisture from the green board to the air (Fig. 1).

Sizes of Gutters and Downspouts

Ques. How are the sizes required for gutters and downspouts determined?

Ans. For semicircular gutters and round downspouts, the following sizes are adequate, except in regions of extremely heavy rainfall:

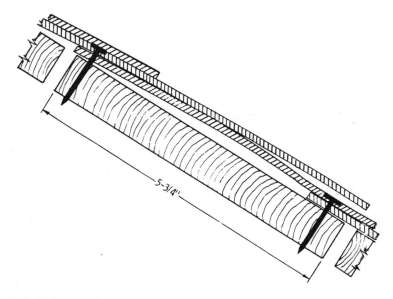

Fig. 1. If sheathing boards are "green" or extremely wet when shingles are applied and if they are wide enough for two courses of shingles to be nailed to the same board, subsequent shrinkage of the boards often causes unsightly buckling of the asphalt shingles.

3-in. diameter gutter for 170 sq. ft. of roof.

4-in. diameter gutter, with 3-in. downspouts spaced 25 to 35 ft. for 360 sq. ft. of roof.

5-in. diameter gutter for 625 sq. ft. of roof.

7-in. diameter gutter, with 5-in. downspouts spaced 40 ft., for 1380 sq. ft. of roof.

8-in. diameter gutter, with 5-in. downspouts spaced 35 ft., for 1990 sq. ft. of roof.

10-in. diameter gutter for 3600 sq. ft. of roof.

12-in. diameter gutter for 6800 sq. ft. of roof.

Where the sizes of the downspouts are not given, allow 1 sq. in. of cross-sectional area of downspout for each 100 sq. ft. of roof drained. The pitch of the gutters should not be less than 1/16" per foot. For steeply pitched roofs, or where the gutters slope more than 1/16" per foot, the above figures may be reduced slightly.

Laying an Asphalt Roof Over an Old Coal-Tar Roof

Ques. On a building with a 10-year-old built-up roof of impregnated felt and coal-tar pitch, it is desired to apply more layers of roofing. Can asphalt be used; or is it necessary to apply the tar-and-felt material for additional layers of roofing that are to be applied?

Ans. It is not advisable to apply asphalt over coal-tar pitch, because the oils in the pitch are an asphalt solvent. However, a complete asphalt built-up roof can be laid over an old pitch roof by first laying down about three layers of red rosin paper, and beginning from there. The red rosin paper should absorb the oils from the old roofing. Why change to asphalt? On level, or nearly level roofs, many users prefer tar-and-gravel roofs to asphalt types of roofs.

Shingles for Dormers or Gables

Ques. How can standard courses of shingles be made to finish evenly when the two sides of a dormer or a low gable are to be shingled?

Ans. As shown in the sketch (Fig. 2), if there is an even number of courses on the left-hand side of the gable, begin the courses on the right-hand side on line *B*, if there is an odd number of courses, begin on line *A*. The starter course is not considered a shingle course.

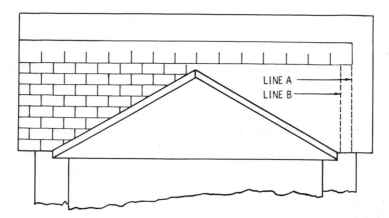

Fig. 2. Illustrating a method of shingling above dormers and low gables. Note that an odd number of courses has been laid on the left-hand side; hence, shingling on the right-hand side begins on line "A."

Roofing Placed Over Old Shingles

Ques. A house with an old wood-shingle roof which has been covered with roll roofing leaks badly. Is it advisable to lay a new asphalt-shingle roof over the roll roofing?

Ans. "Overcoat" jobs of any kinds are seldom advisable, and this job seems to be a particularly makeshift proposition. If the job is worth doing at all, it is surely worth doing better than the job proposed. The old roof covering, including the old wood shingles, should be removed, and the sheathing spaces closed, either by moving the boards together or by placing slats between the spaced boards, so that the new shingles can be nailed properly. Probably, the old sheathing is not in good shape, and most of it will need replacing.

These jobs can be done in some instances by ripping off the old roofing and the shingles, and then covering the spaced sheathing with 5/16″ *Plyscord* plywood. The plywood can be nailed adequately, its surface is smooth and attractive, and the plywood holds well, even if a nail misses the sheathing board.

Preventing Tarnishing of Copper Gutters and Flashings

Ques. How can a tarnishing of copper gutters and flashings that are installed on a new home be prevented?

Ans. Generally, it is useless to attempt to prevent copper from oxidizing in such places; the thin film of oxide does no harm, and usually is not considered to be unsightly. Spar varnish is sometimes used to prevent tarnishing, but it lasts only a short time.

Estimating Material in a Conical Roof

Ques. In estimating a roofing job for the cone-shaped roof of a water tower, how many squares of roofing are required if the roof diameter is 20 ft. and the roof pitch is approximately 6 in. per foot?

Ans. The area A of the cone-shaped roof can be determined by multiplying the circumference C by one-half the slant height, or rafter length, as follows:

1. $C = \pi D$; or $C = 3.1416 \times 20$ ft. $= 62.83$ ft.
2. Slant height, or rafter length $=$
   $$\frac{10 \ (\text{run}) \times 13.42 \ (\text{from framing square})}{12} = 11.18 \text{ ft.}$$
3. When, roof area $A = \dfrac{11.18}{2} \times 62.83 = 352.2$ sq. ft., or

   slightly more than 3-1/2 squares of roofing are required.

A large amount of waste in roofing materials is involved on cone-shaped roofs. If roll roofing is used, the most economical method is to cut the roofing in pieces that equal the slant height, or rafter length of the roof; then split the pieces diagonally, allowing for the laps. Then run the strips up and down on the roof. With this method, the allowance for the laps and the waste material should be approximately 15 percent.

Corrosion of Wet Galvanized Sheets

Ques. In working with corrugated steel sheets of roofing, corrosion often begins when the corrugated steel sheets in the bundles become wet. Why does this occur, and what can be done to prevent its occurrence?

Ans. The "corrosion" is called "wet-storage stain;" it is usually only a white powdery deposit that does not adhere strongly to the corrugated sheets and is noticeable only after the sheets have dried. Although the white deposit is objectionable in appearance, this is only superficial and apparently does not reduce the corrosion resistance of the zinc coating. Some manufacturers are treating their galvanized sheets with chemicals or oils to prevent staining. The bundles can be set on end and their top ends covered, if they are to be stored outdoors.

Ice Dams on Roof

Ques. Moderate to heavy snowfall in winter, with temperatures varying from 57° to $-17°$, is normal in this region. Quite often, ice forms on the projecting eaves, water backs up beneath the shingles, and serious leaks occur. What can be done to prevent this problem (see Fig. 3)?

Ans. These difficulties rarely occur if the roofs are constructed with steep pitches (7 inches or more per foot), or on roofs that are constructed with narrow or no overhanging eaves. On the steeper roofs, the snow does not adhere so readily, and they drain

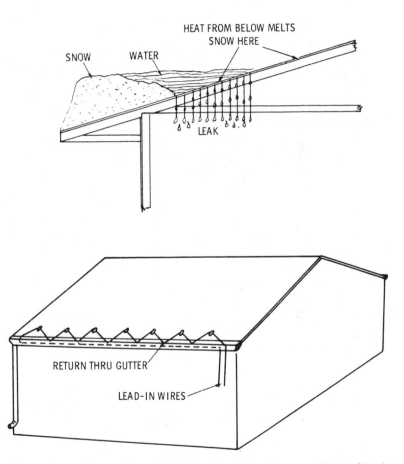

SNOW

WATER

HEAT FROM BELOW MELTS
SNOW HERE

LEAK

RETURN THRU GUTTER

LEAD-IN WIRES

Fig. 3. Illustrating problem created by formation of ice dams on roofs, resulting in leaks (top). Electric resistance wires laid in loops along the eaves of a roof, for ice melting (bottom). The return is usually laid in the gutter. Such assemblies are made at the factory and must not be cut or spliced, but they are obtainable in many different lengths. Approximately 80 ft. of wire are required for the 24-ft. loop shown. At 120 volts, this assembly uses 400 watts. Thermostatic controls are unnecessary, and it may be connected to the house circuit.

quickly. On the flatter roofs, the snow often disappears only by melting in place.

The snow lying over the parts of the roof which are exposed to heat from below and to the rays of the sun from above, melts first. Snow lying on the wide eaves is exposed to the cold outside air on both sides; therefore, it melts more slowly, the wet snow lying above the eaves freezes into dams of hard ice, and the water from the melting snow farther up the roof accumulates behind the dams. Unless the roof is entirely airtight, it will leak. If the roof is shingled, water often backs up underneath the shingle butts.

This problem occurs only when the temperature is favorable, and usually it occurs on roofs with southern slopes. This same phenomenon causes snow to melt on a roof, run over the edges of the eaves, and freeze into icicles. This cannot occur when the air temperature is above freezing, and it usually does not occur when the temperaure is several degrees below freezing

Heavy roof or ceiling insulation helps to prevent these difficulties, because heat from below cannot escape to warm the roof and melt the snow. A satisfactory solution is to install electric resistance cables in zigzag fashion along the eaves where the ice dams usually form. The return cable is usually laid in the gutter, where it prevents accumulations of ice (see Fig. 3).

This problem is one of the reasons why the "ranch-type" home with flat-pitched roof and wide eaves is not practical architecture in the northern regions where snowfall is heavy.

Corrugated Steel Roofing

Ques. What gauge in galvanized corrugated sheets may be used on sheathing that is spaced 24 inches? Is a rise of 3 inches per foot too flat for this type of roof?

Ans. For 28-gauge roofing with 2-1/2-in. corrugations, the sheathing may be spaced up to 2'9"; however, for sheets with

1-1/4-in. corrugations, it is preferred that the sheathing be spaced 1 foot. If reasonably trouble-free service is desired, a rise of 3 inches per foot is entirely too flat for these roofs. It is recommended that corrugated sheets should not be used on pitched roofs that have a rise of less than 6 inches per foot.

Corrugated sheets are made with one edge turned up and the other edge turned down. They should be laid with 1-1/2 corrugations for a side lap and not less than 6 inches of end lap. Some patented types are made with a channel down the side lap, which is supposed to prevent, or retard, water siphoning over the laps of the sheets.

Gravel for Built-Up Roofs

Ques. Why are stone chips, gravel, or crushed slag used on built-up roofs?

Ans. Asphalt-felt roofs are not usually coated with stone, but this is necessary on tar-felt roofs, because coal-tar pitch melts and runs more readily. Cracks and checks in coal-tar pitch roofs are actually "self-healing," but the granules keep the pitch from running too readily when exposed to the sun. It is for this reason that asphalt-felt roofs are preferred if the roof deck slopes more than approximately 2 in. per foot.

In addition, the stone chips or gravel keep the oils in the pitch from evaporating too readily, which makes the pitch brittle and lifeless so that rain washes it away. If the granules are white or light-colored, the roof reflects the sun's radiation, keeping the attic cooler in summer.

Painting Galvanized Steel

Ques. What can be done to prevent paint peeling from gutters and other galvanized ironwork?

Ans. Galvanized steel requires special treatment if the paint is to hold to it. The most satisfactory treatment is a chemical treatment with crystalline zinc phosphate. Although they recommend this treatment, these chemicals are not made by the standard paint manufacturers; they are made by manufacturing chemists, and they are obtainable from most paint dealers. After the phosphate treatment, the galvanized surface can be finished in the same manner as any other iron or steel, using red-lead primer and any type of paint that is suitable for metal. This is a better method than attempting to etch the galvanized surface with acid, which actually removes some of the protective coating.

Blisters in Built-Up Roofs

Ques. A four-ply asphalt-felt roof on an apartment building is blistering badly. It is laid over 1-in. fiberboard insulation, with 3/4-in. sheathing below. On cutting into the blisters, they were found to be filled with water. Where can the water be coming from, and what can be done about it?

Ans. The blisters are a result of no adhesion (or poor adhesion) between the plies of the roofing. If a space is filled with air and water vapor, and the roof is exposed to intense radiation from the sun, the asphalt is softened, the air and vapor expand, and the space increases in volume.

If the indoor humidity is high, which is normal in apartments and residences, while the outside humidity is low, the vapor tends to move from the inside to the outside. If there is no good solid mopping material between the plies, water vapor passes readily through the uncoated roofing felts, and continues moving until it is stopped by the solid mopping material on the top surface. If the surface is cold, water may condense there within the blisters. Although vapor passes through bare (or nearly bare) roofing felts, water in liquid form cannot pass through. It is trapped within the blisters, which continue to increase in size.

The blisters can be cut open in crisscross fashion, the points turned up, the water drained, and the cavity dried with a blowtorch. Then the cavity should be filled with either hot asphalt or cold-patch material, the points pressed down into it, a layer of roofing membrane mopped quickly over the cut, and coated again.

If the inside air is excessively humid, an effective vapor barrier should be placed underneath the roof sheathing. If the insulation is placed inside, the vapor barriers should be placed underneath the insulation; otherwise, water may condense beneath the roof covering, and the sheathing and insulation may be badly damaged by decay before it can be detected from the outside. When it is possible to do so, the attic or space under the roof should be well ventilated, because the vapor barrier itself may become so cold that water condenses on it.

Quantity of Materials Required in a Conical Roof

Ques. The cone-shaped roof of a water tower needs covering. Its diameter is 15 feet, and the rise is approximately 45 inches, with the wood sheathing extending from the eaves to the peak. What method can be used to determine the quantity of roll roofing needed to cover the roof?

Ans. The circumference of the tank can be calculated as follows:

$$D = 3\text{-}1/7 \times 15 = 47\text{-}1/7 \text{ feet, or approximately } 566 \text{ inches}$$

The distance from eaves to peak should be measured accurately, but this should be approximately 8′4″. If the tank is made of hooped wooden staves, they are seldom truly round.

Extend the roll roofing in triangular pieces from the eaves to the peak. Standard roll roofing is 36 inches wide and 36 feet long. Therefore, each roll provides eight triangular pieces, each 8'4" in length. The pieces should be split diagonally, with 2" widths at the top, and 34" widths at the bottom. With 2" for side lap, each triangular piece covers approximately 32" of the circumference. Therefore, 566/32, or 18 strips, or 2-1/4 rolls of roofing are required. Cement the side laps well, since vertical joints in roll roofing are slightly prone to leakage.

Probable Life of Asphalt Shingles

Ques. According to the manufacturers, an expected useful life of ten years may be obtained from the 210-lb. type of asphalt shingles, but in southeastern United States, approximately one-half the expected life is obtained. The shingles curl, become brittle, and break. This may be caused by the climate or heat from the sun; however, it may be assisted by heat from below, because in many instances, the heat in the attics is terrific. Another cause may be the lack of quality in shingles. Are there any suggestions as to the cause of this problem?

Ans. Approximately 80 percent of the asphalts that are used in asphalt shingles are by-products of petroleum distillation. A few manufacturers use a high-quality natural asphalt, or *Gilsonite,* which is produced in Colorado and Utah. These asphalts are too brittle to be used for roofing purposes as they are produced in nature, so they are softened by adding petroleum oils. With the by-product asphalts, distillation is halted before all the oils are driven off.

In all instances, the oils, which are more or less volatile, provide the asphalt with pliability and "life." Sunlight and heat dry out and distill these oils; then the asphalt hardens, scales, powders, and washes or is blown away. The asphalt also becomes hard and brittle at low temperatures. Considering all factors, the manufacturer seems to be doing a commendable job. Builders must recognize the fact that asphalt shingles possess definite and inherent limitations. Unquestionably, low-grade asphalt shingles are available on the market. Perhaps better service may be obtained from the products of the older, well-recognized manufacturers. Probably, the newer heavier types of shingles are worth their extra cost, but in that climate this may be questionable.

Asphalt Shingles Dissolve in Oil

Ques. A workshop is located underneath a two-car garage. The garage floor is made of planks above the joists. In winter, snow and ice accumulations dropped from cars, melted, and ran through the floor. For this reason, the garage floor was covered with 90-lb. slate-surfaced roofing. This was satisfactory for a short time, but oil drippings from the cars have deteriorated the roofing material. Can anything be done, except to trowel on some cold-patch roofing cement and apply another layer of roofing material? What is recommended?

Ans. Probably no more service can be obtained from the new cover than from the first cover. All the asphalts are soluble in petroleum oils. The oily spots are probably well localized, since cars are usually stopped at nearly the same place in a garage. Perhaps the new cover can be laid; some sheets of galvanized iron can be nailed over the new cover where the oil drips are located. The metal can be cleaned easily, whenever necessary. The slate-surfaced roofing may withstand moderate foot traffic for a long period of time.

Tin Roofs Are Generally Satisfactory

Ques. A sheet-metal contractor in this town does much sub-contract work for me. He has been strongly advising me to do more tin roofing. Being unfamiliar with tin roofing, is it entirely satisfactory?

Ans. No type of roof covering is entirely satisfactory under all possible conditions, but on flat to moderately pitched roofs, high-quality tin roofs are usually satisfactory. Present-day roofing tin, however, is not coated with tin. It is more properly called terne-plate, and it is coated with an alloy of approximately 20 percent tin and 80 percent lead. Generally, there is a choice of two available grades, weighing, respectively, 62 and 76 pounds per 100 square feet. This is one of the lightest, one of the most durable, and one of the most satisfactory of the metal roofing materials in use today. It is obtainable in either the standard 20″ × 28″ roofing sheets or in seamless rolls 50 ft. long, and it is usually applied with malleted-down and soldered lock seams. This type of roofing is never nailed through, but is fastened to the deck below by means of clips that are formed and inserted into the seams. Expansion and contraction are usually no problem.

For a century, up to the early 1800's, tin roofs competed successfully with slate, wood shingles, and tile, and then they lost popular favor and settled nearly into oblivion along with some other types of building materials. Only a small number of materials, indeed, recover from similar waves of unpopularity, but the tin roofs seem to have made a rather successful comeback. One objection is that tin roofs are not attractive, despite the fact that they can be painted readily. In fact, they should be kept painted, and any color that is desired may be used. The fact that they do not show "shadow lines" has been overcome in the Bermuda-type stepped-section roofs. For a word of warning, they are noisy, and should never be used on an assembly hall or a church. During a heavy rainstorm, an audience finds that only the rain on the roof can be heard. On a porch roof, the pattering rain on a tin roof is usually audible inside the house, although it may not be loud enough to be annoying at night. In these instances, some people find the gentle pattering of the rain on a tin roof rather pleasant.

Copper Roofing

Ques. Is copper roofing satisfactory? After being called several times to repair leaks in a large flat-seamed copper roof on an office building, it seems impossible to make it stay fixed, although it solders quite readily. Does the roof move with temperature changes?

Ans. Both copper and zinc sheets are often used for roofing purposes, but both materials have a high coefficient of expansion, and to give satisfaction, some provision must be made for changes in dimensions under temperature changes. On a small roof, it may be possible to get by without allowing for temperature changes, but this cannot be avoided on a large roof. Pressed standing-seam joints can withstand temperature changes, but flat soldered seams often cannot. Ribbed-and-capped seams are often used. (Fig. 4).

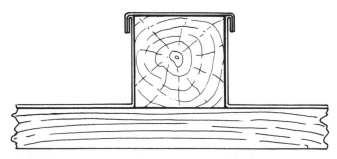

Fig. 4. A ribbed-and-capped joint for sheet copper roofing. The lock seam is not soldered, but it is merely malleted down. The sheets are fastened to the rib by means of clips placed in the turned seams.

Hot-Dip Galvanizing Process

Ques. How is the so-called "hot-dip" galvanizing process done?" Is it an electric, or electrolytic process?

Ans. Hot-dip galvanizing is not an electric, or electrolytic, process (Fig. 5). The steel that is to be galvanized is usually fab-

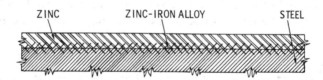

Fig. 5. A hot-dip galvanized steel surface, showing how an intermediate layer of zinc-iron alloy forms underneath the coating. The zinc coating may be 4 to 8 microns (.004 to .008 in.) in thickness. The zinc-iron alloy is not formed in an electroplating process.

ricated before galvanizing, and welds (if any) are carefully cleaned of slag. It is then degreased (if greasy) and "pickled" in a hot solution of either sulfuric or muriatic acid. It is then submerged in a molten zinc bath at about 830° to 860° F. and allowed to remain until its temperature reaches approximately that of the molten zinc. It is then withdrawn slowly, the surplus zinc is allowed to run off, and a coating of zinc 4 to 8 mils thick is left behind.

On the outside, the coating is pure zinc; the steel that was dipped is beneath. Between the zinc and the steel, a layer of zinc-iron alloy is formed, which merges gradually into the steel on one side and into the zinc on the other side, the molecules of the metals actually intermingling and binding the zinc layer firmly to the steel.

Normally, a well-galvanized structure, fully exposed to the weather, is protected from fifteen to twenty-five years, depending on the atmospheric environment. The appearance of reddish patches does not necessarily mean that the zinc coating is entirely gone. After the upper layer of pure zinc is gone, the zinc-iron intermediate coating may oxidize to a reddish color caused by its iron content, but it still furnishes effective protection for the steel underneath for some time.

CHAPTER 12

Floors

Nailing Built-Up Wood Girders

Ques. When building up wood girders that are constructed of two or three planks with continuous length (no end joints), is it necessary to nail them firmly together? Do the spike nails add to the strength of the beam?

Ans. Theoretically, the spike nails do not add to the strength of the beam. Both strength and stiffness of beams that have the same spans and depths are directly proportional to their widths. In other words, there should be no difference in either the strength or the stiffness of three planks each 1-5/8" × 9-1/2" nailed together and one solid wooden beam 4-7/8" × 9-1/2", if their spans are identical.

However, proper nailing is necessary, because the nails force the planks to work as a single member. If they are unsupported laterally along their spans, long planks or joists seldom fail because of ordinary bending stresses. They usually fail either by buckling or by bending sideways and then turning flatwise, even though the ends are held firmly in position at the bearings. If the planks are nailed firmly together, buckling is prevented.

Laying Flexible Tile Over a Plywood Underlayment

Ques. When laying linoleum and vinyl tile, unsatisfactory results usually are obtained with hardboard underlayments, because the tile joints coincide, or nearly coincide, with the joints in the hardboard. Can 1/4″ plywood be used to avoid this problem?

Ans. Cut the 48″ × 96″ plywood panels into 24″ × 48″ pieces, and lay the pieces, staggering the joints over the subfloor. Nail the edges on 3-in. centers, and nail the entire surface both ways on 6-in. centers. Use 3d shingle nails, because they are slightly heavier than 3d common nails (.0915″ to .0800″), and they penetrate the usual 3/4-in. subfloor. If the subfloor is properly dried out, the nails do not "pop" or withdraw. In actual tests, it was found that shingle nails are superior to either deformed or cement-coated nails in this respect, as well as being more economical. Drive the heads flush, or slightly below finish, and smooth with a leveling compound. This is the most satisfactory method of placing underlayment for flexible floor tile; many commercial floor-laying concerns follow this practice on their best jobs. By using smaller pieces of plywood, expansion and contraction are distributed, and the joints do not open widely enough in any one place to be noticeable.

Concrete Floors Placed Over Hollow Tile

Ques. A concrete floor was poured above hollow backing tile which were laid directly on the ground, but serious difficulty in finishing was encountered because the concrete set so quickly that it could not be troweled correctly. What can be recommended to prevent this type of finishing trouble?

Ans. Concrete-over-tile floors usually present no special problems in finishing. Concrete floors are often poured directly on dry gravel, where any free water either runs away or is absorbed almost instantly. Either the concrete is so lean that it will not retain water or too much is expected from the finishers. To slow the drying action, try wetting the tile underlayment with a fine stream of water from a hose before pouring the slabs.

Repairing Porch and Deck Floors

Ques. In repairing exposed porch and deck floors, it is often found that the top edges of the joists are badly damaged by rot, but the rest of the timbers are quite sound. Is there any method of preventing this problem?

Ans. Cut 45-lb. asphalt roofing into 5-in. strips, extending the length of the joists (see Fig. 1). Center these strips on the edges of the joists. and lay the flooring over them in the usual manner.

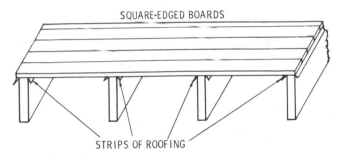

SQUARE-EDGED BOARDS

STRIPS OF ROOFING

Fig. 1. A method used to build rot-resistant porch and deck floors. Since they allow free drainage, square-edged boards are preferable to matched flooring boards for this type of construction.

The edges of the strips sag downward so that the water can drain, and the nails that are driven through the roofing strips are sealed tightly. Square-edged boards last longer than matched boards when they are exposed to the weather, because they drain better.

Steel Joist-Bearing Girders

Ques. An 8-in. steel I-beam is being used instead of the usual built-up wooden joist bearers. Should a nailing sill be bolted over the beams so that the joists can be nailed; or should they bear directly on the metal beam? Is there any way to install steel beams so that the basement ceilings are flush?

Ans. In the interest of good construction, the beams should be set underneath the joists, and a nailing sill should be used. The upper flange of the I-beam should be punched and a $2'' \times 4''$ bolted onto it. The F.H.A. regulations permit the joists to be set on the lower flange of the I-beam, the tops of the opposing joists being held together with steel straps, as shown in the sketch (Fig. 2). The joists should have solid blocking between them on each side of the girder.

Maximum Temperatures for Floor Heating

Ques. In construction of new homes, the hot-water heating coils are embedded in the concrete floors. This type of heating system is very satisfactory, but there is a problem with the floor coverings. When asphalt tile are used, they are softened by the heat, and heavy furniture makes indentations in the tile. What can be done to prevent this?

Ans. Probably, the floor temperature is too high. Under no condition, unless for only a short time, should the floor temperature be above 85° F. When floor temperatures are warmer than 85° F., they are too uncomfortable for the feet, and they may be injurious to crawling infants. Even when the floors are cooler than 85° F., furniture casters and gliders mar the asphalt tile floors seriously. If the amount of radiation surface can be increased, lower floor temperatures might be used.

SPLICE

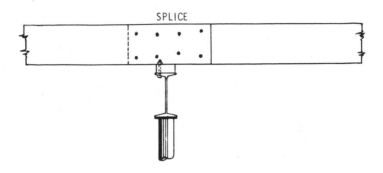

DIAGONAL SUBFLOOR

STEEL STRAP

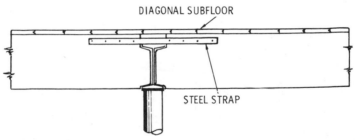

Fig. 2. Use of 8-in. I-beam joist-bearing girders. Although the type of construction in the lower sketch can be used with a flat basement ceiling, the upper sketch shows the better type of construction.

Stopping Squeaks in a Floor

Ques. How can squeaks be eliminated from a 3/8-inch oak floor? Is there an oil or a lubricant that can be used to stop the noise?

Ans. The squeaks are a result of poor or inadequate nailing and the loosening of the boards which is caused by drying out and shrinkage. Lubrication cannot stop the squeak. Renailing, which means face nailing, is the remedy. Use 4d finishing nails; set the nail heads, and fill the holes with either putty or plastic wood. The floor may not need sanding. It is possible that some of the noise may be caused by a loose subfloor. If it is possible to get underneath the floor, glued blocking may solve that problem; otherwise, the only thing that can be done is to face nail through both floors with 10d finishing nails into the joists.

Oak Floors Laid Over Concrete Slabs

Ques. Is it practical to attempt to lay oak flooring directly above a concrete slab? What method should be used in this instance?

Ans. Only when wood blocks are laid in adhesive are they suitable for application directly onto the concrete slab. This method is satisfactory only if the slab is well drained and can be kept reasonably dry. In general, if the top of the concrete slab is at least 8 inches above the grade level, the above method may be satisfactory. The standard size of wood flooring blocks is 9 × 9 inches; they are available in various thicknesses, and they are available either in solid wood or in laminated blocks. All types of blocks are suitable for laying in adhesive applied directly onto the concrete slab.

It is recommended that a roofer first prime the floor, and then apply a two-layer membrane of asphalt and felt with a mop, butting the joints. The blocks are then applied, using an asphaltic adhesive. The adhesive should be applied with a notched trowel, *and allowed to dry thoroughly.* This requires some time, but there is little danger in the adhesive becoming too dry. If the bond between the blocks and the base is broken for any reason, the bond is resumed when the blocks are brought in contact again with the concrete slab.

Magnesite Floors in Residences

Ques. Can magnesite floors for kitchens and bathrooms be used satisfactorily in residences? Can these floors be sealed and waxed?

Ans. Magnesite floors are satisfactory for kitchens and bathrooms in residences. Although magnesite floors are not recommended for places where they will be wetted continuously, considerable daily scrubbing does not damage them. These floors are often built continuous, with a coved base or with wainscots. These floors are available in attractive colors; they may be waxed and polished. When these floors are installed over wooden floors, galvanized, expanded or welded mesh reinforcing material is recommended.

Flooring an Attic Room

Ques. Is it safe to attempt to cantilever the joists for an attic room that is to be built in a house. The house is 28 ft. in width, and has a steeply pitched roof, but the ceiling joists are only 2″ × 4″ boards. The attic is to be floored, but is to be used chiefly for storage space. There are two bearing partitions located below the attic.

Ans. It is entirely satisfactory for the joists to be cantilevered, as indicated in Fig. 3. New 2″ × 8″ joists can be placed between the 2″ × 4″ joists, and the new joists should be nailed beside the old 2″ × 4″ joists. The knee walls and the collar joists will strengthen the framing considerably.

Controlling Vibration Caused by Machinery

Ques. A heavy motor-driven air compressor is mounted directly on a concrete floor, and the vibration is very annoying. Could the

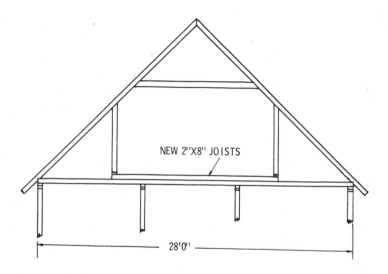

NEW 2"X8" JOISTS

28'0"

Fig. 3. Illustrating cantilevered floor joists for an attic storage room. The knee walls and collar joists increase the stability of the framing.

use of resilient mountings, such as cork or rubber, prevent this annoyance?

Ans. Properly designed resilient mountings should reduce machine-originated vibration greatly, but for maximum efficiency, each installation should be designed to fit the actual conditions. Generally speaking, these jobs should be attempted by experienced engineers only, but the following specifications may serve as a guide for others.

The frequency of the vibrations is directly related to the weight of the machine and the static deflection (or compression) of the resilient mountings that bear the weight of the machine. Cork mountings are useful in controlling vibrations of 1200 cycles or more per minute, and they should compress 1/4 inch or less under the weight of the machine. Rubber pads with a deflection of 1/4 in. to 3/4 in. are effective for vibrations of 700 to 1200 cycles; for less than 700 cycles, steel springs with deflections of 1 inch to as much as 5 to 7 inches are useful. In machines such as the motor-driven air compressor already mentioned, vibrations consisting of two frequencies often occur. The motor may operate at 1200 rpm, while the compressor operates at 360 rpm. It is seldom possible to isolate them separately, so only the lower frequency is usually considered.

The machine must be supported *freely* on the resilient mountings. There should be no bolts or any other type of rigid fastenings used to hold it down. In some instances, this may result in mountings that are so flexible that the machine is almost unstable; thus some kind of compromise must be made. The machine should never be rigidly connected to a wall or any other part of the building by electric conduit.

Vitreous Tile in Bathrooms of Older Homes

Ques. In remodeling an old home, is it desirable to use vitreous tile in the bathroom? Can these be safely laid directly over the old joists?

Ans. Many excellent jobs of laying vitreous tile have been accomplished by laying them in adhesives. If the old joists are sufficiently deep, stiff, and firm and if it is desirable to keep the bathroom floor level with the other floors, the joists should be trimmed to allow for either a 3/4" subfloor, or for a 1/2" or 5/8" plywood underlayment, and for the thickness of the tile. Lay the plywood directly on the subfloor and nail it firmly. Use 6d nails spaced at 3" intervals on the edges and at not more than 6" intervals over the entire panel. There should be no springy places in the floor. See a supplier for suitable adhesives and directions for their use.

Laying Wood Strip Flooring Over Concrete Slabs

Ques. In covering a large concrete slab with maple flooring, can the expense of drilling the slab for lag shells, or for shooting in studs to hold the sleepers, be avoided? Is there another method that can be used?

Ans. The sleepers may be laid in asphalt; then mechanical fastenings are not necessary. If the slab is well drained and can be kept dry, waterproofing should not be required. However, the sleepers (preferably 2″ × 3″ or 2″ × 4″ boards laid flatwise) should be pressure treated with creosote.

The slab should be primed first, either with hot creosote or with one of the commercial concrete primers. Incidentally, these primers are *not* vapor barriers. After the primer has dried, heavy "rivers" of hot asphalt should be mopped down where each sleeper is to be placed; the sleepers are laid and pressed down. If the sleepers do not lie completely flat, kerf them deeply or cut them into pieces, laying them with the joints staggered. The flooring may be laid immediately.

Flexible Tile Laid on Wide Boards

Ques. Two clients are interested in laying flexible vinyl tile over the existing floors, which are 1″ × 6″ D&M boards. Is this advisable?

Ans. It is not advisable unless an underlayment is used. Wide boards, such as 1″ × 6″ boards, are prone to cupping, and the raised edges quickly cut through the thin tile. Also, the shrinkage and swelling of wide boards due to normal changes in humidity tend to open up the tile joints which coincide (or nearly coincide) with the joints between the boards. A 1/4-in. plywood underlayment, cut into 24″ × 48″ pieces and laid with staggered joints, is preferable. This type of underlayment shrinks and swells less than many of the manufactured types of materials.

Deflection of Single-Span and Two-Span Plank Floors

Ques. Is plank flooring that is laid continuously over two spans stiffer than planks of one-half their length laid separately over a single span? On some jobs, the engineers insist that all beams should be single-span beams.

Ans. It is quite true that planks that are long enough for two spans are stiffer. Under a distributed loading, the ratio is 5:384 = 1:165, or approximately 1 to 2.15. The planks of single-span length deflect approximately 2-1/4 times that of planks laid continuously over two spans, under the same distributed loadings (see Fig. 4).

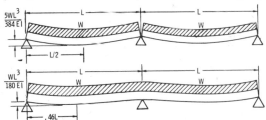

Fig. 4. Illustrating comparative deflections of single-span beams (top) and those beams which are continuous over a center bearing (bottom). Although deflections are greater in single-span beams, shear forces are greater; which may be a governing factor in some instances.

The engineers are probably concerned with deep, heavily-loaded beams, where shears, rather than bending stresses, are more important. Maximum shearing stresses in the continuous-span beams are approximately 25 percent greater than in single-span beams. Shear stresses are not important in plank floors or decks.

Live-Load Allowance on Auditorium Floors

Ques. The specification for a building calls for "no fixed seats." What does this mean?

Ans. If the building is to be used as a public meeting place. this means that a live floor loading of 100 lbs. per sq. ft. must be allowed for to satisfy most codes. If the seats are fastened in position, as in churches, theaters, and similar buildings, the allowance may be reduced to 60 lbs. per sq. ft. In the classrooms of schools and colleges, some codes permit 40 lbs. per sq. ft. live load allowance. These questions usually do not concern the builder. They are incorporated in the design by the architect.

Spacing of End Joints in Flooring

Ques. In end-matched flooring, is there a standard specification for spacing the end joints?

Ans. If there is a standard requirement for spacing the end joints, it is not known, but the following excerpt from an architect's specifications seems to be commonly used (Fig. 5).

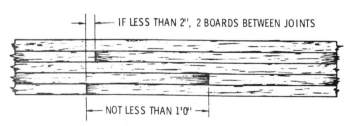

IF LESS THAN 2'', 2 BOARDS BETWEEN JOINTS

NOT LESS THAN 1'0'

Fig. 5. Recommended spacing of end joints in end-matched hardwood flooring.

1. The end joints in adjoining boards should be no closer than 12 inches of directly in line; or if within 2 inches of

directly in line, not less than two boards should be placed between the joints.

2. If the flooring is a grade which allows a large percentage of shorts, the specification can be met only by mixing the shorts in with longer lengths. All the shorts should not be used near the point where the bundle is opened.

House With Cold Floors

Ques. A house with utility room and crawl space was built recently. The walls are concrete blocks, stuccoed on the outside; the inside is furred, lathed, and plastered. All floors are doubled floors, and they are covered with flexible tile. The heating pipes are beneath the floor, and they are not covered. The owner complains of cold floors and high heating costs. What can be done about this problem?

Ans. Some insulation is needed. Either the pipes or the walls of the crawl space should be insulated. Either a cold or a warm crawl space is permissible, but it cannot be both cold and warm. If the space is cold, heat is lost through the bare pipes to the cold air. Usually, only a small quantity of heat is lost to the ground. The heat loss to the ground is so small that, usually, even concrete slab-on-ground floors are not insulated from the ground, but heat loss around the edges is exceptionally heavy through the foundation walls. If the floor is too cold for comfort, the best procedure is to insulate the inside of the crawl space walls properly. Thus, the bare pipes can warm the air in the crawl space and, consequently, the floor above the crawl space. Approximately 2 inches of insulation can be placed beneath the floor, and the pipes can be insulated. With this method, the crawl space will remain cold, and there will be no heat loss in heating it. Heat rises more readily than it moves downward.

The house itself is badly in need of insulation. Approximately 0.31 Btu is lost each hour through each square foot of exposed wall, for each degree of temperature difference between the inside and outside. For comparison purposes, a standard frame wall (no insulation) loses only about 0.25 Btu. Perhaps it is too late to insulate the walls, but the heat loss through an uninsulated ceiling is more important, and the space above the ceiling can be reached without too much difficulty. With only an ordinary plastered ceiling between the inhabited rooms and a cold attic, as much as one-third of the heat loss from the entire house may be through the ceiling. A 4-in. layer of insulation may return its cost in five years, through reduced fuel bills. Thus, the house is badly in need of insulation.

Vibration in Floors

Ques. Excessive vibration in the floors of a new house is a problem. When a person walks briskly across the floor, the vibration rattles the dishes in the sideboard. The joists are 2″ × 10″ timbers on 14″ centers, with 14′0″ spans. On inspection of the job, it was found that the sills are shimmed up in many places where they do not rest directly on the very uneven foundation walls. Can the shimming of the joists be aggravating the trouble? How can this job be corrected?

Ans. If 2″ × 10″ joists are set on 14″ centers above 14-ft. spans, they should be free from excessive vibration, but it is true that all floors possess a natural frequency of harmonic motion; if the cadence of the footsteps is exactly that frequency, a vibration build-up occurs. In bridges, this is a serious consideration. Marching soldiers are always ordered to break step when crossing long bridges. In the floors of homes, this is not often serious, but it may be annoying.

The shimmed-up sills probably contribute to the annoyance. At best, this is slipshod construction and jerry-building. The sills should be bedded in soft mortar, and the anchor bolts should be tightened as the sills are settled into the mortar. Perhaps a quantity of soft grout can be worked into the cracks, but this cannot provide the solid bearing that is obtained when the sills are bedded in mortar.

Wooden Block Floors Above Wooden Subfloors

Ques. Are wooden block floors that are laid in adhesive satisfactory when they are laid above wooden subfloors on joists?

Ans. Both the solid blocks and the thicker laminated types of blocks are approved for laying above wooden subfloors, but the laminated 3/8-inch blocks are not recommended for this purpose. The subfloor must provide the necessary rigidity for block floors, since the blocks possess no bending strength in themselves. If plywood subfloors are used, the following thicknesses are required:

1. For joists on 16-in. centers, 5/8-in. plywood.
2. For joists on 20-in. centers, 3/4-in. plywood.
3. For joists on 24-in. centers, 7/8-in. plywood.

All plywood joints should be placed on the joists; or, if the joints are at right angles to the joists, they should be placed on solid trimmers. Subfloors of 3/4-in. $1'' \times 4''$ or $1'' \times 6''$ boards are satisfactory, either D&M or square-edged. The joists should be placed on not more than 16-in. centers if lumber is used for the subfloor. An underlayment is usually considered unnecessary, except when solid wooden blocks are laid on board subfloors. Then, 15-lb. asphalt felt laid in asphaltic adhesive is recommended.

The adhesives most commonly used are commercial products, and they should be used according to the manufacturer's directions. These may be either asphaltic emulsions or cut-backs, or rubber-base adhesives. Both the cut-backs and rubber-base adhesives are inflammable, and care should be taken to keep them away from fire. The adhesives are usually applied with a notched trowel; after the trowel has been used for some time, the depth of the notches should be checked. It is possible to apply the adhesive in too small a quantity.

Preservations for Wooden Patio Floor Blocks

Ques. A few scrubby and worthless red-oak trees are standing in a fence row where they are not wanted. They are approximately 12 inches through at the butts. It is proposed to cut them into blocks for a patio floor, but without treatment they would rot in a couple of years, if termites did not destroy them first. How are these blocks prepared, what preservatives are used, and how can the work be done at home?

Ans. The blocks can be made and treated at home. Cut them 4 inches in thickness, using any type of saw that is available. Do not remove the bark; it is usually tight if the trees are cut in winter or late summer. The blocks are difficult to treat while they are green. It is better practice to allow them to season for a few months.

A cold treatment with a 5-percent solution of pentachlorophenol in fuel oil is generally used. This preserves timber that is in contact with the ground for an indefinite period of time, and termites do not bother it. The ready-prepared solution may be purchased in farm stores; or it can be mixed at home. Directions for mixing can be found on the cans of the concentrate.

The blocks should be soaked in a 55-gal. steel drum with the head cut out. Pile the blocks in layers with dividers placed between the layers. Pieces of old wire fencing make good dividers.

Place a weight on top to hold down the blocks, leaving them in the solution for approximately two weeks. This soaks red-oak blocks thoroughly, but the heartwood of white oak does not take up preservatives well. Some other timbers, such as elm or basswood (linn), absorb the preservatives in one week or less.

Lay the blocks in a sand bed; the varying diameters are usually laid at random. Unlike timbers that are treated with creosote, penta-treated timber is reasonably clean after it becomes dry, but rubber gloves should be used when handling the wood preservatives.

Extensive experimentation with home treatment of lumber for gates, fence posts, and other farm uses has been done, and is being done, at the Wood Laboratory, Agricultural Engineering Department, Purdue University, West Lafayette, Indiana. Additional information may be obtained from that source.

Warehouse Floors

Ques. A new floor is being installed in a warehouse. The floor loads will be heavy and the merchandise will be handled mostly on pallets with lift trucks. The present floor is double-thickness boards placed on $3'' \times 12''$ joists set on $12''$ centers. It has been proposed to use splined $3''$ decking, but it is feared that it will become splintery under the truck wheels. Can the joists be covered with $3/4''$ plywood and a $2''$ wearing floor of lightweight concrete be poured over it?

Ans. It is entirely correct that flat-sawed softwood floors sometimes become splintery, and a single-thickness plank floor is not easily repaired. Most wooden floors in factories and warehouses are plank floors with a wearing surface consisting of $25/32''$ maple. If it is properly nailed, a maple floor can withstand friction remarkably well. If there is no cutting or abrasive action, the floor polishes to a near glassy finish and wear is negligible. These floors are easily maintained. A factory grade of maple flooring is available that is intended for such purposes. It is not selected for color, and it possesses tight knots and other defects, which do not impair its utility.

Perhaps the most satisfactory floor for these purposes is made of creosoted blocks. They are usually laid in asphalt, and are available in thicknesses of 2 to 4 inches. They are resilient, furnish excellent traction for lift trucks, and last almost indefinitely, but they are slightly difficult to sweep clean, because they are slightly rough. If the client can withstand the expense, the wooden block floors are recommended.

Lightweight concrete should never be used for the wearing surface of a floor. It is much weaker than sand-gravel concrete, and our own experience with concrete slabs over wooden floors has been anything but satisfactory. None of these jobs have given reasonably satisfactory service, even when sand-gravel concrete was used. This type of floor cracks and breaks up, and a cracked concrete floor cannot withstand truck wheels, even with good thickness and a solid base. It is our opinion that the money will be wasted on this type of floor.

Setting Floor-Tile Underlayment in Adhesives

Ques. If hardboard underlayment board for flexible floor tile were to be set in adhesive, would the trouble that is experienced with popping nails and opening joints be avoided?

Ans. It is doubtful that it would solve the problems satisfactorily. If the subfloor is damp and swelled with moisture when the underlayment boards are laid, it is probable that there will still be trouble with popping nails and shrinking underlayment boards; but since fewer nails are necessary when the adhesive is used,

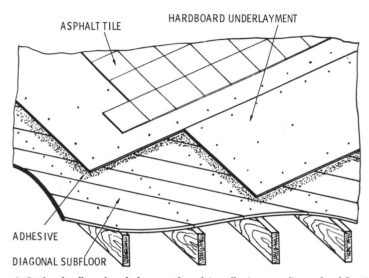

Fig. 6. Setting hardboard underlayment board in adhesives on diagonal subflooring.

the popping nails would probably be less troublesome. Laid over diagonal subflooring, the adhesive bond probably would be strong enough to prevent the joints from opening because of shrinkage, but the adhesive probably would not be as effective when the joints in the underlayment boards parallel the joints in the subfloor (Fig. 6). It is doubtful that the troubles mentioned can be avoided if green or wet subflooring and joists are used beneath the underlayment board.

Removal of Floor Tile

Ques. On a below-grade slab floor, the flexible tile are deteriorated seriously along the edges, probably from moisture. How can we remove these tile cleanly, and what can be used to replace them that will be more permanent?

Ans. The type of tile that is deteriorating was not stated, and the type of adhesive used is not known. If they are linoleum tile, which often deteriorate under the conditions described, a blow-torch may be tried first. If they can be heated, nearly all types of adhesive will loosen. If that treatment does not work, place dry ice on the floor, covering it with a thick blanket and pushing it around to the various spots. Most types of tile, and most adhesives, become hard and brittle under this type of treatment, and the tile can be crushed with a hammer. Probably the residue will have to be scraped up, regardless of the method used.

Asphalt tiles laid in an asphaltic adhesive are probably the best replacement for the old floor covering. The slab should be completely dry before an attempt is made to re-lay the tile. Both the tile and the adhesive can withstand considerable moisture without deterioration.

Waterproof Underlayment for Quarry-Tile Decks

Ques. Can quarry tile be used on the floor of a small inset entrance alcove? Can the tile be used over wood framing? The floor absolutely must not leak.

Ans. Quarry tile, sometimes called promenade tile, can be used satisfactorily on a wood subfloor over the joists, but the subfloor must be rigid and it must have a watertight cover or underlayment underneath the tile. Three-ply, asphalt-felt, built-up roofing is generally used. The tile are approximately 1-inch in thickness and can be purchased in several different colors, various sizes, and in either square or rectangular shapes.

The underlayment roofing is placed, turned up at the edges into flashing where necessary, and a bed of cement-sand mortar 1/2 to 3/4 inch in thickness is spread over it and leveled. Then, the tile are wetted and tapped lightly into place. The bedding mortar is necessary, since the tile vary slightly in thickness. The joints may be grouted with cement and sand; or they may be filled with calking compound. Leave expansion joints around the edges, and fill them with asphalt or other elastic filler. *Do not depend on joint fillers to prevent leaks;* this is equally true when the base is a concrete slab. Leaks in promenade tile floors or decks are sometimes extremely stubborn, but when they are laid properly, the tile makes one of the most attractive and most permanent floor coverings for hard wear.

CHAPTER 13

Plumbing and Sanitation

Expansion of Hot-Water Pipes

Ques. A house in which the water-supply pipes are made of threaded brass was purchased about a year ago. A plumber has had to be called in several times to repair leaks in the joints of the hot-water lines. He said that the leaks were caused by expansion of the pipes, and intimated that the lines were not installed correctly. Can this be explained?

Ans. All metal pipes expand and lengthen when they are heated, and they contract accordingly as they cool. The precise amount of change in length depends on the type of metal in the piping and, of course, on the extent of the temperature changes. Aluminum piping expands more than any other type; then brass or bronze piping, followed by copper tubing. Iron and steel piping expands and contracts the least amount. However, no threaded-joint piping can be held firmly at both ends and subjected to excessive temperature changes without placing heavy stresses on the fittings and possibly causing them to leak. In most residential work, the pipes are relatively short in length, and they are rarely held firmly enough at both ends to cause trouble; however, this

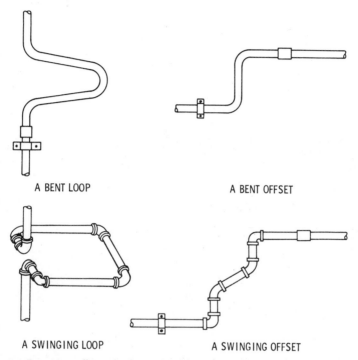

A BENT LOOP

A BENT OFFSET

A SWINGING LOOP

A SWINGING OFFSET

Fig. 1. Illustrating allowance for expansion and contraction of various types of field-constructed pipe joints. Many patented types of joints are available commercially, such as those which permit sliding action—similar to a piston, and other types which employ metal bellows.

is possible. Of course, the stresses are greater in the longer lines. With copper and brass piping, and often with steel piping, expansion loops are sometimes used. The sketches in Fig. 1 show some of the most common expansion loops.

The bent loops and bent offsets are, in general, more satisfactory than the swinging loops made from fittings and nipples, if the arms are adequate in length. In the bent loops, the metal must spring to allow for changes in length; the probability of leaks is greater in threaded joints.

Allowance for Expansion in Embedded Pipes

Ques. Four heat grids are to be installed in a concrete floor, each grid being 28 ft. $\times$ 145 ft. Should the pipes be expanded and the concrete poured while the pipes are hot, to allow for "creep?"

Ans. It is not necesary to allow for expansion. To begin with, concrete should not be poured against the hot pipes; secondly, both concrete and steel possess nearly identical coefficients of expansion. The temperatures being equal, expansion is nearly identical in both the pipes and the concrete.

Dry Wells May Contaminate a Water Supply

Ques. If the greases from kitchen wastes are clogging up a dry well, will installation of a grease trap in the tile line stop this difficulty?

Ans. Without exception, the waste water of any type from homes should not be disposed of in a dry well, because of the possibility of contaminating the ground water supply. Dry wells are forbidden in practically all locations in which the water supply originates from shallow wells. Due to the widespread use of household detergents—even when the most rigid precautions are taken —tap water sometimes foams as it is drawn.

Grease traps have always been a messy contrivance; they must be cleaned periodically, which is always a disagreeable job. If a good septic tank is available, grease traps are unnecessary. Confer either with the County Board of Health, or, if convenient, with the Sanitary Engineering Department at the State University for a waste-water disposal plan which does not endanger the health of the entire neighborhood.

A Septic Tank of 8-In. Concrete Blocks

Ques. Should a septic tank be constructed of 8-in. concrete blocks? The tank should be large enough to hold at least 600 gallons.

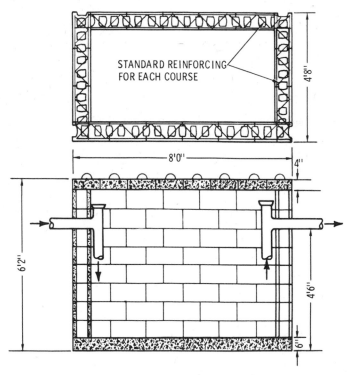

Fig. 2. A septic tank constructed of concrete blocks, having 665 gallons capacity. These tanks are approved by the Board of Health in most states.

Ans. Construction of properly built septic tanks from 8-in. concrete blocks is approved in all regions (Fig. 2). A tank that is 6 blocks in length, 3-1/2 blocks in width, and 8 courses in depth, has a capacity of approximately 665 gallons when the water is 48 inches deep. The cores should be filled with concrete as the blocks are laid, and either standard masonry reinforcing mesh, or 3/8-inch rods may be used in each joint. A 6-in. floor slab is recommended. The covers are sometimes made in sections that are approximately 12 inches in width and 4 inches in thickness, with two 3/8-inch reinforcing rods and either eye-bolts or rod loops placed in each section, so that the sections can be lifted off more readily when cleaning the tank.

Sizes and Slopes of Tile Lines in Septic-Tank Disposal Fields

Ques. In one locality, a difference of opinion exists as to the correct sizes and slopes for tile in septic tank disposal fields. Are there any standard requirements?

Ans. A slope of 2 to 4 inches in 100 feet is generally recommended for the tile in a disposal field, and a 4-in. tile is considered large enough for residences, both for the effluent sewer and the disposal lines. From the house to the septic tank, where local codes or ordinances do not require the use of cast-iron soil pipe, 4-in. vitrified clay sewer pipe with cemented joints is usually satisfactory. The sewer should slope not less than 4 inches in 25 feet, but too much slope in this line may result in undesirable agitation of the contents of the septic tank.

Pass Ground Garbage Through the Septic Tank

Ques. Should the waste from a garbage disposal unit installed in a kitchen be passed through the septic tank, or should the septic tank be by-passed, making a connection beyond the tank?

Ans. The ground garbage should be passed through the septic tank so that it can be digested. Under no circumstances should it be permitted to pass directly into the disposal field, which would undoubtedly clog the lines in a short time. Usually, it is assumed that the quantity of solids in the food wastes is about the equal to that in the sanitary sewage; this may necessitate increasing the volume of the septic tank approximately 30 to 50 percent.

Length of Tile Lines in a Sewage Disposal Field

Ques. How can the required length of tile lines be determined for locating a septic-tank disposal field in a rather tight soil?

Ans. The length of the tile lines depends, of course, on the ability of the soil to absorb water; therefore, a percolation test should be made, as follows (see Fig. 3):

1. Dig a hole *exactly* 1-foot square, down to the depth of the disposal trench.
2. Pour water into the hole to a depth of 6 inches.
3. Insert a ruler in the water, and determine the period of time required for the water to drop a distance of 1 inch. If the soil is unusually dry, allow the water to soak away, then make a second test. Use the data obtained from the second test.
4. The trench width may range from 18 to 36 inches. The required absorption area at the bottom of the trench may be obtained below:

> 2 minutes per inch absorption; allow   50 sq. ft.
> of trench per bedroom.
> 3 minutes per inch absorption; allow   60 sq. ft.
> of trench per bedroom.

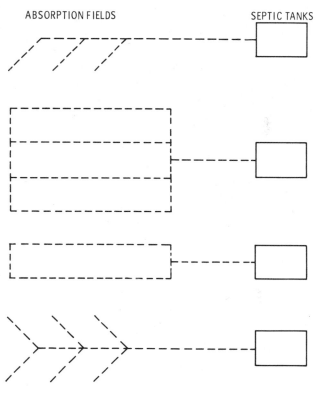

Fig. 3. Approved arrangements of septic tanks and tile lines in the disposal fields.

4 minutes per inch absorption; allow 70 sq. ft. of trench per bedroom.

5 minutes per inch absorption; allow 80 sq. ft. of trench per bedroom.

10 minutes per inch absorption; allow 105 sq. ft. of trench per bedroom.

15 minutes per inch absorption; allow 125 sq. ft.
of trench per bedroom.

30 minutes per inch absorption; allow 180 sq. ft.
of trench per bedroom.

60 minutes per inch absorption; allow 240 sq. ft.
of trench per bedroom.

If the trenches are narrow (approximately 18 inches), the lines may be placed 6 ft. apart, but if they are 36 inches in width, the spacing should not be less than 9 feet.

Clearances for Septic Tanks and Sewage Disposal Fields

Ques. What are the standard clearance requirements for septic tanks and sewage disposal fields from lot lines, dwellings, wells, streams, and lakes?

Ans. There are no "standard" requirements. These vary from state to state, and the requirements of cities and other local authorities are often more rigid than those of the State Board of Health in the various states. For requirements in a local area, the local Board of Health should be consulted. In general, the following requirements meet the recommendations of the U.S. Health Service:

1. For sewage absorption fields;
   From water-supply wells (except deep-driven wells) and all underground pump suction lines, 100 feet.
   From all dwellings and property lines, 10 feet.
   From lakes, streams or ditches, 25 feet.
2. For location of septic tanks;
   From water-supply wells (except deep-driven wells) and all underground pump suction lines, 50 feet.
   From all dwellings and property lines, 5 feet.
   From lakes, streams or ditches, 25 feet.

Improper Venting of Sink for Dishwashing

Ques. Disagreeable odors are a problem at a kitchen sink. The odors seem to be entering through the drain; the water seal does not remain in the trap. Is the sink incorrectly installed (see sketch in Fig. 4)?

Ans. The sink is not vented properly; in these instances, the troubles that are described are quite common. A gurgling noise usually occurs in the trap, and the sealing water may be entirely siphoned out whenever the sink is drained. The installation was probably made after the house was completed, when proper venting would have been exceedingly difficult. In fact, the only way to vent the sink properly is to tear into the wall or to extend a separate and exposed vent upward through the roof. A sketch showing an approved vent is shown in Fig. 4.

A Sand Filter

Ques. In the construction of a sand filter for water from a farm pond, what size tank is required for a capacity of nearly 2500 gallons per day. Plenty of clean sand and gravel are available. How should they be mixed?

Ans. The accompanying sketch (Fig. 5) shows a tank 7'0" × 7'0" and 8'0" deep. Its capacity should meet the requirements. The sand and gravel should not be mixed; it should be screened and graded, and deposited in layers approximately as shown in the drawing.

The depth of the water should be maintained at a point 3 or 4 feet above the sand layer. This area is marked *A* in the drawing. The remaining areas in the sketch are as follows:

Area *B* is 3 ft. of filtering sand, fine enough to pass through a 14-mesh screen.

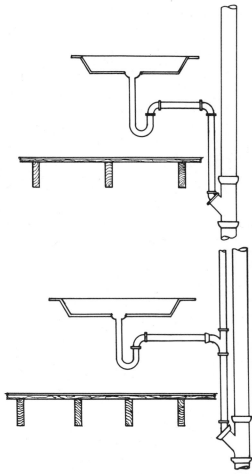

Fig. 4. Kitchen sink installation. An improperly vented kitchen sink is shown (top). In this arrangement, the sealing water in the trap may be siphoned out when the sink is drained. An approved method of venting a kitchen sink is shown (bottom). The vent pipe may be returned into the soil stack, or it may be extended independently through the roof.

Area *C* is 3 in. of 1/8-in. gravel.

Area *D* is 4 in. of 1/4-in. gravel.

Area *E* is 6 in. of 1/2-in. gravel, embedding a 1-1/2-in. outlet pipe with a capped end, perforated with 75 to 100 1/4-in. holes.

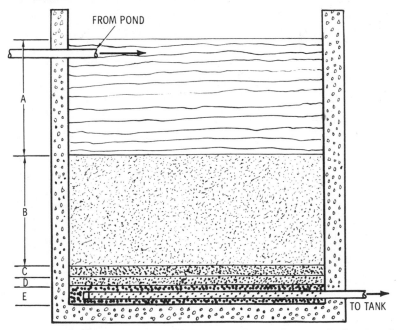

Fig. 5. A sand filter, designed for filtering water from a farm pond. The size of the filter is 7′0″ × 8′0″ in depth; it should have a capacity of nearly 2500 gallons per day, or more.

Overloading a Septic Tank

Ques. Is it safe to discharge the brine from regenerating a water softener into the septic tank? The septic tanks vary in size from 350 to 500 gallons.

Ans. The septic tank and disposal field should not be over-loaded by running water of any description through the tank, if the water does not need the bacterial action. In this instance, this is even more important, because small septic tanks are in use. The U.S. Department of Health Education and Welfare recommends that the septic tank be no smaller than 500 gallons, which is recommended only when the number of persons served is four or less, or for a two-bedroom house.

Hardness of Water in New Cisterns

Ques. The walls of a cistern were recently plastered, using 1 : 2 Portland cement and sand. Now, the owner complains that the water is extremely "hard." Is this caused by the fresh plaster?

Ans. The water in all new cisterns, even with brick walls laid in mortar, is extremely "hard" until the "free" lime in the mortar is leeched away, and the hardness may persist for some time. Usually it is not worthwhile to attempt to soften the water in the cistern, but it may be advantageous to pump the water out, allowing the cistern to fill up again a couple of times. The hardness will disappear in time.

To Calculate the Pressure of a Head of Water

Ques. How can the pressure of a head of water be determined, in pounds per square inch?

Ans. Multiply the height of the head (in feet) by 0.434. The result is the pressure in pounds per square inch.

Air Lock in Water Line

Ques. An excellent farm spring flows into a milk cooling tank; the overflow from the tank then flows to a stock tank located approximately 150 feet away. The fall is nearly 18 inches. During winter, the water flows freely, but it often completely stops flowing during warm weather. What can possibly be the cause of this problem?

Ans. The water line probably becomes air locked. Nearly all water contains some air, and when the water is warmed slightly some of the air is released as small bubbles. When the flow is sluggish, the bubbles collect in any high place in the line and the flow is stopped. Probably, there is a high place in the water line (Fig. 6).

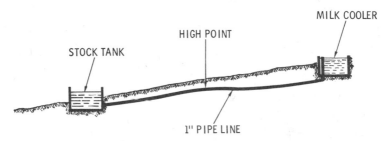

Fig. 6. Illustrating conditions which may result in an air lock in a water line. This action is similar to the "vapor lock" which often stops the flow of gasoline in automobile fuel lines in extremely hot weather.

The logical remedy is to dig up the line and re-lay it, taking care to provide a fall in the line at all points. If the high place can be located without digging up the entire line, a bleeding valve, such as a pipe plug or a boiler try cock, may be installed. If the air is bled out of the line, flow will resume, as through a siphon, but the air lock may recur at any time during warm weather.

Locating a Well Site

Ques. Several one-family residences are being built on 1/4-acre tracts outside the city limits, where the only water supply is individual wells. It may be necessary to drill several of these wells. How can the best locations for these wells be determined? Is there any dependable literature on this subject available?

Ans. It is impossible to predetermine the best location for a well, whether the water is available in sufficient quantity, or whether the water is in a stratum where it can be obtained, unless test borings are made. There has been much rather highly colored guessing done on this subject from time to time, but absolutely nothing that is dependable has resulted. Most professional drillers of wells who have worked in a given area become fairly familiar with the location of the geological strata, and they may be able to provide some idea of the probability of finding water in that area; at best it is a gamble. There is nothing that can be done, except to begin drilling and hoping.

Air in Water Lines

Ques. This city has changed recently to a new water supply system. The water is now very soft, but air collects in the hot-water pipes and tanks. In the early morning, or after the faucet has been closed for a period of time, a hot-water faucet is opened and a blast of air may knock a cup from a person's hand and splatter him with water. Air is not apparent in the cold-water lines. What could be causing this problem?

Ans. The problem may not be air in the water pipes. Assuming that the water formerly was hard, a quantity of scale was probably formed in the hot-water tanks and pipes. The soft water that is now supplied is slightly alkaline and it attacks the scale; one of the products is CO_2, or carbon dioxide gas. It may be that CO_2 gas, rather than air, is collecting in the hot-water lines. This gas is entirely harmless and tasteless; it is the same type of gas that causes the "fizz" in a bottle of carbonated beverage.

The possibility that air in the lines may be causing the problem should not be discounted, however. Water contains a small quantity of air, which is released as tiny bubbles when the water is warmed, and it collects at the higher places in the pipe line. Although this is not likely, it may be possible that air is leaking in the municipal pumps. Centrifugal booster pumps (not often used in small installations) often leak air; or a leak in the pipes may occur on the suction side. The water company usually rectifies these difficulties quickly if they can find the source, since it is much in their interest to do so.

The problem may correct itself in a short time, but extremely soft water is corrosive in iron pipes, and they corrode rapidly. Municipalities which have been provided extremely soft water have discovered this to their sorrow, and usually discontinue the service after a short time.

Water Hardness

Ques. In a subdivision that is being developed, two 12-in. diameter deep wells have been drilled for water supply. The water is unquestionably hard, and complaints have been received. The water has been analyzed, and the chemist reports "10 grains of hardness." What does this mean and what can be done to remedy this situation?

Ans. Chemists and other scientists usually express the mineral content of water in parts per million, but "hardness" is more often expressed as equivalent grains of calcium carbonate; however, all of the hardness may not be calcuim carbonate. Calcium carbonate is lime. Grains are a measure of weight. A common aspirin tablet, for example, weighs 5 grains.

In general, water is classified into four hardness groups, as follows:

1. *Low hardness,* 0 to 60 parts per million; or 0 to 3.5 grains hardness per gallon.
2. *Moderately hard,* 61 to 120 parts per million; or 3.5 to 7.0 grains per gallon.
3. *Hard,* 121 to 180 parts per million; or 7.0 to 10.0 grains per gallon.
4. *Very hard,* over 180 parts per million; over 10.0 grains hardness per gallon.

The chemist's report, then, indicates that the water from the wells is extremely "hard" (10 grains of hardness per gallon). Incidentally, the water from deep wells is usually much "harder" than water that is found nearer the surface or from surface supplies, such as lakes or streams. Few water companies or municipalities supply water that is sufficiently soft for the optimum satisfaction of homeowners; thus home-type water softeners are in general use in practically all regions where the water is extremely "hard."

Contents of Cylindrical Cistern and Tanks

Ques. How can the capacity, in barrels, of round cisterns be determined?

Ans. The United States does not have a legal standard for a liquid barrel. By custom, a barrel of unrefined petroleum is equivalent to 42 gallons, and a barrel of refined oils is equivalent to 50 gallons. A barrel of water is usually (not always) equivalent to 31-1/2 gallons. The U.S. gallon is a legal standard, fixed by law at 231 cubic inches, and a cubic foot is approximately 7.48 U.S. gallons. The following list indicates the capacity, in barrels, (31-1/2 gal.), of cylindrical cisterns or tanks, for each foot of depth:

5-ft. diameter = 4.66 barrels per foot of depth
6-ft. diameter = 6.71 barrels per foot of depth
7-ft. diameter = 9.13 barrels per foot of depth
8-ft. diameter = 11.93 barrels per foot of depth
9-ft. diameter = 15.10 barrels per foot of depth
10-ft. diameter = 18.65 barrels per foot of depth

Cleaning Septic Tanks

Ques. A septic tank has been in use for nearly five years, so an experienced man was hired to dig down, lift the cover, and pump it out. This was needed, and he did an excellent job, scrubbing and flushing the sides. He did not replace the earth, advising that the bacterial action might be slow in resuming, and that if the action was too slow in starting, he might have to return and add "bacterial feed" to resume the action. This preparation is expensive, and a neighbor advises that the action can be restored readily by dumping in a few yeast cakes. Is it true that the bacterial action has not resumed? After two weeks there is only a small quantity of scum on the surface.

Ans. There is no reason why you should be "cleaned," as well as the tank. The so-called bacterial feeds and other such preparations are unnecessary, to say the least, and some of these preparations are positively detrimental. The yeast treatment is also useless. Yeast organisms possess the ability to change starches and sugars into alcohols, but they do not have the power to break down organic solids, and 90 percent of the substances carried in household sewage are organic solids. Cover up the hole and forget about the septic tank for a period of time. The bacterial action will resume on its own initiative. The bacteria which are active in septic tanks are present in a normal atmosphere, and they need only time and favorable conditions to live and multiply. The sides of the tank should not have been scrubbed and cleaned. This is quite useless; and if it is not done, the bacterial action usually resumes quite readily. When septic tanks are newly installed, it is sometimes advantageous to aid them in starting. This is usually accomplished by dumping a bucketful of scum from a working tank into the newly installed tank.

Septic Tank Disposal Fields

Ques. Most septic tank disposal lines in this locality are placed only 18 inches below the surface, and they do not seem to work satisfactorily. Is it more desirable to place the lines deeper, for example, at basement floor level? Would the use of seepage pits, rather than the open-jointed tile lines be more satisfactory?

Ans. Perhaps it is necessary to place the disposal fields shallow in your area because of impermeable soil that is located deeper. In any instance, 18 inches of covering above the tile is not too little covering, if the soil is porous and if tractors or trucks are not passing above it. The shallow lines are much preferred to deeper lines in impermeable clay. Although a good porous soil, sand, or gravel is available at the basement depth, it is doubtful that health authorities would permit placing the disposal lines at that level, because of the possibility of contaminating the ground water.

Seepage pits are allowable only when a tile disposal field cannot be made to work properly. Health authorities do not permit their use where the natural water table is near the surface or where the general water supply source is shallow or dug wells. As with the disposal field, the ground must be permeable, and where a seepage pit is practical, the tile disposal lines are usually practical and preferable. Septic tanks, regardless of their efficiency, do *not* remove all disease bacteria from the sewage, nor do they break down household detergents in the waste water. In many instances, the tap water foams like draft beer.

Storm Water Into Perimeter Drains

Ques. Seepage into a basement is occurring along the edges of the floor and at the bottom of the walls, although the walls have membrane waterproofing outside and there is a 6-in. tile line around the house just outside the footings. This city has no sanitary sewers, and the code requires that rain water leaders empty into the drain tile. It seems that this overloads the perimeter drains. What can be done about this problem?

Ans. Probably, the code provisions have been misunderstood. Probably the code demands that both the footing drain and the storm water drain should have outlets into the storm water sewer; however, it does not seem reasonable to interpret this to mean that the roof leaders should be emptied into the footing drains, because this would produce the very condition that the footing drains were intended to prevent. This would be running the roof water directly to the open-jointed perimeter tiling, which is the very place where it could most readily seep into the basement. It is doubtful that the roof water could seriously overload a 6-in. tile line, but the setup is similar to a septic tank disposal field in which water seeps outward through the open joints in the tile lines (see Fig. 7).

The roof leaders should be directed into a separate line of cemented-joint vitrified pipe. The line need not be placed deeply in the ground. Rain water from roofs is not unsanitary or otherwise objectionable, and most codes permit it to be drained into the street gutter. Consult the city building inspector about a proper installation; it seems that someone has misunderstood the meaning of the code.

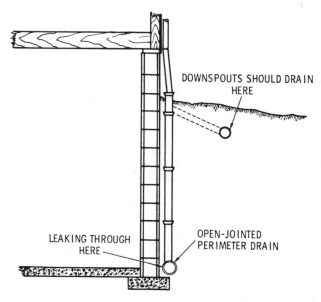

Fig. 7. An extremely poor arrangement for disposing of storm water from a roof. Inevitably, water infiltrates into the basement from the open-jointed type of perimeter drain.

Odors From Plumbing Drains

Ques. The wife of a client who purchased a house from me complains about odors which come up through the drain of a dishwashing sink. She thinks that it is "sewer gas," and that it is probably explosive. The plumbing is the same design as that used on other houses, which have been perfectly satisfactory. Is there a suggestion as to what can be done about this complaint?

Ans. Probably, it is not sewer gas. Sewer gas is mostly methane, which is a product of decaying organic matter. Although it is explosive when it is mixed with air in the correct proportions, it is not often found in dangerous quantities in good drains that are connected to a public sewer and where plumbing fixtures are properly vented to the open air. Sewer gas is, however, generated in septic tanks and most types of sewage-treatment plants. Many other bad-smelling gases are found in the air in drains. Probably the worst-smelling of these gases is sulfuretted hydrogen, which provides the odor for rotten eggs. It is perfectly true that this gas, and others, diffuses through the water in traps to some extent, but the possibility of a noticeable odor passing through the trap is remote indeed. More important than odors from this source are the odors which result from the decomposition of organic particles which stick to the walls of the pipe between the fixture and the trap. It is entirely possible that the lady is not flushing the sink drain properly.

Of course, this assumes that the fixture is properly vented. If it is not vented properly, the water may be siphoning out of the trap, then the lady has a legitimate gripe. Even though "sewer gas" is not escaping into the house, drain air is never agreeable.

Sewage Disposal Fields in Tight Soils

Ques. The subsoil in this location is red clay. A shelly, impervious red shale is found beneath the subsoil. During the rainy season of winter, the septic tank overflows, because there is practically no absorption in the disposal field; however, during the dry weather in summer, it works reasonably well. A sanitary sewer is available, but its level is too high, and a booster pump would have to be installed at my own expense. Is there another alternative?

Ans. It is doubtful whether there is another alternative. The red clays rarely meet the standard absorption requirements even when they are dry; when they are saturated, absorption, of course, does not occur. It may be fortunate that a sewer is available, even though it is at a level that requires use of a booster pump. If the neighbors are having the same difficulty, a type of community booster station might solve the collective problems, saving money for all. A survey should be made by a competent sanitary engineer. Probably, it will be necessary to abandon the absorption fields sooner or later.

Water Required by Plumbing Fixtures

Ques. How much water is used by plumbing fixtures, per operation?

Ans. Due to the variations in models, the quantities may vary, but the following quantities are nearly average.

Water closet, per flushing	3-1/2 to 5 gallons
Tub, bath	15 gallons
Laundry tubs, per filling	9 gallons
Automatic clothes washer, per load	18 gallons
Automatic urinals, per stall per hour	4 gallons
Automatic dishwasher, per load	7 gallons
Shower baths, per minute	3 gallons
Dishwashing sink, per meal	3 gallons
Drinking fountain, per operation	3 quarts
Drinking fountain, continuous flow, per minute	1/2 gallon
Factory cleanup, per man	3-1/2 to 4 gallons

Types of Flush Toilets

Ques. The action of the water in flush toilets is not clear; and there seems to be no uniformity in designs. What is the difference in the various types, and what advantages are claimed for each type?

Ans. Three basic types of flush toilets are in general use, with some modifications among different manufacturers (Fig. 8). All

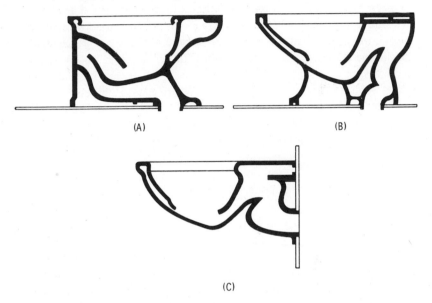

(A)   (B)

(C)

Fig. 8. Illustrating the three types of flush toilets, all in common use today: (A) The wash-down toilet; (B) The reverse-trap toilet; and (C) The wall-hung toilet.

these basic types efficiently fill the purpose for which they were originally designed.

The first, and oldest, is the wash-down type of toilet, with the trap turned toward the front. This type of toilet arrived on the market around the year 1890, and today, nearly 30 to 40 percent of the toilets that are installed are of this type. It is the cheapest, the noisiest, and probably the most difficult to keep clean of any of the types of toilets, but it is efficient enough to receive wide acceptance after all these years.

The second type is the reverse-trap toilet, with the trap turned toward the rear. It was introduced around 1906. It is quieter, easier to keep clean, and some models cost the same, or only a few dollars more, than the wash-down types. Most new installations and most replacements are of this type. Many of them are made with an elongated bowl, introduced about 1930, which is supposed to reduce spatter inside the bowl. The siphon-jet models have a deep water seal, and they produce a more positive flushing action.

The third type of toilet is the relatively new wall-hung type. It was introduced commercially in 1935, although it probably originated about 1905. Frank Lloyd Wright is supposed to have been the inventor of the model which is supported by the soil stack. The chief advantage of the wall-hung type of toilet is that it does not set on the floor, making it easy to clean beneath it. Its popularity is probably due to the fact that some manufacturers have priced some of the deluxe models of the older types nearly out of the market.

So, let your conscience be your guide. Any of the types of toilets that are now available, properly installed and properly maintained, can fulfill the purpose for which they were intended in a satisfactory and sanitary manner.

Unsanitary Sewage System

Ques. Sanitation is a problem in the sewage system of a country home where the sewage from the toilets is disposed of through a septic tank and a tile-line disposal field. The system is satisfactory, as the soil is very sandy. All the other waste water, from the bathroom, lavatories, and the kitchen sink are piped out approximately 150 feet through a fiber pipe to a low place, or draw. For a short period of time the water soaks away fairly quickly, until a scum forms on the soil and holds the water, which makes a smelly mess that must be cleaned off frequently. Can a settling tank which would catch this mess and drain the clear water into another disposal field be used to solve this problem?

Ans. This is not a sanitary way to dispose of sewage, and this can be avoided. If the present septic tank is of adequate size for the family, additional disposal facilities are not needed, except possibly to extend the present disposal field tile lines. A septic tank of adequate size can take care of all the waste water from a single-family home, including greasy and soapy waste water from the kitchen. Septic tanks cannot break down some of the older types of household detergents in the water, but they can handle the newer types of detergent without difficulty. Connect the waste-water line to the present septic tank if it is adequate in size (400 to 500 gallons capacity); if it is not large enough, build a septic tank that is large enough. It is standard and approved procedure that all household waste water should pass through the septic tank and disposal field. If the disposal field becomes overloaded, it can easily be extended.

Copper Tubing for Plumbing

Ques. The specifications for a new house originally called for galvanized-iron water pipes, but the plumbing contractor, with the consent of the architect, substituted copper tubing which is one size smaller than the iron-pipe sizes originally specified. Is this substitution generally allowable?

Ans. It is sometimes, but not always, allowable for certain portions of the installation. The recommendations of the Bureau of Standards allow it generally, and some plumbing codes follow these recommendations, but many (perhaps most) codes do not allow this rule-of-thumb reduction. Although the reduction may be permitted for supply pipes to water closets, sillcocks, and hot-water boilers, it is not allowable to most other fixtures; it is not generally allowable to reduce the size of the usual 3/4" service line by using smaller copper tubing. Possibly the plumber did not reduce the size of *all* of the water pipes. It is likely that the architect knew the rules of good practice and the requirements of the local code and that he was governed by them.

CHAPTER 14

Windows

Reflection of Light

Ques. Why do rooms that have dark-colored or dirty walls and ceilings become gloomy, with poor visibility, as compared to rooms that have clean, light-colored boundaries, even though the light in the two rooms is identical?

Ans. When light rays strike a smooth surface, they may be either reflected or, if the material is a transparent material such as plastic or glass, they may be transmitted through the surface; or, they may be absorbed and changed into heat on dark-colored surfaces. The light rays that are absorbed are irretrievably lost, and it may be mipossible to utilize light rays that are transmitted; but light rays that are reflected may reinforce the light rays that fall on an object viewed directly from the light source. Objects can be seen and perceived only because they reflect light rays, and the different colors vary widely in the amount of incident light that they reflect. The color cards of some paint manufacturers list the reflective values of the various paints that they manufacture. The following list provides the average reflective value in percentage of some of the common colors:

White	89% reflected	Dead black	2% reflected
Ivory	82% reflected	Orchid	67% reflected
Canary yellow	77% reflected	Cream gray	66% reflected
Cream	77% reflected	Ivory tan	66% reflected
Caen stone	76% reflected	Sky blue	65% reflected
Silver gray	46% reflected	Bright sage	55% reflected
Olive tan	43% reflected	Shell pink	55% reflected
Forest green	22% reflected	Pale green	59% reflected
Coconut brown	16% reflected	Buff	63% reflected

The following colors are usually called "warm" colors; they are especially desirable in rooms which have access only to northern sunlight:

Yellow	Orange
Gold	Cherry red
Yellow-red	Rose

Metal-Sash Putty

Ques. A considerable quantity of whiting and linseed oil putty is already on hand for use on wood sash. What material can be added to make the putty suitable for metal sash?

Ans. It can be made satisfactory for metal sash by adding approximately 5 percent of litharge. Another type of putty that can be used for metal sash is composed of 60 percent whiting, 30 percent white lead, and 10 percent litharge, with enough linseed oil to make it workable.

Grinding the Edges of Plate-Glass Shelves

Ques. How can the edges of plate-glass display shelving be smoothed?

Ans. It is advisable to take the glass to a glass dealer. Many dealers have special grinding machines for this type of work. If the equipment is not available, and if the edges are cut reasonably smooth, the job can be done with almost any type of medium-grain carborundum stone or a piece of grinding wheel. Use plenty of medium-heavy oil, and rub the stone over the edge. First chamfer or round the corners, using light pressure or fine chips will be knocked off. With reasonable care, a good job can be done.

Radiation-Resisting Glass

Ques. A client with a newly-built house has a problem with floor-to-ceiling glass walls on the south side of the living room. In the summer months when the sun is higher, a wide outside canopy keeps out the direct sunshine; but during the winter, fall, and spring months, the sunshine is objectionable. Are there any types of glass available which will solve this problem?

Ans. There are several types of glass available which are capable of shutting out the sun's radiant rays and reducing glare, but these may not solve the problem to the client's satisfaction; or he may not be willing to pay the price. The most commonly used type of glass has a greenish or bluish tint. This type of glass absorbs the heat-carrying red and infrared rays; it becomes hot in direct sunlight, but it excludes approximately 35 percent of the heat-carrying radiation. It is also available in polished plate. A more satisfactory glass is the gray plate glass which excludes 25 percent of the heat-carrying rays and also reduces glare. This glass is available, but it is rather expensive. A very attractive golden-colored plate glass is also available, which is not especially heat-resistant or glare-resistant, but it stops the ultraviolet rays which fade the colors in rugs and draperies. This type of glass is not often used in homes, but it may have possibilities.

Should Bed Putty Glass That has Removable Stops

Ques. Heavy wood sash, with double glazing, was set recently. The owner complained that they were leaking around the glass. The glass was reset, but the leaks still occur. Are the sash set with the wrong side outward, with the stops set on the inside surface of the glass?

Ans. The sash are set correctly with the solid sticking on the outside (Fig. 1). When glazing this type of sash (with nailed-on

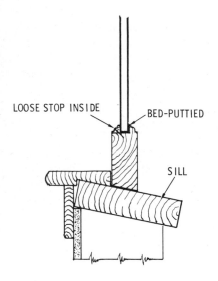

LOOSE STOP INSIDE — BED-PUTTIED

SILL

Fig. 1. Showing the correct method of setting glass in the sashes by means of nailed-in stops. These panes should always be set with the stops on the inside surface and bed-puttied in.

stops), it is convenient, but not absolutely necessary, to take them down and lay them flat on trestles. The rabbet should be well soaked with lead-and-oil primer, allowed to dry, and then a heavy strip of rather soft glazing compound should be laid in the rabbet. Then the glass should be pressed firmly into the glazing compound until the crack between the glass and the sticking is completely filled. One can see through the glass when it is filled. Then the putty should be cut off and removed inside the glass; the stops should be nailed in, and the cracks, if any, between the stops and the glass should be pressed full of the putty. The putty on the outside of the glass should be cut off and smoothed down flush with the edge of the sticking. This is the correct way to glaze all sash and doors with loose stops; glass set in this way will *not* leak, and the stops will not become soft and rot, as they invariably will in a short time when the stops are set on the outside surface of the glass in the weather.

Photochromic Glass

Ques. It is our understanding that a type of glass is available which automatically darkens and shuts out direct sunlight and then becomes clear again when the sun's rays do not strike it. Is this true, and where is this type of glass obtainable?

Ans. There is such a glass, but to our knowledge it was not available commercially at this writing (March, 1964). More than one of the major glass manufacturing companies, however, have produced this glass in their laboratories, and it may be on the market soon.

This glass is called "photochromic." Exposed to violet rays from the sun, or from any other source, the clear glass darkens very decidedly, within one minute, until only approximately 28 percent of the visible light can pass through; then when the light is discontinued, the glass clears again in about the same period of time. The photochromic glass contains a small percentage of silver halide crystals, submicroscopic in size, which, since they are sealed from the air, retain indefinitely their ability to react to light changes.

Reasons for Tinted Glass Windows

Ques. Why are so many of the newer apartment buildings using blue glass windows? Is there any reason other than to add color?

Ans. The bluish or greenish panes are used for the same reason that the upper parts of the windshields of some makes of automobiles are tinted—to shut out glaring sunlight and to reduce the amount of sun heat that passes through. The glass in the bluish panes contains a small percentage of iron, which enables it to absorb some of the radiant energy in sunlight. The glass becomes hot, and the heat is reradiated on each side, but one-half of the absorbed heat is excluded. The resistance of the tinted glass to heat *conduction* is similar to that of clear glass, but it is obtainable in double panes with sealed edges, which improves this characteristic.

Other glare-resistant panes are available, including the gray plate and sheet glasses which are also obtainable as double panes, and a newly introduced double pane which depends on a coating to resist glare; its color is not so apparent as that of some other types.

Setting Glass in Adhesives

Ques. Why cannot the glass in wooden doors be set in some type of adhesive, thus preventing water leaks and rattling glass once and for all? What types of adhesives can be used to bond the glass to the wood?

Ans. It is satisfactory to set the glass in wooden doors in an adhesive; at least some millwork houses are doing it. Nothing is objectionable about this practice, unless it might be difficult to remove the pieces if it is ever necessary to replace a broken glass.

The common animal glues (*not* fish glues) can be used to bond glass to wood, as can the epoxy synthetics and the "pressure sensitive" vinyl-ethyl-ester resins; the rubber-base adhesives also can be used. The sodium silicate adhesives that are used in some of the cheap plywoods and in the corrugated paperboards bond so strongly with glass that they can be removed only by grinding and repolishing. It is not advisable to set the glass in metal sash or doors with strong adhesives, because of the difference in expansion of the two materials under temperature changes.

CHAPTER 15

Residential Problems

Widths of Awnings to Exclude Sunlight

Ques. When building sun shades and awnings, how should their widths, in relation to the heights of the openings that are to be shaded, be calculated?

Ans. The height of the sun above the horizon varies with the latitude, the season, and from day to day. Usually, the opening should be completely shaded at noon on June 21, which is the longest day in the year. Your approximate latitude can be obtained from almost any state map. A degree or two is not important. When the latitude is known, the height of the sun at noon on June 21 can be obtained from the graph in Fig. 1A. When the height of the sun is known, a coefficient can be obtained from the graph in Fig. 1B. By multiplying the height of the opening by the correct coefficient, the awning width that is necessary to shade the opening completely on that date can be determined.

As winter approaches, the sun's rays enter the bottom of the opening at a gradually increasing height, until on December 21, the shortest day of the year, nearly the entire area of the opening is exposed to the sun at noontime. Usually, though by no means

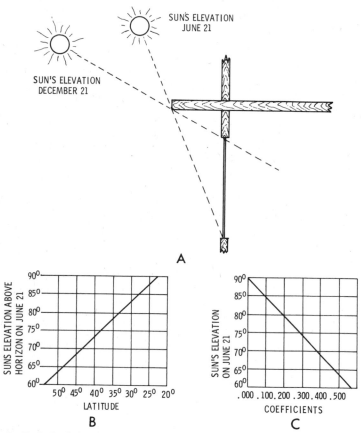

Fig. 1. Method of determining required width of canopy (Fig. 1A). To use the first graph (Fig. 1B), enter at the proper latitude on the lower line. Project this position upward to its interception with the slanting line, and then read the sun's height on June 21 on the vertical line at the left-hand side. To use the second graph (Fig. 1C), enter on the vertical line at the left-hand side at the sun's elevation as determined in Fig 1B. Project this point to the right-hand side, to its interception with the slanted curve, and then downward to the line marked "coefficients." The height of a window multiplied by the determined coefficient gives the width of the canopy required to shade the window completely at noontime, June 21.

always, the sun's rays are desirable on that date. After December 21, the exposed area gradually shortens, until it is completely shaded again on June 21. The figures given in the diagrams, of course, assume that the opening faces directly southward.

For example, in Indianapolis, Indiana, which is located on the 40th parallel, the above data can be determined. Enter the graph (Fig. 1A) at the 40° point on the bottom line. Follow a vertical line upward from that point until it intercepts the slanted line; project from there to the left-hand side until the line marked "elevation" is intercepted at approximately 73-1/3 degrees. Then enter the graph (Fig. 1B) at 73-1/3° at the line on the left-hand side marked "elevation," and project to the right-hand side until it intercepts the slanting curve; then project downward to the correct coefficient (0.300). If the window height is 8-1/2 feet, the awning width that is required to shade the opening completely at noon on June 21 can be determined as follows:

8-1/2 $\times$ 0.300 = 2.55 feet, or approximately 2 ft. 6-1/2 in.

Soil Poisoning to Control Termites

Ques. Is soil poisoning an effective method for controlling termite infestations? What chemicals are used, and how are they applied? Are the poisons injurious to shrubbery or other plantings?

Ans. Treatment of the soil beneath, and adjacent to, a house is an extremely effective way to control termites; this method is being used more widely, because metal shields are, in many instances, ineffective. Many different chemicals are used; some of them are *Chlordane,* dieldrin, DDT, aldrin, *Lindane,* and trichlorobenzene. All these chemicals are toxic, and they must be handled with care. This type of work should be done by pest control firms who are experienced. The chemicals may be absorbed through the skin; rubber gloves should be worn when using them.

Water emulsions of *Chlordane* and dieldrin are probably the most inexpensive and effective preparations that are used. *Chlordane* is classed as moderately toxic, but a dose ranging from 1 ounce to 1 pint can kill a person. Dieldrin is extremely toxic—at least equal to Paris green or lead arsenate; from 7 drops to a teaspoonful causes death.

In using the toxic chemicals, dig a shallow V-shaped trench along each side of the foundation walls, digging around piers or other critical places. If there is a basement, dig the trench only on the outside. If *Chlordane* is used, mix 1 gallon of 45-percent *Chlordane* emulsifiable concentrate with 44 gallons of water. For dieldrin, mix 1 gallon of 15-percent dieldrin emulsifiable concentrate with 44 gallons of water. Pour the emulsion into the trenches at the rate of 2 gallons per 5 feet of trench length; pour the solution on both sides of the walls; or, if there is a basement, use 4 gallons per 5 feet only on the outside wall. If applied properly, the treatments should last at least five years. These chemicals are not injurious to shrubbery, flowers, or foundation plantings.

Odors in Kitchen Cupboards

Ques. Food that is stored in kitchen cabinets constructed of birch-faced paneling with pine shelving absorbs a strange, woody, musty odor. The cabinets are painted inside. What can be done about this problem?

Ans. Although this was not indicated, the cabinets are probably mounted on an outside wall; problems are fairly common in these instances. Since the doors are normally closed, the backs of the cabinets may become cold during severe winter weather, causing enough moisture to condense on them for mold fungi to live and grow.

A fungicide cannot be used, because most of them are virulent poisons and their odors are worse than the mustiness. Charcoal is one of the best absorbents of odors. "Activated" charcoal may be obtained from a pharmacist. If the cabinet doors are left open during cold weather, the mustiness may be reduced. When cabinets are to be mounted on outside walls, heavy insulation should be installed in the walls behind the cabinets. Then, the backs of the cabinets remain at a warmer temperature, probably remaining higher than the dew point of the kitchen air.

Wood-Borer Infestations

Ques. The pine floors in a house over a crawl space are infested with white worms, or grubs, and there is no indication of tunnels, as when termites are present. What are these grubs, and what can be done to get rid of them?

Ans. Probably, these grubs are the larvae of a beetle known as the old-house borer. When they are at work, these grubs make a ticking sound, similar to that of a watch, and they are sometimes called "wall-watches," — superstitious persons formerly called them "death watches,"—because the characteristic sound was supposed to foretell a death in the family. When the grubs emerge as beetles, they leave a hole 1/4 inch in diameter; then they fly away to begin a new family of their own.

Try soaking the infested wood with a spray of two-percent solution of *Chlordane* in oil. This halts the trouble, unless they are inside a wall or place where they cannot be reached. In these instances, they can be eliminated only by employing a competent pest-control firm to fumigate the house with hydrocyanic acid gas. The house cannot be lived in while they are doing this, because the gas is a deadly poison. Individuals should never attempt this control themselves.

Comparative Fuel Costs

Ques. It is difficult to compare heating costs when different fuels are used. Comparison of monthly fuel bills is difficult, because weather and temperatures are not uniform, and the various homes rarely have identical insulation. Is there a logical and workable method for making these calculations?

Ans. There is a workable method. To begin with, heat units must be used that are identical for all fuels compared. Although it is an inconveniently small unit, the Btu, or British thermal unit, is universally used in all English-speaking countries for calculations involving combustion fuels; the kilowatt-hour unit is used in the electrical heating industry.

In round whole numbers, the following relations in heat units (Btu) can be used:

1. One pound of Ohio high-grade bituminous coal contains approximately 12,500 Btu of available heat. This is equivalent to 25,000,000 Btu per ton.
2. One pound of No. 2 fuel oil contains approximately 131,500 Btu of available heat.
3. One cubic foot of natural gas contains approximately 1000 Btu of available heat.
4. One kilowatt-hour of electricity is equivalent to 3413 Btu of available heat.

For the combustion fuels, these calculations vary to some extent. Dealers and distributors of fuels are usually happy to explain the heat content of the fuels they market. However, when any of the combustion fuels are used, a considerable percentage of the available heat may be lost up the chimney, because of incomplete combustion, faulty equipment, and incompetent or careless operation of the heating plant. Unburned coal that is carried out in the ashes is heat that is lost. It is generally accepted that the following utilization efficiencies are attained readily over an entire heating season, using good equipment and intelligent operation:

gas-fired furnaces, designed units ....average 78%
oil-fired furnaces, designed units ....average 72%
bituminous coal, stoker-fired ....average 60%
direct electric heating 100%

Using 100,000 Btu (commonly called a "therm") as a basis, comparative estimates of fuel costs can be made by the following equation:

$$\text{cost per therm} = \frac{\text{cost per unit} \times 100,000}{\text{available heat per unit} \times \text{utilization efficiency}}$$

For coal at $14.00 per ton, the calculation is:

$$\text{cost per therm} = \frac{14.00 \times 100,000}{25,000,000 \times .60} = \$0.09333$$

For electricity at 2c per kwh, the calculation is:

$$\text{cost per therm} = \frac{.02 \times 100,000}{3413 \times 1.00} = \$0.506$$

Solar Heat Collectors Have Limited Capacity

Ques. A high-school teacher has built a 48-in. concave solar heat collector that is made of wood, with foil reflecting surfaces. It seems to be extremely efficient. Is this principle practical for heating the water in homes?

Ans. The focusing heat collector is extremely practical for some purposes, but its capacity must not be overestimated. The heat-carrying rays are concentrated in a small area; the smaller the area, the higher the intensity of the heat, but a 48-in. reflector does not have enough capacity to heat a large quantity of water. In other words, it cannot collect enough energy.

In Central United States on June 21, the maximum sun energy striking the earth is approximately 290 Btu per hour per square foot, and the day is approximately 15 hours in length. On December 21, the incident heat available is approximately 220 Btu per hour per square foot, and the day is approximately 9 hours in length. The average intensity for an entire day is probably approximately one-half those figures listed above. The area of a 48-in. circular reflector is 12.57 square feet, and the maximum efficiency of the collector is probably 60 percent, since the loss of a high percentage of the radiation is inevitable. The amount of heat collectible on a sunny June 21, then, is approximately:

$$\frac{290 \times 15 \times 12.57 \times .60}{2} = 16,400 \text{ Btu}$$

On December 21, the amount of collectible heat is approximately:

$$\frac{220 \times 9 \times 12.57 \times .60}{2} = 7465 \text{ Btu}$$

These are not large quantities of heat. The Btu is a small unit. A gallon of No. 2 fuel oil contains approximately 132,000 Btu of available heat; therefore, more than a week of good weather is necessary for the 4-ft. reflector to collect as much heat as can be obtained by burning a gallon of fuel oil. It requires 500 Btu to heat a gallon of water from a ground temperature of 40° to

100°F. For home use, desired hot-water temperature is usually 140°F.

A reflector larger than 4-ft. in diameter is necessary for a practical home hot-water heater. Authorities, such as the *A.S.H.A.E.*, recommend a storage tank with a capacity of 75 to 100 gallons, and a collector which can heat 135 to 180 gallons a day, or 17 to 23 gallons per hour, to meet the needs of a family of four. This requires a collector with 100 to 128 square feet of exposed surface, which means a focusing-type round reflector with a diameter of 11 to 13 feet. The focusing reflector requires a mechanism to keep it constantly facing the sun, and no attempt is usually made to heat the water to a high temperature. A large storage tank is necessary to carry through the night time and other periods when the sun does not shine. There are many solar water heaters, most of them homemade, in Florida, Arizona, and California.

Performance Specifications

Ques. A job is available for bids on a "Performance Specification." The drawings and specifications are not available as yet. Being unfamiliar with such specifications, can you advise as to the difference in these specifications, from the usual architect's standard specification?

Ans. The typical standard specification may read: "All interior partitions shall be $2'' \times 4''$ studs plastered both sides on metal lath, plaster to be three-coat dry work." The performance specification may read: "All interior partitions shall have a fire-resistance rating of 1 hour, based on standard fire tests." Therefore, the standard specification permits only one type of wall, three coats of plaster on metal lath, while the performance specification allows, plaster on metal lath, perlite plaster on gypsum lath, 5/8-inch dry wall, and some other types.

A standard specification might read: "The boiler shall be No. UR-120, made by the Chicago Steel Furnace Company." This leaves the contractor no alternative. He must furnish the boiler of the specified make and capacity. A performance specification might read: "The boiler shall have a standard rating of 120,000 Btu per hour." This leaves the contractor considerable leeway as to the particular make of furnace that he furnishes.

The specification which unequivocally calls for a special make or brand of materials or equipment is very much frowned on. Some private owners may still specify the makes or brand they want; but on most public work, these specifications are forbidden. Many architects still specify a named brand, but add "—or equal." This is not much improvement, because it may mean "—or else," since the architect decides what is equal, leaving the contractor over the barrel. The performance specification certainly leaves something to be desired, but it is generally much to be preferred.

Cannot Change Plans and Specifications

Ques. If a job is being bid on, and the architect's drawings could be changed to allow the use of $2'' \times 6''$ joists rather than $2'' \times 8''$ joists, and $4'' \times 6''$ joist bearers could be used rather than $4'' \times 8''$ timbers, could the bid be made on that basis? This would save money.

Ans. This should *not* be attempted, because the bid may be thrown out without any consideration. The owner has engaged the architect to make a design. If the architect approves the substitution, well and good. Then, an alternate bid may be placed and the other bidders given an opportunity to bid on the same alternate plan, thereby no one bidder receives an unfair advantage. The architect probably will not allow an alternate bid, because he would have asked for alternate bids if he had wanted them.

If the builder and the owner should agree on changes (*any* changes), neither can ignore the architect. The architect has a contract to furnish the design and, probably, to see that the contractor does the work according to the design; the design is fully protected by law. There is no easier way to get yourself into trouble than by taking liberties with the designs, even though no question of ethics is involved.

Red Clover Mites or Red Spiders

Ques. The owners of new houses in a recently opened subdivision are being plagued by infestations of red clover mites which collect in millions around the eaves and window sills of their homes. The owners of a local greenhouse have been consulted and the preparations they recommended have been used, but they are ineffective. Is there an effective control for these pests?

Ans. Undoubtedly, they are difficult to control. Usually, they infest only the young grass in new lawns, which is the reason they are such a nuisance in new subdivisions. In the fall, they attempt to move into the houses to avoid the cold, and since they are so small, some of them usually succeed.

Their migration can usually be stopped, if it is done in time, by spading up and cultivating a 12-in. strip of soil around the foundations. They are not readily controlled with the common insecticides, but good results have been obtained by spraying with aramite, dimite, and chlorobenzilate. The best results may be obtained by spraying the ground with rotenone or malathion. Malathion is probably the best preparation for this purpose, but its odor is extremely disagreeable. Its odor has been compared with that of a dead rat, and no one has disagreed. Probably, it is best to confer with a qualified pest-control service to obtain the most satisfactory results.

Controlling Odors

Ques. A building is to be remodeled into three apartments. For three years, the building was used to house poultry, and the very distinctive smell of all chicken houses prevails. Of course, the odor must be eliminated. The walls and ceiling are presently covered with a waterproof impregnated fiberboard, but it is proposed to cover them with gypsum board dry-wall material. It is doubtful whether the fiberboard has absorbed any odor. What can be done about this problem?

Ans. Probably, the fiberboard *has* absorbed odor, since poultry odors are extremely persistent. Odors are caused by vapors, and wood products are not vapor-resistant. It will have to be sealed, and one of the most economical and effective vapor barriers is a polyethylene film. The fiberboard on the walls and ceiling should be covered with the film and the dry-wall material placed over it. If 1″ × 2″ furring strips are used over the fiberboard, a reflective foil vapor barrier should be used instead of the film, because it increases the heat-insulating value of the walls. The vapor barrier may be desirable for other than its odor-sealing value.

Much of the odor is probably coming from the floors. A vapor barrier is needed there as well as in the walls. Linoleum and vinyl floor coverings are of themselves effective vapor barriers, but if an underlayment board is required, place a film underneath it. It is likely that the odor cannot be completely eliminated immediately, and it may not disappear for some time, but the building can be made habitable. Oil paints and the acrylics are excellent vapor barriers, but the water-mixed coatings are not so good. Use paint freely.

If it is desired to attempt to mask the odors, use oil of sassafras. It is one of the oldest and most effective preparations for this purpose. Its odor is pleasant, and persistent. Of course, *Lysol,* creosote, carbolic acid, or another of the phenolics may be used, but their "hospital" smell is distinctive, and not agreeable. These preparations are widely used in jails and prisons.

Control of Wood-Boring Bees

Ques. In a summer home that is located in woods, wood-boring bees are honeycombing the redwood fascia with neat round holes; after only three years, the fascia should be replaced. To add to the difficulty, the woodpeckers peck at the boards to obtain the larvae from the holes. What can be done about this problem?

Ans. Either a one-percent solution of *Chlordane* in water, or a one-half percent solution of dieldrin may be used. Spray with the solution; soak the wood thoroughly, shooting the solution well into the holes. If interested in the possibility of a "silent spring," the birds may be poisoned by eating the larvae and insects which are killed by the insecticides; therefore, a decision may be necessary to determine whether it is more desirable to put up with the bees and replace the cornice boards, rather than run the risk of poisoning the birds. Possibly, the risk of killing the birds may not be too great; however, a great "to-do" has been made about the "indiscriminate" use of insecticides.

The Authentic Colonial-Style Home

Ques. Many of the so-called "colonial" homes now being built seem to be poor imitations of colonial-type homes. What are some of the attributes of the authentic colonial architecture?

Ans. It is quite true that many details of present-day "colonial-style" homes are not of true colonial origin. This is unavoidable in many instances, because modern concepts of homes are widely different from those of our ancestors, but their tasteful designs and sturdy utilitarianism can be adapted to our modern homes. Following are some of the attributes of the New World homes of the Georgian period extending from approximately the year 1700 to about 1790. These homes were built in those regions of the country which were under British influence during that period.

The Georgian colonial roof was steep; on one-story houses, 10 to 12 inches rise per foot of run was common, and not less than 7-1/2 inches rise per foot of run was common on two-story houses. Dormers were small, always with single windows, and they were set back a distance of 3 or 4 feet from the ends of the roof. The dormers were usually placed directly above the windows or doors in the walls below. Facades were preferably balanced, the same on each side of the central entrance; or, if the facade was not perfectly balanced, which was unusual, the upstairs windows were aligned either with the windows in the lower story or with the entrance doorway. Twin and triple windows were not used in the colonial-style home. The panes were always small; they were often six-over-six in the upper-story windows and six-over-nine in the lower windows. The shutters fit the windows, and they were operable. Personally, it seems that "shutters" which are screwed to the siding only catch dirt and hold water.

The flush-type door was not used in the colonial home, since plywood was unknown in those days. The doors had raised panels, T-cross rails, and small, nearly square, panels placed near the top were common. In the earlier Georgian homes, the entrance doors were exposed to the weather, but some of the later and more pretentious homes possessed heavily pedimented and pilastered entrances. A small number of the homes possessed inset entrances for protection from the weather, but only near the end of the period was the Georgian home built with a covered stoop or entrance porch. Double-entrance doors were common in colonial-style homes.

The chimneys were extremely large and usually placed in the center of the home; or, in the larger homes, a chimney was placed in each gable. The chimneys were *always large*. A small chimney destroys the authentic look of any colonial-model home, but do not corbel chimneys out into the attic, if they are to work satisfactorily.

Although 10- and 12-in. siding is sometimes called "colonial," this type of wide siding was seldom, or never, found on the colonial house. The siding on these homes was rarely more than 5 in. exposed to the weather, and in some instances, only 2 in. were exposed. Shingled walls were very common, and relatively wide corner boards were generally used. Some of the older New England homes were built with an overhang or "garrison" on the second story. Garrison-type overhangs should be used with caution, because the house may look top-heavy, or beetle-browed, but properly proportioned garrisons of 12 to 18 inches may often be used with good effect.

Effects of Water on Plaster

Ques. As a plastering contractor, the dry-wall people are continually giving me a difficult time because of the water that is used, contending that this results in permanent damage to a home. What is your opinion of this? How much steam or vapor is produced when a week's washing is done in a home?

Ans. It is agreed that "there is no substitute for good plastering," but a real mess can be made with the water that must necessarily be used in plastering. Approximately 700 gallons of water is used in plastering a six-room house, and if it is occupied during the fall or winter, it may not be completely dried out until the following summer. However, permanent and serious structural damage caused by the dampness cannot be recalled.

Regarding the water vapor produced from a week's washing inside a house, an average family of four persons, with a conventional washing machine, releases approximately 4.33 pounds of water as vapor or steam. If a roller-type wringer is used and the washing is dried inside the house, approximately 26 pounds more water is released. If a spin-type dryer is used and the laundry is finish dried inside the house, approximately 1 pound of water is released per pound of dry weight of the clothes. If a gas-fired drier is used, add 2 pounds of water to the total for combustion products.

Desirable Temperature Environment

Ques. What, in your opinion, is the proper temperature that should be maintained in homes, offices, and schools in winter?

Ans. This is entirely a matter of personal preference. In a home, active adults are usually comfortable at 68°F., while inactive older people and younger children need a temperature of approximately 72°F. In offices, it has been found that there is often a difference of opinion. The girls usually want the temperature maintained at about 70°, but the men are better satisfied at 68°F. A compromise is generally made at approximately 70°F.

In schoolrooms, a check by the New York Committee on Ventilation showed that 15 percent more work was accomplished at 68°F., then at 74°F. Experiments in Indiana showed that a class did its best work at about 68°F., but, at 66°F., one-half the class fell below the average. At 72°F., the class was restless; at 80°F., it was both restless and dull.

Two Species of Redwoods

Ques. Is it probable that redwood lumber may disappear from the market in the near future? Supposedly, the United States Government is incorporating stands of these trees into the national parks and, of course, public sentiment discourages logging the big trees.

Ans. There is a probability that stock redwood lumber may disappear from the Eastern and Midwestern markets in the not too distant future, because the supply, never large, is greatly diminished. So far as is known, the stands of redwood saw timber are not being taken over by the parks, but redwood lumber is so expensive that it is being replaced by less expensive timbers which are chemically treated if rot-resistance is desired. The aforementioned "public sentiment" is largely misguided, or merely plain ignorant. The "big trees" belong to the species *Sequoia gigantea*, the Sierra redwood, whose wood is so soft and brashy that the trees are often smashed and split when they are felled. These trees are sometimes sawed into lumber, but the lumber is so soft and brittle that it is almost useless, even for siding. The redwood lumber in commerce is from trees of the species *Sequoia sempervirens*, the Coast redwood, which is a much smaller botanical relative of the big trees, although it is still sometimes very large. The wood of these trees is harder, stiffer, and stronger.

Turning Down Thermostat at Night

Ques. How much fuel can be saved by turning down my room thermostats from the usual 70°F. daytime temperature to, perhaps, 60°F. at night?

Ans. It is not practical to reduce room temperature during the night hours, if a so-called "radiant" heating system is used. The heating surfaces in these systems, either electrical or hot-water systems, must necessarily operate at relatively low temperatures; these temperatures cannot safely be raised to supply extra heat during the morning warm-up time. Consequently, the rooms may be uncomfortably chilly for several hours in the forenoon.

Even with conventional heating apparatus, the fuel saved during the cool-down period may not equal the excess fuel used during the warm-up time. Accurate calculations must include many factors. Some of these factors are the quantities of different materials in the walls, floors, and ceilings, and their specific heats, because, in all instances, these materials must be returned to their "steady-state" temperatures during warm-ups. The heat thus expended is irretrievably lost.

A formula that is sometimes used in these instances, although it may be doubtful as to dependability, may be used. It is as follows:

$$A = \frac{0.0625\ (n\text{-}1)\ W}{z}$$

A is the amount of heat, in Btu's, which is added to the normal heat loss

W is the normal heat loss per hour, in Btu's

n is the number of hours during which heating is discontinued

z is the number of hours from beginning reheating to the time when the rooms are satisfactorily heated

Calculating the Elevations of the Sun at Various Seasons

Ques. A sun shade is to be built on the south side of a store building. Is there any method that can be used to calculate the height of the sun during a given season?

Ans. These calculations are simple, if the declination of the sun (its distance north or south of the equator) and the latitude of the project are known. The latitude can be obtained accurately enough from a good map, and a table of declinations of the sun (at noontime) can be obtained from several sources. The "Old

Farmer's Almanac," obtainable at newsstands, contains these tables. A typical calculation for the season extending from March 22 to September 22, when the declination is *north,* is as follows:

1. Sun's altitude = 90° − latitude + declination. From September 22 to March 22, when the declination is *south,* the calculation is: Sun's altitude = 90° − latitude − declination.
2. If located exactly on the 40th parallel at noontime on June 22 (the longest day), the calculation is: Sun's altitude = 90° − 40° + 23°26′ = 73°26′. For December 22 (the shortest day), the calculation is: Sun's altitude at noon = 90° − 40° − 23°27′ = 26°33′.

Using a protractor to measure the angles, a drawing of the proposed sun shade should be made. The drawing may then be scaled for actual dimensions. A list indicating the *approximate solar declinations,* in degrees north or south of the equator, is as follows:

January 1,	23° S.	July 1,	23° N.
15,	21° S.	15,	21.5° N.
February 1,	17° S.	August 1,	18° N.
15,	15.5° S.	15,	14° N.
March 1,	7.5° S.	September 1,	8° N.
15,	2° S.	15,	3° N.
April 1,	4.5° N.	October 1,	3° S.
15,	10° N.	15,	8.5° S.
May 1,	15° N.	November 1,	15.5° S.
15,	19° N.	15,	18.5° S.
June 1,	22° N.	December 1,	22° S.
15,	23.5° N.	15,	23° S.

CHAPTER 16

Miscellaneous

Dead-Load and Live-Load Allowances

Ques. What is meant by the terms "dead loadings" and "live loadings" in building design? What is the difference between the two terms?

Ans. Dead loads are the weights of the *permanent* parts of the building, such as walls, floors, roofs, partitions, etc. Live loads are the weights of the *moving or movable* contents of the building, such as people, furnishings, machinery, and the weights of stored goods. Snow loads on the roofs and wind loads against walls are classified as live loads. The live loadings that should be allowed for in buildings are usually specified arbitrarily in building codes and ordinances.

Canvas Roof Deck Covers

Ques. How should canvas roof deck covers, which are required to withstand a light to moderate amount of foot traffic, be laid? Lock-jointed tin roof covers are now in use, but the noise during rainstorms is objectionable. What is the average length of life of canvas deck covers?

Ans. There are several approved methods of laying canvas deck covers, but the following method is recommended: Use tight, dressed-and-matched roof sheathing, nailing it down well and making sure that there are no projecting nail heads or cupped boards. Use boards that are no wider than standard 1 × 6 D&M, —1 × 4 flooring boards are better. If the boards become cupped or warped, the raised edges form ridges that quickly cut through the canvas.

Prime the sheathing with a heavy lead-and-oil primer, mixed with about 25 pounds of heavy-paste white lead, 1 gallon of raw linseed oil, 1/2 gallon of turpentine, and 1/4 pint of liquid drier. Allow the primer to dry; then give the deck a coating of the heavy-paste white lead. The canvas then should be pressed and rolled down into the white lead, preferably with a linoleum roller. Lead the joints well, allow a 1-1/2″ lap, and nail the lap with 3/4″ copper, aluminum, or galvanized tacks placed at not more than 1″ intervals. The canvas should be primed with a white-lead and oil primer, and followed with two successive coats of an outside paint. Aluminum paints and other types of metallic paints have not been satisfactory for this purpose.

The canvas should be unbleached, unsized, closely-woven, and not lighter than 10-oz. grade, but No. 6 and No. 2 grades are often used where the roof is to be subjected to heavy traffic, or where the canvas covers are used on the decks of boats. If they are kept painted, canvas deck covers should, and many covers do, last 25 to 30 years or more.

An Easily Made Bench Stop

Ques. A sharp-notched steel bench stop has the advantage of being adjustable for height, but it mars and sometimes splits the ends of boards, and occasionally a chisel or a plane rams into it. Is there a better type of bench stop?

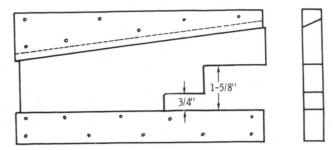

Fig. 1. A satisfactory bench stop, made of 1-in. lumber. It holds either 1-in. or 2-in. stock firmly, with the edge placed upward.

Ans. The wooden stop shown in the sketch (Fig. 1) is much better. It is easily made from almost any 1-inch scraps; it can hold either 1-in. or 2-in. stock, and very thin boards can be held firmly by driving the beveled-edge wedge inward against them.

Calcium Chloride to Control Dust

Ques. In the process of building an open-air pavilion at a fair-ground, the ground has been graded, but dust is a serious problem. What can be done about this problem, besides wetting the ground, which makes it muddy?

Ans. Treat the ground with calcium chloride, which is also used to accelerate the setting of concrete. It can be obtained from a materials dealer. Spread the chloride flakes, applying approximately 2 lbs. per square yard. The calcium chloride absorbs moisture from the air, causing the soil to pack. If the treatment is repeated in a few weeks, a hard crust forms on the surface. This is, of course, not a permanent solution for the problem, but it is effective for some time, and is easily renewed. Calcium chloride is not a poison and does not damage clothing, except to bleach it.

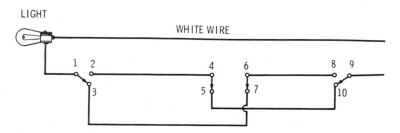

Fig. 2. Wiring diagram used to control an electric light from any one of three switches. In the three-way switch at the left-hand side, pole No. 1 is always connected with either pole No. 2 or pole No. 3. Similarly, in the three-way switch at the right-hand side, pole No. 9 is always connected with either pole No. 8 or with pole No. 10. In the four-way switch at the center of the diagram, if the switch is turned in one direction, poles No. 4-5 and No. 6-7 are connected; turned in the other direction, poles No. 4-6 and No. 5-7 are connected.

Control of Lights from One of Three Switches

Ques. How should the switches be wired to control a hall light from one of three doorways?

Ans. One four-way switch and two three-way switches are needed. All of these switches fit into standard outlet boxes. Three-way and four-way switches are always in one closed position. See the wiring diagram (Fig. 2).

Calculating Tank Capacity in Gallons

Ques. How can the total capacity in gallons of square, rectangular, or round tanks be calculated?

Ans. A gallon of water occupies a volume of 231 cubic inches, and a cubic foot of volume holds 7.48 gallons of water. For either square or rectangular tanks, multiply the height by the length by the width (all in feet), and multiply the result by 7.48. For cylindrical tanks, multiply the *square* of the radius (in feet) by the height (in feet), and multiply the result by 5.875.

Swimming Pool Below Ground-Water Level

Ques. In building a swimming pool (12 × 32 feet, maximum depth 8 feet), the ground water level is only 42 inches below the grade level. Is it practical to use a 5-in. reinforced concrete floor with 8-in. concrete-block walls?

Ans. Several problems may be encountered. The head of water against the floor at the deep end of the pool is going to be nearly 300 lbs. per sq. ft., and the weight of the floor itself is going to be approximately one-fifth of that pressure. Since the floor cannot be built in the water, the soil must be drained first. Well-point systems are often used for this purpose. If the soil is sandy, it may require pumping a large quantity of water. All these items should be checked before starting a project that cannot be finished. After the pool has been completed and filled with water, it should give no trouble; but several problems may be encountered in building it—or later, when it is desired to empty the pool.

Fire-Clay Liners in Chimneys

Ques. When building a chimney, is it necessary to fill the space between the liners and the bricks with mortar? What is the easiest way to cut out holes in the liners for smoke pipes?

Ans. The Underwriter's Code specifies that the space should *NOT* be filled with mortar. The liner sections should be set up *ahead* of the brickwork, and the joints between the sections should be mortared. Coinciding joints between the brickwork and the liners should be avoided, if possible.

The best way to cut holes in sewer pipe and chimney liners is to use a common carpenter's nailset; first carefully pick a small hole through the liner, and then gradually enlarge it chip by chip. This method is safer if the liner is filled with damp sand.

A Quonset-Type Farm Machinery Shed

Ques. A 36′ × 74′ machine shed is to be constructed, using laminated semicircular arches. How heavy should the arches be made, and what kind of roofing should be used?

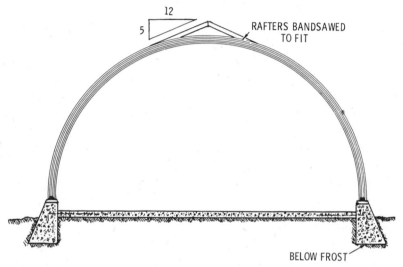

12

5

RAFTERS BANDSAWED
TO FIT

BELOW FROST

Fig. 3. A Quonset-type farm machinery shed. When the shorter straighter rafters are used at the peak, practically any type of roofing is satisfactory. The foundations should be designed to withstand the outward thrust of the arches.

Ans. (See Fig. 3). The arches should be set on 24″ centers, and they should be built from five thicknesses of 1″ × 4″ boards, but seven thicknesses of 1″ × 3″ boards, ripped from 1″ × 6″ boards are preferred. A form should be built; short, flat-sided posts have been used, set firmly in the ground at the required arc. Bend the first lamination, and tack it to the posts. Subsequent laminations are glued. Casein glues are commonly used. The glue should be spread only on one of the contacting surfaces; and each lamination should be nailed with 7d cement-coated nails, placed at 9-in. intervals. Keep the joints well distributed—not closer than 24" to any one section. To do this, the strips should be no less than 16 ft. in length. After the first arch has been completed, leave it in place and build the others over it, using the first arch as a pattern. It is necessary to hold the ends of the arches together by some means, such as twisted wires, as they are removed from the form and as the arches are erected.

Roofs of this type are somewhat prone to leak in the flat part of the arch near the crown. To prevent this difficulty, false rafters, approximately 8 ft. in length, may be used at the tops of the arches. These may be bandsawed to fit the curve, or nailed to the sides of the arches. Almost any type of roofing may be used. The sheathing may be spread 1" × 4" boards, and wood shingles used; or the roof may be sheathed tight, and either asphalt shingles or roll roofing used. Purlins (2" × 4") spaced at 24" intervals may be used with either 1-1/4" corrugated galvanized sheets or corrugated aluminum, but 2-1/2" corrugated sheets are too stiff to bend.

The foundations must be designed to resist the outward thrust of the arches. The foundation walls should be tied to the edges of the floor slab with reinforcing rods. Use 3-1/2" × 3-1/2" × 1/4" angle clips to fasten the ends of the arches to the 2" × 8" sill; and use 1/2" × 12" anchor bolts, placed on 72" centers, to fasten the sills to the foundation walls. Poured concrete, rather than hollow-block masonry, should be used for the foundation.

Pressure of Grain in Deep Bins

Ques. A customer plans to build three silos for grain storage; each silo is to be 14 ft., inside diameter; 60 ft., high; and constructed of 4-in. concrete staves. The soil is sandy and the ground water level is normally 8 to 10 ft. below the ground surface, but often rises to within 3 or 4 ft. of the surface. Will the proposed foundation (see Fig. 4) be satisfactory for these silos?

Ans. Pressures caused by grains in deep bins are not the same as the pressures of fluids. Most small grains weigh approximately

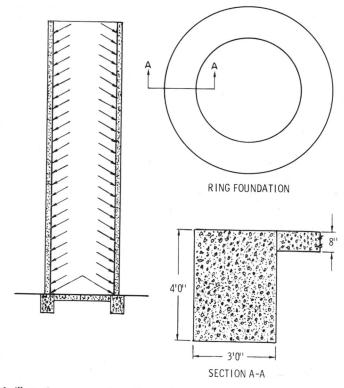

RING FOUNDATION

8"

4'0"

3'0"

SECTION A-A

Fig. 4. Illustrating pressure in a silo used for grain storage. The inside diameter is 14 ft., and the height is 60 ft. Due to the downward and outward action of the grain, a large portion of the weight of the contents exerts pressure on the sides; the proposed foundation shown above may not be adequate.

50 lbs. per cu. ft.; when dumped on a floor, they tend to pile up into an inert cone—the slant of the sides is approximately 28° from the horizontal. The grain tends to slide downward and outward until it is restrained by the sides of the bin. Thus, the cone rises continually as the bin is filled, and some outward pressure is exerted, but the grain tends to adhere to the sides of the bin; much of the weight of the contents is transmitted to the sides as vertical pressure. From the sides of the bin, of course, this loading is transmitted to the foundations and footings, and from them to the soil that bears the entire load.

Calculations indicate that the load on the circular foundation, including the weight of the structure itself, is approximately 200 tons, and the area of the soil beneath the footings is approximately 132 sq. ft. The soil pressure is approximately 1-1/2 tons per sq. ft. It is doubtful that wet sand can bear the loading safely. Dry sand, or even moderately damp sand, can bear the load safely. Since calculations indicate that the loading is near the danger line, it is suggested that a good engineer who can make a personal inspection of the premises, and who understands all of the problems involved, be employed. Several problems other than the bearing qualities of the soil are involved, and they should be investigated. The engineer may insist on a soil bearing test. Since so much money is involved, risks that can be avoided should be eliminated.

Brown Stain in Western White-Pine Lumber

Ques. A considerable quantity of Western white-pine boards are available; some of these boards are siding and dimension lumber that shows considerable brown stain. Some persons advise that this lumber is structurally unsound and that it should not be used; yet, it cuts and handles in the same manner as sound lumber. Is this advice unfounded?

Ans. This is probably the "chemical stain," sometimes called "yard stain," which is fairly common in air-dried lumber of nearly all species. It is believed to be the result of oxidation of the water-soluble substances present in the sap of the living tree. It is not decay, and it does not affect either the cell structure or the strength and utility of the lumber. It can be used for any purpose where white-pine lumber might be used, except, of course, where the wood is to be finished natural. Even then, if the lumber is carefully selected, attractive and unusual effects may be obtained.

Step-Cutting for a Weld in an I-Beam

Ques. A welder advises that the proper way to make a weld in an I-beam is to step-cut the ends, as indicated in the sketch (Fig. 5). Why is this type of weld stronger than a straight butt weld?

Ans. The weld is no stronger. In an I-beam, the stresses that are caused by bending are concentrated almost entirely in the

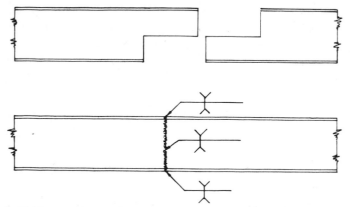

Fig. 5. Welding an I-beam. The step cut (top) is unnecessary. The welded joint is no stronger than the plain butt weld (bottom).

flanges—compression in the upper flange and tension in the lower flange. These stresses cannot be altered in either intensity or direction by changing the shape of the weld. Shearing stresses are heavily concentrated in the web of the beam. Good welds are strong in shear, but there is no advantage in placing an unnecessary weld in shear. In other words, the shape of the weld is not important if the welding is done properly.

Straight butt welds are as strong as possible, if the welding is done skillfully. The metal in the flanges is relatively thick; therefore, the junctions must be filled solidly with weld metal to develop the full strength of the beam. The edges of the weld must be scarfed by burning, grinding, or milling. A single pass cannot fill the welds; the passes must begin near the center of the thickness to assure full penetration. This type of welding operation requires a skilled operator; preheating may be necessary. In any instance, care must be used in applying the heat, if the beam is to be kept straight.

Grain Bins Usually not Overdesigned

Ques. In building a grain bin 40′ × 100′ with 12-ft. walls, it is proposed that 2″ × 6″ studs placed on 16-in. centers with plywood lining be used. Will the bin be strong enough? Is it true that grain bins are frequently designed too strongly, making them unnecessarily costly?

Ans. The proposed bin is not strong enough for a bin of that width. The pressure of small grain or other granular materials stored in bins is not comparable with fluid pressure. When filled with water or other fluid, the pressure against the sides of a tank that is 2 feet wide is the same as the pressure against the sides of a tank that is 20 feet wide. When a grain bin is filled with grain, a portion of the contents at the bottom is roughly pyramidal, or conical, and around this relatively inert pile the grains tend to slide downward and outward, exerting pressure similar to a wedging action; its intensity is relative to the *width* (not the *depth*) of the grain bin. In a bin that is 12 feet deep, maximum pressure is reached when the width is approximately 45 feet. The proposed bin approximates 45 feet in one dimension, but it is larger in the other dimension. According to our calculations, the pressure against the side walls, when the bin is filled with wheat, is approximately 3000 pounds per lineal foot of wall. The 2″ × 6″ studs set on 16-in. centers cannot withstand that much pressure (see Fig. 6).

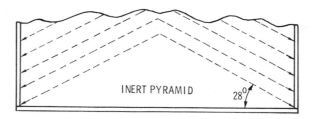

INERT PYRAMID   28°

Fig. 6. Illustrating the pressure forces in a wide, shallow grain bin. The sketch shows why pressure against the walls of relatively shallow grain bins varies not only with the depth but also with the width of the fill.

Cracked Rivets, and Different Types of Iron and Steel

Ques. The inspector on steel framing jobs often marks various rivets that are to be cut out and replaced. How does he determine which rivets are unsound? Also, what is the basic difference between cast iron, malleable iron, and steel?

Ans. Structural rivets are driven hot, and on cooling they shrink, drawing the joint tightly. A rivet may be loose, flawed, or the tension in shrinkage may snap off the head. The rivets are tested by striking the rivet head a sharp blow with a hammer. If the rivet is sound, a *solid* sound can be heard. If the rivet is cracked, the sound of the blow is similar to that of a *rattle*. Perhaps this is a poor description of the sound produced, but experience is required to judge the meaning of the sound, and the test is not infallible. A loose rivet may sometimes be tightened by bucking it and driving it slightly after it is cold, but do not let this be seen by the inspector.

Cast iron, malleable iron, and steel are different mixtures of the two basic elements, iron and carbon, combined with other elements which may be alloying agents, such as manganese or chromium; or the two basic elements may be combined with impurities, such as sulfur and phosphorous. The carbon content of cast iron may range from 2 to 4 percent. Malleable iron is cast iron which has been annealed to make it less brittle. Carbon steel, or structural steel, contains 0.06 to 0.4 percent carbon. The modern high-strength or high-tensile structural steels are alloys that contain one or more alloying ingredients, such as manganese, chromium, nickel, vanadium, columbium, molybdenum, and other elements in carefully controlled quantities.

Stopping Leaks Around Guy Cables

Ques. After using roofing cement to stop leaks that occurred where guy cables are fastened to a flat roof, the leaks reappeared in a few months. How can these leaks be repaired so that they will stay repaired?

Ans. Run the guy cables into an asphalt well (Fig. 7). Place a shallow box or collar made of tin or galvanized iron approximately 1-1/4 to 1-1/2 in. in height around the guys. With the nailing flanges turned inward, nail them to the roof; fill either with hot asphalt or with roofing cement. This should eliminate the problem. Asphalt wells are often used to halt leaks around guy cables fastened to a flat roof.

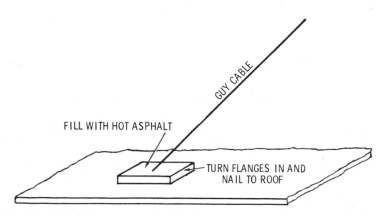

Fig. 7. Illustrating the use of an asphalt well to halt leaks around the guy cables that are fastened to a flat floor. If the asphalt pool is fractured, it is self-healing. The asphalt well has many practical applications.

Standard Colors for Danger Areas

Ques. What are the standard colors that may be used to signify danger areas?

Ans. Apparently, no firm "standard" colors are used, but colors recommended by the American Standards Association are as follows:

Red, *danger*	Blue, *electricity*
Orange, *be on guard*	Purple, *radiation*
Green, *safety*	Black and white, *dead end*
	Yellow, *hazard*

Various firms apply these differently, but, in general, the yellow color indicates moving equipment, such as cranes, lift trucks, the dangerous moving parts of machinery, and strike-against hazards of all types. Fire equipment, such as fire buckets, extinguishers, hose cabinets, and fire-alarm boxes are usually painted a fire-engine red color. The black and white markings that denote dead ends of streets, passages, and corridors are used almost universally.

In some industrial plants, the different colors are used to identify various pipe lines, such as electrical conduit lines (blue), gas lines (orange), cold water pipes (light green), etc. Thus, the colors are distinguishing markings that are used to identify valves, by-passes, etc.

Dimensions of Swimming Pools

Ques. The swimming pool in a city park is 30′ × 60′, and the diving area has a springboard at one end. How many persons can this pool accommodate?

Ans. Allow 27 square feet of space per person in the swimming area, and allow 20 to 25 square feet of space per person in the diving area. If the diving area is 15′ × 30′, the capacity would be 18 to 22 persons in that area and approximately 50 persons in the remainder of the pool. Thus, approximately 70 persons could be accommodated.

Technical Terms

Ques. What are engineers talking about, in regard to wood framing, when they use such terms as: forces, stresses, tension, compression, bending, and shear.

Ans. *Force* has approximately the same meaning as power, or energy. Intensity of force is expressed as pounds, or kips, or tons. It is impossible for a force, such as the weight of a loading on a beam or a column, to be applied at a *point,* although for calculating purposes, this may be so assumed. Forces are always partially distributed over an area and, when so distributed, a force becomes a *stress.* Stresses are expressed as *force per unit* *of area;* in wood framing, stresses are usually expressed in pounds per square inch.

Only three types of stresses are possible: (1) *tension,* which tends to tear the timber apart; (2) *compression,* which tends to crush the timber; and (3) *shear,* which tends to push or pull one portion of the timber past another portion.

Bending is the tendency of beams to sag under loads which may be applied at any point in the span. This produces compression in the upper portion of the beam, extending downward to a plane at approximately one-half the height, which is called the *neutral axis.* At that plane, the forces change direction; below the neutral axis, the stress is in the form of tension. The tensile and compressive forces are equal in intensity and opposite in direction; stresses are greatest at the extreme top and bottom surfaces of the beam, where they are called *stresses in extreme fibers.*

In the effort to sustain the loading, *shearing* forces are set up within the beam. *Vertical shear* is the effect of force, which tends to push the beam downward between its supports. In extreme instances, it could cut off the ends of the beam, leaving them in place on the supports. This type of action is not usually serious in wood beams, because wood possesses excellent resistance to stresses of this type across the grain. However, wherever vertical shearing forces are present, another set of shearing forces are set up within the beam itself. They act at right angles to the vertical shearing forces, and are equal to them in intensity. These forces are termed *horizontal shears,* and in wood beams they may be dangerous, because wood possesses relatively low resistance to shearing forces with the grain. The carrying power of wood beams is seriously reduced if they are badly season checked near the ends, because horizontal shearing stresses are always at a maximum, or equal to the maximum, at the supporting ends of the beams.

Unlike stresses in bending, which are normally highest at the outermost fibers at top and bottom of the beam, shearing stresses are greatest at, and near, the neutral axis.

Space Requirements for Coal Storage

Ques. When building coal bins, how much space should be allowed for one ton of coal?

Ans. The space requirements for coal are:

1. 1 ton of bituminous coal occupies approximately 40 cubic feet of space.
2. 1 ton of anthracite coal occupies 37-1/2 cubic feet of space.
3. 1 ton of coke occupies 70 cubic feet of space.

Pressure in Shallow Grain Bins

Ques. In relatively shallow grain bins, what, if any, extra force is exerted by the grain when it is heaped higher than the sides? Is the extra weight carried by the floor alone, or does the extra weight also cause additional outward pressure?

Ans. The sketch (Fig. 8) illustrates a commonly accepted theory. As the bin is filled, the grain forms a cone or pyramid at the bottom, and that portion of the fill exerts direct downward pressure. As the filling progresses, the grain tends to slide downward and outward around the cone area. The cone rises as the bin is filled until, if the grain is heaped up, it projects above the walls. If the depth of the bin is equal to twice its width or thereabouts, and the grain is piled higher than the wall line, the outward pressure is nearly the same at all points from the bottom to the top of the walls. In bins made of wood, concrete, or other rough-surfaced materials, the grain tends to stick to the walls, and the walls

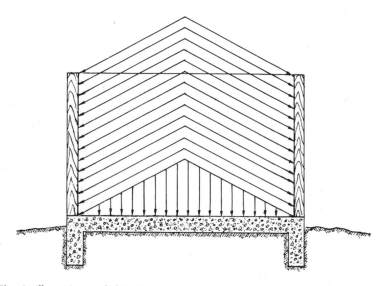

Fig. 8. Illustrating probable lines of forces active in a shallow grain bin. If the grain is heaped higher than the wall line, pressure against the sides is nearly constant from the top to the bottom.

carry a great portion of the weight of the grain. If the height of the walls is about 1.4 times the width of the bin, nearly one-half the weight of the grain is carried by the walls of the bin to the foundations as a straight vertical load; the foundations should be designed accordingly.

If the depth of the bin is less than its width, and if the bin is filled only to a level even with the top of the walls, the outward pressure decreases as the top level is approached. Because of this fact, the pressure in relatively shallow bins is sometimes compared with fluid pressure. This is the "equivalent fluids" theory, and shallow bins are sometimes designed, assuming that the pressure exerted by the grain is similar to the pressure exerted by a fluid weighing approximately 21 pounds per cubic foot, which is approximately one-third the weight of water. Satisfactory bins have been designed by this simple method, but it should be used with caution, because the pressure in grain bins varies not only as the height but also as the width. In no instance should this rule-of-thumb method be used for either wide or deep bins. As aforementioned, if the grain is heaped up, the outward pressure is nearly constant from the top to the bottom of the walls, and is not comparable with fluid pressure.

Darkening Brass Hardware

Ques. Is there any method by which bright brass hardware can be darkened?

Ans. To darken brass hardware, the following solutions should be made:

1. 120 grains of silver nitrate in 5 ounces of water.
2. 120 grains of copper nitrate in 5 ounces of water.

Mix the solutions together, dip the brass into the mixture, and then heat in an oven until the hardware is as dark as desired.

Hand-Ties for Block Retaining Walls

Ques. A retaining wall 5-ft. high was built four years ago of 8-in. concrete blocks. The wall is now pushed outward by frost action. What can be done when the wall is relaid to prevent this happening again?

Ans. Probably, it was earth pressure, and not necessarily freezing, that pushed the wall over. Hollow 8-in. concrete blocks do not have sufficient weight to make a satisfactory retaining wall 5-ft. high, or even 3 ft. high. To be stable, retaining walls should be made of solid concrete or solid masonry; their base width should be approximately four-ninths (4/9) their height. If the blocks are reused, buttresses should be built on the face side; or counterforts should be built behind the wall. Hand-ties extending back to deadmen buried in the earth are effective, but these are considered a makeshift arrangement for construction of these types of walls.

Place a 1/4-inch reinforcing rod in each mortar joint along each edge, and fill the cores of the blocks with concrete as the wall is laid. Dig a trench at 8- to 10-ft. intervals backward into the earth and place the hand-ties. Galvanized rods approximately 8 ft. in length are preferred, if available, but galvanized wire may be used satisfactorily. Uncoated steel placed in the ground lasts only a short time. Pour a sizable chunk of concrete on the ends of the hand-ties for the deadmen (see Fig. 9).

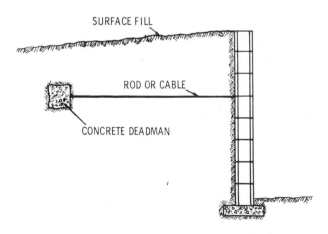

Fig. 9. Hand-ties extending backward to deadmen buried in the ground may be used to prevent lightweight retaining walls from overturning. This is considered a makeshift arrangement, but it is more or less effective.

Grade the fill to turn the water away from the retaining wall. It is impossible to build a retaining wall strong enough to withstand freezing, if water is permitted to stand against the wall.

Correct Sizes of Butt Hinges

Ques. Serious difficulty has been experienced in obtaining proper clearance of the inside edges of recently hung heavy 2-1/4″ oak doors. It was necessary to bevel the doors more than was desired. Are 6″ butt hinges too large for 2-1/4″ doors?

Ans. The 6″ butt hinges are recommended for large 2-1/4″ doors. The doors should be beveled to provide clearance for the inside edges, and the bevel is more apparent on the thicker doors. Possibly, the hinges were unnecessarily wide; or they may have been set out farther than necessary, either of which would have required more bevel. The butt hinges need only enough width for the doors to clear the trim. Following are the recommended heights of butt hinges, or the lengths of the joints (in specifying butt sizes, the length of the joints is always given first) as:

```
3/4″ and 7/8″ cupboard doors, to 24″ wide..2-1/2″ butt hinges
7/8″ and 1-1/8″ screen doors, to 36″ wide..........3″ butt hinges
1-1/8″ doors, to 36″ wide ............................3-1/2″ butt hinges
1-1/4″ and 1-3/8″ doors, to 32″ wide ........3-1/2″ butt hinges
1-1/4″, 32″ to 37″ wide ...................................4″ butt hinges
1-9/16″, 1-3/4″, 1-7/8″ doors,
   to 32″ wide.....................................4-1/2″ butt hinges
1-9/16″, 32″ to 37″ wide ...................................5″ butt hinges
1-9/16″, 37″ to 43″ wide ..............5″ butt hinges (extra heavy)
1-9/16″, 43″ to 50″ wide ..............6″ butt hinges (extra heavy)
2″, 2-1/4″, 2-1/2″, to 43″ wide ....5″ butt hinges (extra heavy)
2″, 43″ to 50″ wide .......................6″ butt hinges (extra heavy)
```

Restrictive Electrical Codes

Ques. The city council has passed a new wiring code, making it mandatory to use rigid conduit in all types of buildings. This is going to make house wiring exceedingly expensive. What is your unbiased opinion, and do you agree that this is an unnecessary expense?

Ans. Such an ordinance is probably the result of the political clout of electrical contractor's associations, or electrician's unions, or both. There are no valid reasons for restrictions such as those mentioned. The National Electrical Code of the Board of Fire Underwriters permits several more economical types of electrical installations in homes, including old-fashioned open wiring and concealed knob-and-tube work. The restrictive code should be repealed and replaced by the Underwriters Code, or a similar standard code. These codes are not biased, other than their bias against any person to electrocute himself or to burn his house down, and they are not "make work" codes that favor a special group.

A Stairway Repair Job

Ques. A stairway which was built without skirting boards is in need of repair. The risers and treads were cut flush against the plastered walls. The owner is unhappy, because the walls are always dirty for a least 12 inches above the treads, and he wants skirt boards installed. It seems impossible to notch skirting boards above the risers and treads and still do a workmanlike job. The joints cannot be scribed, and some of the cross-grained corners are sure to break off if an attempt is made to nail them correctly, providing there is anything to nail to. Is there any possible way to do this job correctly, providing the owner with a satisfactory and workmanlike repair job?

Ans. This job has been done and a workmanlike job can be done, but, of course, reasonable skill and care are required. As in all types of stairway work, this is not a job for a saw-and-hatchet man, but a skilled carpenter should be able to do the job satisfactorily.

The job can be done as follows (see Fig. 10):

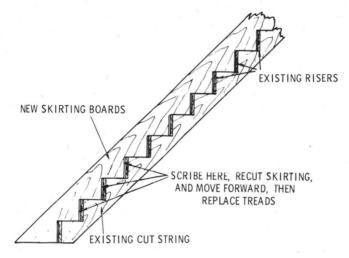

EXISTING RISERS

NEW SKIRTING BOARDS

SCRIBE HERE, RECUT SKIRTING,
AND MOVE FORWARD, THEN
REPLACE TREADS

EXISTING CUT STRING

Fig. 10. Illustrating a practical method for installing skirting boards in a stairway which originally was built without them.

1. Remove the treads, leaving the risers in place. The nails may have to be sawed.
2. Roughly notch the skirting boards, placing the boards above the horses, as shown in the sketch.
3. Scribe the joints at the fronts of the risers. Cut to the scribed lines, and the joints should fit. The horizontal joints do not have to be fitted.

4. Nail the skirting boards, and cut the treads to fit between them in the usual manner.

If the walls are reasonably straight and true, the notches will not be broken out, the notched skirting will be held firmly in place, and a workmanlike job should be the result.

Adobe Brick Construction

Ques. A large area, or "playa," of adobe soil is available for making adobe bricks. How are they made? Is it true that some of the oil companies can furnish a product to mix with the clay for making good bricks without burning them? Is it true that stable manure should be mixed with the clay?

Ans. Adobe clays can be burned into excellent bricks, but the true adobe blocks are not burned, they are sun dried. The oil product mentioned is a petroleum-derived asphaltic emulsion which is added to make the adobe wall more suitable for rainy climates, but it increases the cost of the adobe wall to nearly the cost of good wood-framed construction. In the arid parts of New Mexico, Arizona, and California, plain adobe walls are strong enough, and they are sufficiently weather-resistant without an additive.

Adobe workers are usually Mexican or Indian. They merely loosen the soil with mattocks, throw a quantity of stable manure on the soil, wet it well, and then they take off their shoes, roll up their pants, and tramp the entire mass into the proper consistency, adding water as necessary. The brick molds are usually made of 2″ × 4″ members that are used for two blocks, each approximately 12″ × 12″ and 3-5/8″ thick. The molds are soaked well, laid on a smooth place on the ground, and the mud packed into them by hand. Then the wet mold is removed to be wetted well again and reused immediately. After drying for a few days, the blocks are set on edge and allowed to "season."

The walls are approximately 12″ thick, or equal to the width of a single block. They are ordinarily laid in the adobe mud, but lime and sand have been used. The walls may be finished with stucco on the outside and plaster on the inside, applied directly to the bricks; the wall must "season" thoroughly before applying either of these finishes, since they continue to season and shrink for some period of time.

Adobe walls possess excellent heat-transmission resistance and high capacity for heat. They warm up slowly under the rays of the sun. Properly built, the adobe house is anything but makeshift. Many of these homes are definitely in the luxury class.

Mixing manure with the clay is strictly a Mexican idea. They insist that it is necessary for keeping out termites. This is not true, and the idea is offensive to most United States citizens. Chopped hay or straw does as well, or better, and a small quantity of DDT added to the mixing water is effective in controlling termites; however, they rarely infest an adobe house anyway.

Moving a Garage

Ques. A three-car garage is to be moved approximately 8 feet. What is the easiest way to move this type of building? It is too heavy to drag behind a tractor.

Ans. Almost any building can be moved with a tractor if proper equipment is available, but it may be torn to pieces if an attempt is made to drag it. For a distance of only 8 feet and with a minimum of equipment, probably the easiest method is to jack the building across the 8-ft. distance. Practically the only equipment needed is a couple of railroad track jacks, or step-type jacks (Fig. 11). The new foundation or extension to the old foundation should be built before an attempt is made to move the building to the new site.

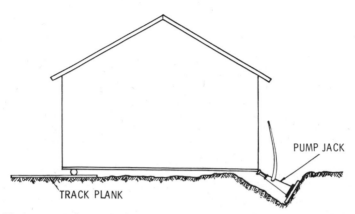

Fig. 11. An easy and economical method of moving a small building a short distance.

If the "step" of the jacks can be placed in a 2-in. crack, little digging is necessary to set the jacks. Jack up the far side of the building, place a track plank under each sill at each side, and place rollers between the track plank and the sill. Then, on the near side, dig holes for the jacks at each corner, place some blocking, and set the jacks at an angle. When set at the correct angle, the jacks *lift* as well as *push*. If the building does not move, the jacks lift until it does move, rolling on the track at the far side; therefore, the building will not be torn apart. Insert more rollers as the building moves. Pieces of 2″ or 3″ pipe make excellent rollers. Place blocks in the holes for the jacks as the building is moved. It is not difficult to move this type of building if good judgment and patience are exercised; no more than a two-man crew is needed.

Dry Storage of Loose Materials in Deep Bins or Silos

Ques. A client has a very large silo, 18′ × 40′, made of steel plates with the edges turned, punched 4″ on centers, and bolted.

The silo probably was twenty years old and the plates were slightly rusted and pitted inside, but the structure appeared to be sound. The next day after the silo was filled, two sections of the plates near the bottom buckled and folded, and the entire structure fell. Not one of the plates was torn, and none of the bolts were broken.

The inspectors for the insurance company reported that age and rust had weakened the steel and that the initial cause of the failure was shifting of the contents. It is difficult to understand how shifting of the ensilage could cause such a failure. If any of the plates had broken or bulged, it might be understandable; however, to move the center of gravity far enough to cause the silo to fall, it seems that the contents would have had to move a distance greater than 9 ft., or one-half the width of the silo. Is this logical reasoning?

Ans. The reasoning is logical as far as it goes, and you are correct. Shifting of the contents was not the initial cause of the failure. The line of reasoning can be continued.

When loose material is piled, it tends to form a natural cone; the material slides down the sides of the cone until it comes to rest, and the sides form an angle with the horizontal at a slope that varies with the nature of the material (Fig. 12). With granular materials, such as sand, gravel, or grain, the slope (called the "angle of repose") is comparatively flat (25° to 45°), but with fibrous materials, such as ensilage, the sides are steeper. When this type of cone is formed in the silo, even though the top of the material is kept level, the material tends to slide *outward* and *downward,* but it is restrained by the sides of the silo. If the material is tamped thoroughly as the filling is done, especially around the walls, it sticks more tightly to the slightly roughened walls; in addition to the outward pressure, much of the weight of

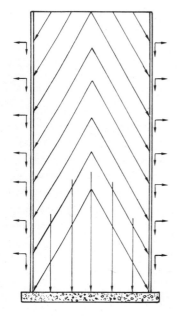

Fig. 12. Illustrating the probable lines of force that are active inside a large silo filled with ensilage. Note that the forces are by no means comparable with fluid pressure, but they are somewhat proportional to the width or diameter of the silo.

the contents is transferred to the sides as a direct vertical load. The friction of the ensilage with the roughened surface is considerable, and it is much greater than if the plates are new and smooth.

Data is unavailable as to the effect of the angle of repose (the slant of the sides of the cone) for materials such as ensilage. Probably, it varies widely, depending on the moisture content, the length of the cut, the amount of compaction, and similar factors. The angle of repose for materials such as coal, sand, gravel, and grains is well known. Without this type of data, calculations as to the intensity of the actions against silo walls, both vertical and horizontal, are impossible. It is likely that the angle of repose for ensilage is very steep, probably 60°, or greater. Thus, the *outward* pressure is relatively light, and the downward pressure, depending largely on the roughness of the inside surface, is much greater. Unlike water pressure, the outward pressure is quite uniform from the top to the bottom of the silo, but the downward pressure is cumulative. The pressure increases from the top toward the bottom. The aforementioned silo did not burst, because the outward component is not only relatively light, but it is fairly well distributed. It was the *downward* pressure, or direct weight, on the sides that caused the silo walls to buckle at a lower point on its weakest side. As the silo leaned, the friction on the lower side increased, and more and more of the weight was applied at that point, until the structure fell. It is worthwhile to note that these forces, both vertical and horizontal, are greatest in bins or silos of large diameter. They are not comparable in any manner with fluid pressure, which varies directly with the depth, and only with the depth.

Wind Pressure on Signboards

Ques. My business is construction of roadside signs. Some of these signboards are set high off the ground, and the actual erection of the high ones is sublet, but the plans for the supporting framework are furnished. My brother is a good engineer, and a design wind pressure of 20 pounds per exposed square foot is used, but some serious failures have been very expensive. Are there any suggestions that may eliminate some of these failures?

Ans. There is no method that can eliminate the possibility of wind damage, but the probability of these failures can be reduced by building stronger supporting structures. The United States Weather Bureau suggests the following equation for estimating the actual positive pressure against structures such as sign boards:

$$P = .00256 \ V^2$$

in which:

P is the positive pressure, in pounds per square foot of exposed surface

V is the wind velocity, in miles per hour

In the Northern states near the Great Lakes, the highest recorded wind velocity (outside of tornadoes) is approximately 72 miles per hour. Thus, velocity pressure is calculated at 13.27 pounds per square foot.

In addition to the direct positive pressure against the exposed face of the signboard, the wind rushing around the edges of the obstruction produces *negative* pressure, or *suction,* on the leeward side (Fig. 13). This is of indefinite intensity, depending on the shape, the size, and possibly some other characteristics of the signboard. A common assumption is that negative pressure equals 0.7 times the velocity pressure, which adds 9.29 lbs. per sq. ft. to the wind action, or a total of 22.56 lbs. per sq. ft.

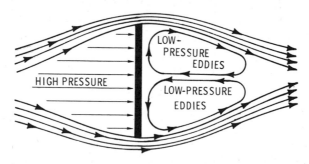

Fig. 13. Illustrating the effect of wind action against exposed surfaces of signboards.

In addition to this sustained wind action, when the work is important, good designers usually consider the action of gusty winds It is impossible to measure the velocity of gusty winds, but it is assumed that if the sustained wind velocity is 75 mph or less, the gusts may easily reach a 50-percent higher velocity. If the wind velocity were to reach the 72 mph that was assumed, the pressure intermittently may reach as much as 33.74 lbs. per sq. ft.

It should be remembered that the wind blowing at right angles to the face of the signboard exerts these same unit forces against the sides of the members in the supporting framework. If the framework is built of relatively wide planks, as is customary, the action may be serious. It is assumed that the overturning moment has been provided for, as it was not mentioned.

If a high degree of assurance against costly wind damage is desired, the supporting structures are under-designed, perhaps as much as 50 to 75 percent. If you are willing to assume this risk or willing to pay for insurance coverage, this is merely a matter of probabilities, and it should be a calculated risk, which is entirely your own affair. Where no hazard to human life is involved and where a replacement cost is nominal, it may be a financial advantage to assume at least part of the risk. This matter should be taken up with a representative of an insurance underwriter, as we cannot advise as to probabilities and financial risks that may be involved.

The foregoing suggestions were given without considering the possibilities of tornadoes. They are not especially prevalent in your part of the country, but they may occur anywhere. It is not considered feasible to erect wooden structures of any type to withstand full exposure to a tornado; the wind velocity in the periphery of storms of this type has been estimated to reach 500 mph in some instances.

Boiler Horsepower

Ques. A good, small, hand-fired steam boiler, formerly used on a construction hoist, is available for heating a garage building. This boiler is marked "9 HP." What is its heating capacity?

Ans. Modern heating boilers are not rated in horsepower. The term was used when boilers were used primarily to generate steam for engines, and the value of the unit has been changed officially several times, but after the last change, *one boiler horsepower* is equivalent to 33,475 Btu per hour. At that rating the capacity of the 9HP boiler is (9 $\times$ 33,475), or 301,275 Btu per hour. This is not a great quantity of heat, but if the boiler is installed properly it could be satisfactory for heating a rather large garage in that part of the country (South Carolina). The boiler should be able to handle approximately 1000 sq. ft. of radiation. High efficiency cannot be expected from the boiler. Some of the older types of steam boilers were extremely inefficient and expensive to operate.

Gas Heaters Should be Vented

Ques. In a wood-framed house that is finished inside with gypsum dry-wall, and stuccoed outside; only the ceiling is insulated, and the walls become so damp that they are mildewed. It is heated with open-flame gas heaters, unvented, and a change to electric heating is being considered. Will electric heating solve the condensation problems?

Ans. Probably, electric heating would solve the problem. The unvented gas heaters discharge one pint of water, in the form of vapor, into the house for each 10 cubic feet of gas that is burned. A gas-fired space heater of only 30,000 Btu per hour capacity generates 3 pints of water per hour.

If it is desirable to eliminate the wet walls and retain the gas heaters, vent them properly to the outside and insulate the walls. The inside surfaces become so cold that they are condensing water from the highly humid air inside. It is doubtful whether a reputable electrical contractor is willing to install electric heating in a house with walls that are so highly heat-conductive as these. Electrical heat energy is expensive, and unless the walls are insulated heavily, satisfaction will not result.

Enlarged Tops for Chimneys

Ques. Several chimneys which are corbeled out in the attic beneath the roof to give a larger, heavier, appearance have heating plants which burn gas, and all of the chimneys leak. Water drips off the corbels in sufficient quantities to wet the insulation and the ceiling below. Treating the brick with silicone sealers has been tried, and one of the chimneys has been painted, but this was ineffective. Will filling the steps in the corbels smoothly with mortar, or choking down the top opening with chimney tops solve this problem?

Ans. The enlarged tops will act as very efficient funnels to catch rain, and they may be more or less effective as condensers to distill water out of the flue gases, but there is no useful purpose that they can serve, and their appearance certainly will not compensate for the nuisances that they create (Fig. 14).

Taking the tops down and laying the chimneys up straight can solve the problem effectively. Other than that, if it is desirable to preserve the heavy appearance, insert one of the commercial flue liners downward to the furnace, and connect it. Pour the cap solid except for the opening. Either of these two expedients can solve the water problem, and will probably result in increased furnace efficiency.

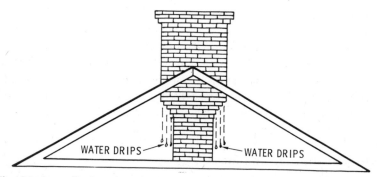

Fig. 14. A needlessly enlarged chimney top, illustrating the problem that often results when it is used.

If coal or wood had been used as a fuel, the result would probably have been messier than it is now. The enlarged chimney tops allow the ascending flue gases to expand, velocity is slowed down, and the enlarged tops are the coldest parts of the chimneys. This setup is nearly ideal for condensing tars, oils, and creosotes from coal or wood smoke, as well as condensing water from the flue vapors of gas furnaces.

Lightning Protection

Ques. A friend wants me to build him a summer home in the mountains; severe electrical storms are common, and some type of lightning protection is called for. Is it effective to extend a 1/2-inch copper tube downward through the chimney masonry to a good ground?

Ans. Why not use a standard lightning-rod system (Fig. 15), with at least *two* terminals? This is safer, and is surely worth its cost under the conditions described. Single-mast conductors *do* afford a fairly high degree of lightning protection within a cone whose apex is the top of the air terminal, and the radius of whose

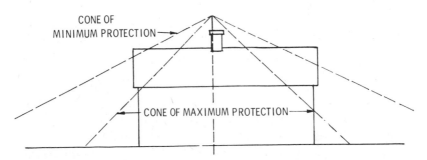

CONE OF
MINIMUM PROTECTION

CONE OF MAXIMUM PROTECTION

Fig. 15. Illustrating the cones of protection which may be expected from a grounded single-mast conductor. The building shown in the sketch does not receive even minimum protection.

base is equal to the height of the terminal above the ground. It has been found that a somewhat lesser degree of protection is found within a cone whose apex is the air terminal and whose base has a radius equal to *twice* that height, but occasionally lightning has been known to strike inside this cone. Apparently, there is a relation between the height of the air terminal and the height of the storm cloud above the earth, but figures cannot be supplied to substantiate this theory.

Glues for Wood

Ques. Local dealers do not seem to be familiar with adhesives, knowing only brand names which are meaningless to me. Can information be provided concerning the following types: (1) casein resins; (2) resorcinol resins; (3) urea resins; and (4) polyvinyl resins?

Ans. All these adhesives are used for wood, and all make a bond that is stronger than the wood they join; however, they are all handled differently, and if a shop setup is being planned, this should be taken into consideration. Many of the commercially obtainable adhesives are mixtures of two or more types, and only the manufacturers can advise as to their proper use. In general, the following descriptions apply only to the uncompounded basic adhesives.

Casein is not a synthetic resin; it is a natural phosphoprotein that is obtained from milk, and it is probably the easiest to handle and most economical of the water-resistant adhesives. It sets moderately slowly, depending on the air temperature, and it is not suitable for fast factory assemblies, but it is almost universally used for both factory- and field-built glue-lam timbers and all other types of structural gluing. This adhesive is gap-filling, requiring no heavy clamping. It works at all temperatures above the freezing points of water, but at low temperatures, it may require 36 hours to set. After it is set, the adhesive is exceptionally hard and may be damaging to woodworking tools.

Resorcinols are synthetic resins; they are dark colored, have a smoky, tarry odor, and they stain some woods badly. Most resorcinols require hot-pressing to set; however, in some formulations they may be set up at room temperatures by using strong catalysts. The resorcinols are gap-filling, extremely water-resistant, and may be used for outside work. They are often combined with other adhesives, such as the phenolics. Resorcinols can be set quickly under heat and are adaptable to fast factory assemblies, but they are still rather high priced. The catalysts used are irritating if allowed to contact the skin.

Urea resins are often combined with other synthetics, such as the resorcinols and the melamines, to make them more heat-resistant. They are thermoplastic, melting or softening at approximately 180°F.; a urea-bonded joint falls apart quickly in boiling water, but below that temperature, they withstand water-immersion for a long period of time. The urea compounds are widely used for bonding plywood.

Polyvinyl resins are also somewhat thermoplastic, softening under moderate heat, and set at room temperatures; they are extremely easy to use. These resins do not stain woods, and they make strong joints, although they are slightly inclined to "creep" when placed under high and sustained stresses. Polyvinyl resins are not especially water-resistant, but they are often used for shop-built millwork; they are one of the most valuable adhesives.

Trees Injured by Building too Close

Ques. A home in the country is being planned. It is to be located in a grove of shag-bark hickory trees, some of them 70-feet tall. The house will have a slab-on-ground floor, with foundations extending below the frost line. How close can the house be built to the trees without injuring them?

Ans. Expert foresters have been consulted on this question, and they advise that, although the hickory is a sturdy and persistent grower, a tree which has grown and matured under forest conditions cannot tolerate a disturbance of its root system; also, there may be danger of injuring the tree described if the roots are cut closer than approximately 25 feet along one side. Normally, from a circle immediately outside the crown, the main feeder roots extend outward and downward at an angle of approximately 45 degrees, and sometimes these roots go very deep. In addition, a system of very shallow roots, approximately 12 to 24 inches beneath the surface of the ground, extends outward in all directions. These roots also carry water to the trunk of the tree, and serve to anchor the tree upright in the soil. These are the roots that will be injured by digging for the foundations of the house.

Actually, there is no way to accurately foretell the reaction of the trees. Stay away from the trees as far as possible. The disturbed trees should be supplied with plenty of water and heavy feedings of fertilizer for some time to enable them to regain the loss of strength occasioned by disturbing the roots in the affected areas of the root system.

A Lawn Fountain for Home Cooling

Ques. Is it true that an ornamental lawn fountain may be used to cool a home satisfactorily? How does this type of installation work?

Ans. This has been more or less satisfactory in some regions, but figures on cooling capacities or costs of operation are not available. The principles employed are identical to those employed in atmospheric evaporative cooling towers. The cooling towers are widely used, and very satisfactorily, in the low-humidity conditions of the Southwest, in Arizona, and in Southern California; however, they are not highly successful in the highly humid South and Midwest regions, especially where the wind is obstructed by tall trees or buildings.

The warm water from the cooling unit is pumped to the jets in the fountain; it is sprayed into the air, and some evaporation and cooling action takes place. The cooled water falls into the bowl of the fountain, and it is pumped back to the cooling unit. One problem that is encountered is the inevitable collection of trash, leaves, and silt, which may damage the apparatus. Wind drift of the spray may be a problem.

These installations should be made where the wind has a free sweep over the fountain. They do not work satisfactorily where the wind is obstructed by trees, shrubs, or a building which is too close on the windward side. The major expense of operating these installations is, of course, the electrical power required to run the pump, but a considerable quantity of water is evaporated into the air.

Compressibility of Water

Ques. How many gallons of water can be held in a 50-gallon tank if the pressure is increased, for example, from 0 to 20 pounds per square inch?

Ans. The tank can hold 50 gallons of water. A gallon of water occupies a space of 231 cubic inches, regardless of pressure. Presumably, the capacity of the tank cannot be increased by placing its contents under pressure, because an increase in pressure reduces its volume.

Water is only slightly compressible. Increasing its pressure by one pound per square inch, reduces its volume approximately 1/300,000. Therefore, for the 50-gallon tank, if the pressure is increased 20 pounds per sq. in., the volume of the water within the tank is reduced by:

$$\frac{50 \times 20}{300,000} = \frac{1}{300}, \text{or } .00333 \text{ gallons, which is approximately}$$
$$0.77 \text{ cubic inches.}$$

If no additional water were to enter the tank, the water volume would be:

$$(50 - 0.00333), \text{ or approximately } 49.997 \text{ gallons.}$$

Usually, the changes in the volume of water caused by pressure can be safely ignored, but the volume changes caused by temperature changes are often quite important. If water is heated from 37°F. to the boiling point, it expands approximately 4-1/3 percent; if water is cooled from 37°F. to the freezing point, it expands approximately 9 percent, and the expansion is quite sudden and violent.

Flame-Resistant Draperies

Ques. In an apartment house, a serious fire was narrowly averted when window drapes blew in over the top of the kitchen range. Is there any chemical which can be used to treat draperies where there is a possibility of their becoming ignited?

Ans. Noncombustible draperies are much better and safer where there is a possibility of this type of accident. Nearly all drapery materials, especially the lightweight cottons, are highly combustible. These draperies are sometimes "flameproofed" by saturating them in a solution of 3 ounces of boric acid and 7 ounces of borax in two quarts of water, and allowing the draperies to dry. The fabrics are slightly stiffened, and the flame-resistant properties disappear after laundering. Even when treated in this manner, the fabrics are not entirely flameproofed and they can be burned.

Two-Wire and Three-Wire Receptacle Circuits

Ques. Today, while inspecting a new house along with the architect, it was noticed that the duplex receptacles were all on three-wire circuits. The architect did not, or could not, explain this other than "we always do it that way, nowadays." Can the advantage gained by using three-wire circuits, if any, be explained in language intelligible to a layman?

Ans. For the owner, the principal advantage is that with the three-wire circuit the other receptacle is still hot when a fuse is blown on one of the duplex receptacles; and this is true on the entire circuit. The entire circuit is not put out of service by blowing either fuse. Although there may be an advantage in having 240 volts available at each outlet, if it should ever be necessary, this contingency may be remote.

From the contractor's viewpoint, the three-wire circuit may be cheaper than two-wire circuits. A three-wire 120-240 volt circuit has the same capacity as two 120-volt two-wire circuits; it can carry the same load three times as far, and with less voltage drop. This results in a 25-percent reduction in copper. Also, a three-

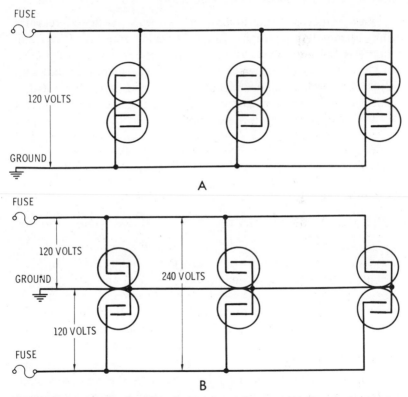

Fig. 16. Two methods of wiring duplex receptacles are: (A) The usual two-wire method (if the fuse is blown all outlets on the circuit are out of service); and (B) The three-wire method (if either fuse is blown, one receptacle at each outlet remains in service).

wire circuit may be placed in a single conduit, and receive 100-percent rated capacity; however, two two-wire circuits in the same conduit must operate at a 20-percent reduction, according to the National Electric Code (see Fig. 16).

Lang-Lay and Regular-Lay Wire Rope

Ques. Some used 1/2-inch wire rope was purchased recently, with the intention of using it for light timber frame hoisting. This rope was formerly used on an elevator, but it is not badly worn, and is very flexible. It was found that a load suspended on a single line tends to spin and untwist the rope; it is impossible to splice it, and I learned to splice wire rope in the Navy. Do you know what type of rope this may be?

Ans. It is strongly suspected that it is Lang-lay rope, and to complicate matters, it may be flat-strand rope which is often used on elevators. Elevator cables are never spliced, and Lang-lay rope is rarely spliced, since it is extremely difficult to do so. It is doubtful whether it can be spliced, although it may be possible. In Lang-lay rope, both the wires in the strands and the strands themselves are twisted in the same direction, usually in a left-hand direction. In regular-lay rope, the wires in the strands are usually twisted in the left-hand direction, and the strands themselves naturally twist in the right-hand direction. It does not untwist nearly so readily as the Lang-lay rope. All of the Navy wire rigging probably was galvanized regular-lay rope.

Yearly Fire Losses

Ques. Is it true that losses from home fires are increasing every year in greater proportions than the proportional increase in population? Is it probable that modern building methods are to blame? Are dependable records of home fires available?

Ans. Records of reported fire losses are kept by the National Fire Prevention Association, but, of course, there must be many losses which are not reported. It is true that fire losses have been climbing almost steadily since the depression years in the 1930's, but it is probable that the actual material loss has not exceeded the birth rate proportionally. The dollar loss is a different matter. From 1945 to 1961, the value of the building dollar decreased approximately 45 percent, so the dollar loss is now much higher per amount of actual destruction. As reported by *NFPA,* the losses from 1958 to 1963 were as follows:

1959: 542,000 fires in homes, 5,600 lives lost, $312,000,000 loss.
1960: 563,000 fires in homes, 6,000 lives lost, $346,200,000 loss.
1961: 534,000 fires in homes, 6,200 lives lost, $337,500,000 loss.
1962: 562,000 fires in homes, 6,400 lives lost, $339,000,000 loss.
1963: 566,500 fires in homes, 6,500 lives lost, $326,800,000 loss.

In our opinion, the "modern" home building methods and types of homes are slightly less fire resistant than the older, heavier, and sturdier buildings, but the older buildings are frequently more vulnerable because of deterioration and neglect.

Visibility of Signboards

Ques. Is there an accepted rule for minimum sizes of lettering for good visibility on outside advertising signs? In many instances, our signs are set back some distance from the road or street.

Ans. There is no rule known, but it is an accepted fact that the average human eye does not perceive objects which subtend a visual angle of less than approximately 1 minute(see the sketch in Fig. 17 for an explanation of this statement). The tangent (and also the sine) of a 1-minute triangle is 0.000291. At a distance of 200 feet, for example, the lettering should be at least:

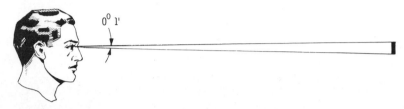

Fig. 17. The human eye is unable to distinguish an object with its surroundings if it does not subtend a visual angle of more than approximately one minute (0°1'), even with a favorable color contrast.

$$0.000291 \times 200 \times 12 = \text{approximately 3/4-inch in height}$$

In other words, to be visible at 200 feet, a line of lettering should be at least 3/4-inch high, but it would be only visible— not readable. To be readable, the lettering should be four to five times that height. Other factors, such as coloring and lighting, are vitally important. The color of the letters and the color of the background should be highly contrasting. It may be noted that black on white, or black on yellow, are universally used for official street and road signs, because these two color combinations furnish the greatest color contrasts. Nothing, and we repeat, *nothing,* is going to attract the attention of drivers passing by at 70 mph, nor should this be an object in roadside advertising signs. It is doubtful whether roadside advertising ever actually sells a product or a service,but it may create an interest that is followed up later. Only a small (if any) advantage is to be gained by using long sentences lettered in small-sized letters.

Type of Metal in Sprinkler-Head Links

Ques. Because our shop ceilings are rather low and the sprinkler heads are close together, the workmen have several times accidentally bumped a sprinkler head with a long piece of material, obtained a shower bath for themselves, and ruined the sprinkler-head links. As new links are often not on hand or readily obtainable, replacement links were made out of lead. Are they allowed?

Ans. This should never be done at any time or under any conditions. Fusible links are *not* made of lead, but are made of an alloy called Wood's metal; it ordinarily melts at 150°F., but lead does not melt until it reaches approximately 621°F. Wood's metal melts at 150°F. and it is composed of: 49% bismuth; 27.7% lead; 12.9% tin; and 10% cadmium. It melts in boiling water, but melted lead can ignite a piece of wood. The installers of sprinkler systems often make periodic inspections. If either the installers or the insurance company inspectors discover the lead links in the sprinkler heads, they will probably have heart failure.

Saving the Elm Trees

Ques. In a subdivision that was developed some years ago, extensive use was made of American elm shade trees, but, of course, the present owners have lost them because of the Dutch elm disease. Many elm seedlings, some of them 1 inch or more in diameter, are now being found in out-of-the-way places, and they seem to be disease-free. Is it possible that these seedlings may have developed immunity from this disease? Has any chemical control for this disease been found?

Ans. In our opinion, the seedlings have not developed natural immunity to the disease; probably, the bugs simply have not found them. Only one toxic insecticide has been found to be effective against the disease; it has only recently been placed on the market, and is available only through trained foresters or tree experts. Its chemical composition and the trade names or manufacturer's addresses are unknown to us, but a firm of recognized tree experts can be consulted for details. This treatment reportedly is not injurious to birds. The chemical is injected directly into the trunk of the tree.

Ironworker's "Old Man"

Ques. Today, the ironworker's foreman told me to "go down and bring up a 7/8″ ratchet and the old man." The ratchet was found easily, but much time was wasted by running all over the place while trying to find the superintendent. Can you please describe an "old man," so that other greenhorns can avoid the embarrassment and razzing that resulted?

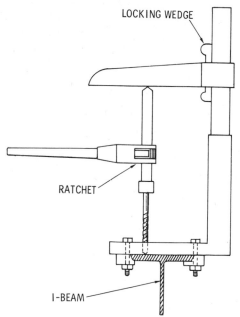

LOCKING WEDGE

RATCHET

I-BEAM

Fig. 18. A steel erector's "old man," used to bring pressure to bear on a ratchet when drilling or reaming mismatched holes.

Ans. The steel erector's "old man" (Fig. 18) is an arrangement similar to the frame of a heavy drill press, which is used to exert heavy pressure on a ratchet when drilling or reaming mismatched holes. While working around the steel erectors, other rather bizarre names for equipment may be learned. For example, if you are sent for a "cow-sucker," take along a wheelbarrow. This is the iron ball on the fall line of the erection crane; it is located immediately above the hook, to pull the line downward when the drum is released, and it may weigh 50 pounds or more. Both these names are commonly heard on steel erection jobs.

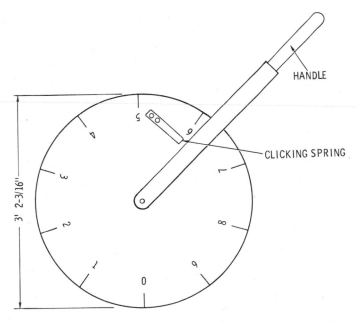

Fig. 19. A land-measuring wheel. It is reasonably accurate, but it follows the contour of the ground.

Measuring Wheel

Ques. Is there a quick-and-easy method for estimating distances with reasonable accuracy, other than actual taping? This would be used to measure drain lines, for example, where measurement to the exact inch is not vital.

Ans. For accurate measurement, of course, there is no substitute for carefully taping a given distance, and a knowledge of the correct procedure is desirable. For reasonably accurate estimates, experienced land surveyors use the stadia method. For the unskilled, an excellent method is to use the "measuring wheel," which can easily be made from plywood (Fig. 19). It is convenient to make the circumference of the wheel exactly 10 feet. Thus, a diameter of approximately 3 ft. 2-3/16 in. is required. The wheel is rolled along over the unknown distance, counting the revolutions; the number of revolutions is then multiplied by 10. This measurement, of course, follows the contour of the ground and is not a true horizontal measurement, but it is quite accurate for estimating the length of drains. To make errors in counting the number of revolutions less probable, screw a flexible "flapper" spring to the wheel, so that a distinct "click" is heard each time the wheel passes the 10-ft. mark. Under favorable conditions, allow for a possible error of plus or minus 3 percent.

Fairy Tale Concerning Fireplaces and Lightning

Ques. Some friends say that fireplace chimneys attract lightning and that it travels downward through the chimney, through the opening, and outward into the room. Can this be prevented by placing a metal cap on the chimney?

Ans. That idea is a fairy tale. Lightning usually strikes the highest and the most exposed point in the immediate area. If this point is a tree, a high tower, or a chimney constructed of masonry or some other low-conductive material, the structure may be damaged; and the material may be ignited if it is flammable. If the object that is struck happens to be a well-grounded lightning rod, a steel smokestack, or a steel framed or sheathed building, the electrical charge may be, and usually is, conducted harmlessly to the ground. If the fireplace chimney stands isolated on a high rise of ground, a grounded lightning rod should be placed on it as a precaution, but a metal cap would have no effect whatsoever. Lightning does not behave like Santa Claus—running downward inside the chimney and then jumping outward into the room. Usually, lightning strikes the television antenna, rips the siding off the house beneath the lead-in wire, and jumps across to an eaves gutter if one is nearby, tearing it off; or, if a water pipe is nearby, the lightning may jump across to the plumbing system, damaging it severely. The house may, or may not, be set afire. The ground wire of a television set is not a satisfactory conductor of lightning. If there is no lightning arrestor on the lead-in wire, the television set is almost certain to be damaged seriously.

Humidity Inside Homes

Ques. Most persons are much annoyed by the drying out of the woodwork and furniture in their homes during winter when the homes must be heated. Is it desirable to humidify the air in homes during winter, so that the humidity is uniform during the entire year?

Ans. That is virtually impossible, if the house is to be ventilated adequately during cold weather, because the usual outside air during severe winter weather may contain only 1/50, or possibly even less, moisture than it contains during humid summer weather. Also, excessive humidity in a home in winter invariably results in moisture condensation problems. Windows, especially metal windows, fog and frost up, and the vapor may penetrate the walls, condensing beneath the outside paint and causing it to peel; or in lightly-insulated or uninsulated houses, the inside wall surfaces may become damp, clammy, or noticeably wet. The following humidities, with the usual 70°F. inside temperature, are recommended; usually, artificial humidifying is not necessary to maintain them:

20% relative humidity; for outside temperature of −10°F.
25% relative humidity; for outside temperature of   0°F.
30% relative humidity; for outside temperature of   10°F.
35% relative humidity; for outside temperature of   20°F.
40% relative humidity; for outside temperature of   30°F.

In regions where the average winter temperature is approximately 35°F., which includes most of the United States near the 40th parallel, the winter humidity in homes normally averages 40 to 45 percent, which is generally satisfactory. However, when the outside temperature is 0°F., condensation begins to form on single-glazed window panes when the inside humidity reaches 17 percent, and on double-glazed windows at 45 percent. During severe winter weather, condensation, often in the form of frost or ice, gathers on the bars of metal sash, even though the windows are double-glazed, and it may be a continuing nuisance, even when the inside humidity is comparatively low.

Considering the amount of moisture which is added to the air in a normal home in the routine course of living in it, the average home has little need for additional humidification, although there are homes where it may be desirable. It is impossible for the population to seal itself inside thermos jugs to control the inside climate, even though it is desirable theoretically.

Glossary

Air-Dried Lumber—Lumber that has been piled in yards or sheds for any length of time. For the United States as a whole, the minimum moisture content of thoroughly air-dried lumber is 12 to 15 percent, with the average somewhat higher.

Asphalt—Most native asphalt is a residue from evaporated petroleum. It is insoluble in water but is soluble in gasoline and melts when heated. Used widely in building for waterproofing roof coverings of many types, exterior wall coverings, flooring tile, and the like.

Attic Ventilators—In home building, usually openings in gables or ventilators in the roof. Also, mechanical devices to force ventilation by the use of power-driven fans. Also see Louver.

Back Fill—The replacement of excavated earth into a pit or trench or against a foundation wall.

Base or Baseboard—A board placed against the wall around a room next to the floor to provide a proper finish between the floor and plaster.

Base Molding—Molding used to trim the upper edge of interior baseboard.

Base Shoe—Molding used next to the floor on interior baseboard. Sometimes called a carpet strip.

Batter Board—One of a pair of horizontal boards nailed to posts set at the corners of an excavation, used to indicate the desired level. Also a fastening for stretched strings to indicate the outlines of foundation walls.

Beam—A structural member transversely supporting a load.

Bearing Partition—A partition that supports any vertical load in addition to its own weight.

Bearing Wall—A wall that supports any vertical load in addition to its own weight.

Bed Molding—A molding in an angle, as between an overhanging cornice or eaves, of a building and the side walls.

Blinds (Shutters)—Light wood sections in the form of doors to close over windows to shut out light, give protection, or add temporary insulation. Commonly used now for ornamental purposes, in which case they are fastened rigidly to the building.

Blind Nailing—Nailing in such a way that the nail heads are not visible on the face of the work.

Blue Stain—A bluish or grayish discoloration of the sapwood caused by the growth of certain mold-like fungi on the surface and in the interior of the piece, made possible by the same conditions that favor the growth of other fungi.

Bolster—A short horizontal timber resting on the top of a column for the support of beams or girders.

Boston Ridge—A method of applying asphalt or wood shingles as a finish at the ridge or hips of a roof.

Brace—An inclined piece of framing lumber used to complete a triangle, and thereby to stiffen a structure.

Brick Veneer—A facing of brick laid against frame or tile wall construction.

Bridging—Small wood or metal members that are inserted in a diagonal position between the floor joists to act both as tension and compression members for the purpose of bracing the joists and spreading the action of loads.

Built-up Roof—A roofing composed of three to five layers of rag felt or jute saturated with coal tar, pitch, or asphalt. The top is finished with crushed slag or gravel. Generally used on flat or low-pitched roofs.

Butt Joint—The junction where the ends of two timbers or other members meet in a square-cut joint.

Cap—The upper member of a column, pilaster, door cornice, molding etc.

Casing—Wide molding of various widths and thicknesses used to trim door and window openings.

Casement Frames and Sash—Frames of wood or metal enclosing part or all of the sash which may be opened by means of hinges affixed to the vertical edges.

Cement, Keene's—The whitest finish plaster obtainable that produces a wall of extreme durability. Because of its density, it excels for a wainscoting plaster for bathrooms and kitchens and is also used extensively for the finish coat in auditoriums, public buildings, and other places where walls will be subjected to unusually hard wear or abuse.

Checking—Fissures that appear with age in many exterior paint coatings, at first superficial, but which in time may penetrate entirely through the coating.

Collar Beam—A beam connecting pairs of opposite rafters above the attic floor.

Column—In architecture: A perpendicular supporting member, circular or rectangular in section, usually consisting of a base, shaft, and capital. In engineering: A structural compression member, usually vertical, supporting loads acting on or near and in the direction of its longitudinal axis.

Concrete, Plain—Concrete without reinforcement, or reinforced only for shrinkage or temperature changes.

Condensation—Beads or drops of water, and frequently frost in extremely cold weather, that accumulate on the inside of the exterior covering of a building when warm, moisture-laden air from the interior reaches a point where the temperature no longer permits the air to sustain the moisture it holds. Use of louvers or attic ventilators will reduce moisture condensation in attics.

Construction, Dry-Wall—A type of construction in which the interior wall finish is applied in a dry condition, generally in the form of sheet materials, as contrasted to plaster.

Construction, Frame—A type of construction in which the structural parts are of wood or dependent upon a wood frame for support. In codes, if brick or other incombustible material is applied to the exterior walls, the classification of this type of construction is usually unchanged.

Coped Joint—See Scribing.

Corbel Out—To build out one or more courses of brick or stone from the face of a wall, to form a support for timbers.

Corner Braces—Diagonal braces let into studs to reinforce corners of frame structures.

Counterflashing—A flashing usually used on chimneys at the roof-line to cover shingle flashing and to prevent moisture entry.

Cove Molding—A three-sided molding with concave face used wherever small angles are to be covered.

Crawl Space—A shallow space below the living quarters of a house. It is generally not excavated or paved and is often enclosed for appearance by a skirting or facing material.

Deck Paint—An enamel with a high degree of resistance to mechanical wear, for use on such surfaces as porch floors.

Dimension—See Lumber, dimension.

Direct Nailing—To nail perpendicular to the initial surface or to the junction of the pieces joined. Also termed *face nailing*.

Doorjamb, Interior—The surrounding case into which and out of which a door closes and opens. It consists of two upright pieces, called jambs, and a head, fitted together and rabbeted.

Dormer—An interal recess, the framing of which projects from a sloping roof.

Downspout—A pipe, usually of metal, for carrying rainwater from roof gutters.

Dressed and Matched (Tongue and Groove)—Boards or planks machined in such a manner that there is a groove on one edge and a corresponding tongue on the other.

Ducts—In a house, usually round or rectangular metal pipes for distributing warm air from the heating plant to rooms, or air from a conditioning device. Ducts are also made of asbestos and composition materials.

Eaves—The margin or lower part of a roof projecting over the wall.

Expansion Joint—A bituminous fiber strip used to separate blocks or units of concrete to prevent cracking due to expansion as a result of temperature changes.

Facia or Fascia—A flat board, band, or face, used sometimes by itself but usually in combination with moldings, often located at the outer face of the cornice.

Fire-Resistive—In the absence of a specific ruling by the authority having jurisdiction, applies to materials for construction not combustible in the temperatures of ordinary fires and that will withstand such fires without serious impairment of their usefulness for at least one hour.

Fire Stop—A solid, tight closure of a concealed space, placed to prevent the spread of fire and smoke through such a space.

Flagstone (Flagging or Flags)—Flat stones, from 1 to 4 inches thick, used for rustic walks, steps, floors, and the like. Usually sold by the ton.

Flashing—Sheet metal or other material used in roof and wall construction to protect a building from seepage of water.

Flue—The space or passage in a chimney through which smoke, gas, or fumes ascend. Each passage is called a flue, which, together with any others and the surrounding masonry, make up the chimney.

Flue Lining—Fire clay or terra-cotta pipe, round or square, usually made in all of the ordinary flue sizes and in 2-feet lengths, used for the inner lining of chimneys with the brick or masonry work around the outside. Flue lining should run from the concrete footing to the top of the chimney cap. Figure a foot of flue lining for each foot of chimney.

Footing—The spreading course or courses at the base or bottom of a foundation wall, pier, or column.

Foundation—The supporting portion of a structure below the first-floor construction, or below grade, including the footings.

Framing, Balloon—A system of framing a building in which all vertical structural elements of the bearing walls and partitions consist of single pieces extending from the top of the soleplate to the roofplate and to which all floor joists are fastened.

Framing, Platform—A system of framing a building in which floor joists of each story rest on the top plate of the story below or on the foundation sill for the first story, and the bearing walls and partitions rest on the subfloor of each story.

Furring—Strips of wood or metal applied to a wall or other surface to even it, to form an air space, or to give the wall an appearance of greater thickness.

Gable—That portion of a wall contained between the slope of a single-sloped roof and a line projected horizontally through the lowest elevation of the roof construction.

Girder—A large or principal beam used to support concentrated loads at isolated points along its length.

Grounds—Strips of wood, of the same thickness as the lath and plaster, that are attached to walls before the plastering is done. Used around windows, doors, and other openings as a plaster stop and in other places for the purpose of attaching baseboards or other trim.

Grout—Mortar made of such consistency by the addition of water that it will just flow into the joints and cavities of the masonry work and fill them solid.

Gutter or Eave Trough—A shallow channel or conduit of metal or wood set below and along the eaves of a house to catch and carry off rainwater from the roof.

Gypsum Plaster—Gypsum formulated to be used with the addition of sand and water for base-coat plaster.

Header—(*a*) A beam placed perpendicular to joists and to which joists are nailed in framing for chimney, stairway, or other opening. (*b*) A wood lintel.

Hip—The external angle formed by the meeting of two sloping sides of a roof.

Hip Roof—A roof that rises by inclined planes from all four sides of a building.

Humidifier—A device designed to discharge water vapor into a confined space for the purpose of increasing or maintaining the relative humidity in an enclosure.

I-Beam—A steel beam with a cross section resembling the letter "I."

Insulating Board or Fiberboard—A low-density board made of wood, sugarcane, cornstalks, or similar materials, usually formed by a felting process, dried and usually pressed to thicknesses of 1/2 and 25/32 inch.

Insulation, Building—Any material high in resistance to heat transmission that, when placed in the walls, ceilings, or floor of a structure, will reduce the rate of heat flow.

Jack Rafter—A rafter that spans the distance from the wallplate to a hip, or from a valley to a ridge.

Jamb—The side post or lining of a doorway, window, or other opening.

Joint—The space between the adjacent surfaces of two members or components joined and held together by nails, glue, cement, mortar, or other means.

Joint Cement—A powder that is usually mixed with water and used for joint treatment in gypsum-wallboard finish. Often called "spackle."

Joist—One of a series of parallel beams used to support floor and ceiling loads, and supported, in turn, by larger beams, girders, or bearing walls.

Landing—A platform between flights of stairs or at the termination of a flight of stairs.

Lath—A building material of wood, metal, gypsum, or insulating board that is fastened to the frame of a building to act as a plaster base.

Leader—See Downspout.

Ledger Strip—A strip of lumber nailed along the bottom of the side of a girder on which joists rest.

Lintel—A horizontal structural member that supports the load over an opening such as a door or window.

Louver—An opening with a series of horizontal slats so arranged as to permit ventilation but to exclude rain, sunlight, or vision. See also Attic Ventilators.

Lumber—Lumber is the product of the sawmill and planing mill not further manufactured other than by sawing, resawing, and passing lengthwise through a standard planing machine, crosscut to length, and matched.

Lumber, Boards—Yard lumber less than 2 inches thick and 2 or more inches wide.

423

Lumber, Dimension—Yard lumber from 2 inches to, but not including, 5 inches thick, and 2 or more inches wide. Includes joists, rafters, studding, planks, and small timbers.

Lumber, Dressed Size—The dimensions of lumber after shrinking from the green dimension and after planing, usually 3/8 inch less than the nominal or rough size. For example, a 2-by-4 stud actually measures 1-5/8 by 3-5/8 inches.

Lumber, Matched—Lumber that is edge-dressed and shaped to make a close tongue-and-groove joint at the edges or ends when laid edge to edge or end to end.

Lumber, Ship Lap—Lumber that is edge-dressed to make a close rabbeted or lapped joint.

Lumber, Timbers—Yard lumber 5 or more inches in the least dimension. Includes beams, stringers, posts, caps, sills, girders, and purlins.

Lumber, Yard—Lumber of those grades, sizes, and patterns which are generally intended for ordinary construction, such as framework and rough coverage of houses.

Mantel—The shelf above a fireplace. Originally referred to the beam or lintel supporting the arch above the fireplace opening. Used also in referring to the entire finish around a fireplace, covering the chimney breast across the front and sometimes on the sides.

Masonry—Stone, brick, concrete, hollow-tile, concrete-block, gypsum-block, or other similar building units or materials or a combination of the same, bonded together with mortar to form a wall, pier, buttress, or similar mass.

Metal Lath—Sheets of metal that are slit and drawn out to form openings on which plaster is spread.

Millwork—Generally all building materials made of finished wood and manufactured in millwork plants and planing mills are included under the term *millwork*. It includes such items as inside and outside doors, window and doorframes, blinds, porchwork, mantels, panelwork, stairways, moldings, and interior trim. It does not include flooring, ceiling, or siding.

Miter—The joining of two pieces at an angle that bisects the angle of junction.

Moisture Content of Wood—Weight of the water contained in the wood, usually expressed as a percentage of the weight of the oven-dry wood.

Mortise—A slot cut into a board, plank, or timber, usually edgewise, to receive the tenon of another board, plank, or timber to form a joint.

Molding—Material, usually patterned strips, used to provide ornamental variation of outline or contour, whether projections or cavities, such as cornices, bases, window and doorjambs, and heads.

Nonbearing Wall—A wall supporting no load other than its own weight.

Nosing—The projecting edge of a molding or drip. Usually applied to the projecting molding on the edge of a stair tread.

O. C. (On Center)—The measurement of spacing for studs, rafters, joists, and the like in a building from center of one member to the center of the next member.

O. G. (Ogee)—A molding with a profile in the form of a letter S; having the outline of a reversed curve.

Paint—L, pure white lead (basic-carbonate) paint; TLZ, titanium-lead-zinc paint; TZ, titanium-zinc paint.

Panel—A large, thin board or sheet of lumber, plywood, or other material. A thin board with all its edges inserted in a groove of a surrounding frame of thick material. A portion of a flat surface recessed or sunk below the surrounding area, distinctly set off by molding or some other decorative device. Also, a section of floor, wall, ceiling, or roof, usually prefabricated and of large size, handled as a single unit in the operations of assembly and erection.

Paper, Building—A general term for papers, felts, and similar sheet materials used in buildings without reference to their properties or uses.

Paper, Sheathing—A building material, generally paper or felt, used in wall and roof construction as a protection against the passage of air and sometimes moisture.

Parting Stop or Strip—A small wood piece used in the side and head jambs of double-hung windows to separate the upper and lower sash.

Pier—A column of masonry, usually rectangular in horizontal cross section, used to support other structural members.

Pitch—The incline or rise of a roof. Pitch is expressed in inches or rise per foot of run, or by the ratio of the rise to the span.

Plate—(*a*) A horizontal structural member placed on a wall or supported on posts, studs, or corbels to carry the trusses of a roof or to carry the rafters directly. (*b*) A shoe, or base member, as of a partition or other frame. (*c*) A small, relatively flat member placed on or in a wall to support girders, rafters, etc.

Ply—A term to denote the number of thicknesses or layers of roofing felt, veneer in plywood, or layers in built-up materials, in any finished piece of such material.

Plywood—A piece of wood made of three or more layers of veneer joined with glue and usually laid with the grain of adjoining plies at right angles. Almost always an odd number of plies are used to provide balanced construction.

Preservative—Any substance that, for a reasonable length of time, will prevent the action of wood-destroying fungi, borers of various kinds, and similar destructive life when the wood has been properly coated or impregnated with it.

Primer—The first coat of paint in a paint job that consists of two or more coats; also the paint used for such a first coat.

Putty—A type of cement usually made of whiting and boiled linseed oil, beaten or kneaded to the consistency of dough and used in sealing glass in sash, filling small holes and crevices in wood, and for similar purposes.

Rabbet—A rectangular longitudinal groove cut in the corner of a board or other piece of material.

Radiant Heating—A method of heating, usually consisting of coils or pipes placed in the floor, wall, or ceiling.

Rafter—One of a series of structural members of a roof designed to support roof loads. The rafters of a flat roof are sometimes called roof joists.

Rafter, Hip—A rafter that forms the intersection of an external roof angle.

Rafter, Jack—A rafter that spans the distance from a wallplate to a hip or from a valley to a ridge.

Rafter, Valley—A rafter that forms the intersection of an internal roof angle.

Rail—A horizontal bar or timber of wood or metal extending from one post or support to another as a guard or barrier in a fence, balustrade, staircase, etc. Also, the cross or horizontal members of the framework of a sash, door, blind, or any paneled assembly.

Rake—The trim members that run parallel to the roof slope and from the finish between wall and roof.

Reflective Insulation—Sheet material with one or both surfaces of comparatively low heat emissivity that, when used in building construction so that the surfaces face air space, reduces the radiation across the air space.

Reinforcing—Steel rods or metal fabric placed in concrete slabs, beams, or columns to increase their strength.

Resin-Emulsion Paint—Paint, the vehicle (liquid part) of which consists of resin or varnish dispersed in fine droplets in water, analogous to cream, (which is butterfat dispersed in water).

Relative Humidity—The amount of water vapor expressed as a percentage of the maximum quantity that could be present in the atmosphere at a given temperature (the actual amount of water vapor that can be held in space increases with the temperature).

Ridge—The horizontal line at the junction of the top edges of two sloping roof surfaces. The rafters are nailed at the ridge.

Ridge Board—The board placed on edge at the ridge of the roof to support the upper ends of the rafters.

Rise—The height a roof rises in horizontal distance (run) from the outside face of a wall supporting the rafters or trusses to the ridge of the roof. In stairs, the perpendicular height of a step or flight of steps.

Riser—Each of the vertical boards closing the spaces between the treads of the stairways.

Roll Roofing—Roofing material, composed of fiber and saturated with asphalt, that is supplied in rolls containing 108 square feet in 36-inch widths. It is generally furnished in weights of 55 to 90 pounds per roll.

Roof Sheathing—The boards or sheet material fastened to the roof rafters on which the shingles or other roof covering is laid.

Rubber-Emulsion Paint—Paint, the vehicle of which consists of rubber or synthetic rubber dispersed in fine droplets in water.

Run—In reference to roofs, the horizontal distance from the face of a wall to the ridge of the roof. Referring to stairways, the net width of a step; also the horizontal distance covered by a flight of steps.

Sash—A single frame containing one or more panes of glass.

Saturated Felt—A felt which is impregnated with tar or asphalt.

Scratch Coat—The first coat of plaster, which is scratched to form a bond for the second coat.

Scribing—Fitting woodwork to an irregular surface.

Seasoning—Removing moisture from green wood in order to improve its serviceability.

Shake—A hand-split shingle, usually edge grained.

Sheathing—The structural covering, usually wood boards, plywood, or wallboards, placed over exterior studding or rafters of a structure.

Sheathing Paper—See Paper, Sheathing.

Shellac—A transparent coating made by dissolving lac, a resinous secretion of the lac bug (a scale insect that thrives in tropical countries, especially India), in alcohol.

Shingles—Roof covering of asphalt, asbestos, wood, tile, slate, or other material cut to stock lengths, widths, and thicknesses.

Shingles, Siding—Various kinds of shingles, some especially designed, that can be used as the exterior side-wall covering for a structure.

Ship Lap—See Lumber, Ship Lap.

Siding—The finish covering of the outside wall of a frame building, whether made of weatherboards, vertical boards with battens, shingles, or other material.

Siding, Bevel (Lap Siding)—Used as the finish siding on the exterior of a house or other structure. It is usually manufactured by resawing dry square-surfaced boards diagonally to produce two wedge-shaped pieces. These pieces commonly run from 3/16 inch thick on the thin edge to 1/2 to 3/4 inch thick on the other edge, depending on the width of the siding.

Siding, Drop—Usually 3/4 inch thick and 6 inches wide, machined into various patterns. Drop siding has tongue-and-groove joints, is heavier, has more structural strength, and is frequently used on buildings that require no sheathing, such as garages and barns.

Sill—The lowest member of the frame of a structure, resting on the foundation and supporting the uprights of the frame. The member forming the lower side of an opening, as a door sill, window sill, etc.

Soffit—The underside of the members of a building, such as staircases, cornices, beams, and arches, relatively minor in area as compared with ceilings.

Soil Cover (Ground Cover)—A lightweight roll roofing or plastic used on the ground of crawl spaces to minimize moisture permeation of the area.

Soil Stack—A general term for the vertical main of a system of soil, waste, or vent piping.

Sole or Soleplate—A member, usually a 2-by-4, on which wall and partition studs rest.

Span—The distance between structural supports, such as walls, columns, piers, beams, girders, and trusses.

Square—A unit of measure—100 square feet—usually applied to roofing material. Side-wall coverings are often packed to cover 100 square feet and are sold on that basis.

Stain, Shingle—A form of oil paint, very thin in consistency, intended for coloring wood with rough surfaces, like shingles, but without forming a coating of significant thickness or with any gloss.

Stair Landing—A platform between flights of stairs or at the termination of a flight of stairs.

Stair Rise—The vertical distance from the top of one stair tread to the top of the one next above.

Stair Carriage—A stringer for steps on stairs.

Storm Sash or Storm Window—An extra window usually placed on the outside of an existing window as additional protection against cold weather.

String, Stringer—A timber or other support for cross members. In stairs, the support on which the stair treads rest; also *stringboard*.

Stucco—Most commonly refers to an outside plaster made with Portland cement as its base.

Stud—One of a series of slender wood or metal structural members placed as supporting elements in walls and partitions. (Plural: studs or studding.)

Subfloor—Boards or sheet material laid on joists over which a finish floor is to be laid.

Tail Beam—A relatively short beam or joist supported in a wall on one end and by a header on the other.

Trimmer—A beam or joist to which a header is nailed in framing for a chimney, stairway, or other opening.

Termites—Insects that superficially resemble ants in size, general appearance, and habit of living in colonies; hence, they are frequently called *white ants*. Subterranean termites do not establish themselves in buildings by being carried in with lumber but by entering from ground nests after the building has been constructed. If unmolested, they eat out the woodwork, leaving a shell of sound wood to conceal their activities, and damage may proceed so far as to cause collapse of parts of a structure before discovery. There are about 56 species of termites known in the United States; but the two major species, classified from the manner in which they attack wood, are ground-inhabiting or subterranean termites, the most common, and dry-wood termites, found almost exclusively along the extreme southern border and the Gulf of Mexico in the United States.

Termite Shield—A shield, usually of noncorrodible metal, placed in or on a foundation wall or other mass of masonry or around pipes to prevent passage of termites.

Tread—The horizontal board in a stairway on which the foot is placed.

Truss—A frame or jointed structure designed to act as a beam of long span, while each member is usually subjected to longitudinal stress only, either tension or compression.

Trim—The finish materials in a building, such as moldings, applied around openings (window trim, door trim) or at the floor and ceiling of rooms (baseboard, cornice, picture molding).

Undercoat—A coating applied prior to the finishing or top coats of a paint job. It may be the first of two or the second of three coats. In some usage of the word it may become synonymous with priming coat.

Valley—The internal angle formed by the junction of two sloping sides of a roof.

Vapor Barrier—Material used to retard the flow of vapor or moisture into walls and thus to prevent condensation within them. There are two types of vapor barriers, the membrane that comes in rolls and is applied as a unit in the wall or ceiling construction, and the paint type, which is applied with a brush. The vapor barrier must be a part of the warm side of the wall.

Varnish—A thickened preparation of drying oil, or drying oil and resin, suitable for spreading on surfaces to form continuous, transparent coatings, or for mixing with pigments to make enamels.

Vehicle—A liquid portion of a finishing material; it consists of the binder (nonvolatile) and volatile thinners.

Veneer—Thin sheets of wood.

Vent—A pipe installed to provide a flow of air to or from a drainage system or to provide a circulation of air within such systems to protect trap seals from siphonage and back pressure.

Vermiculite—A mineral closely related to mica, with the faculty of expanding on heating to form lightweight material with insulation quality. Used as bulk insulation and also as aggregate in insulating and acoustical plaster and in insulating concrete floors.

Wallboard—Wood pulp, gypsum, or other materials made into large rigid sheets that may be fastened to the frame of a building to provide a surface finish.

Weatherstrip—Narrow strips made of metal, or other material, so designed that when installed at doors or windows they will retard the passage of air, water, moisture, or dust around the door or window sash.

Index

Index

AUDEL BOOKS *practical reading for profit*

APPLIANCES

Air Conditioning   (23159)

Brand new from Audel. Domestic, commercial, and automobile air conditioning fully explained in easily-understood language. Troubleshooting charts aid in making diagnosis and repair of system troubles.

Gas Appliances and Heating   (23104)

A reliable guide to acquaint repairmen and home owners with the construction, operation and servicing of modern gas-fired appliances such as may be found in the average home.

Home Appliance Servicing   (23016)

A practical "How To Do It" book for electric & gas servicemen, mechanics & dealers. Covers principles, servicing and repairing of home appliances. Tells how to locate troubles, make repairs, reassemble and connect, wiring diagrams and testing methods. Tells how to fix electric refrigerators, washers, ranges, toasters, ironers, broilers, dryers, vacuums, fans, and other appliances.

Home Refrigeration and Air Conditioning (23133)

NEW AND UP-TO-DATE. Covers basic principles, servicing, operation, and repair of modern household refrigerators and air conditioners. Automobile air conditioners are also included. Troubleshooting charts aid in trouble diagnosis. **A gold mine of essential facts for engineers, servicemen, and users.**

Oil Burners   (23151)

Brand New. Provides complete information on all types of oil burners and associated equipment. Discusses burners—blowers—ignition transformers—electrodes—nozzles—fuel pumps—filters—controls. Installation and maintenance are stressed. Troubleshooting charts permit rapid diagnosis of system troubles and possible remedies to correct them. This book replaces the popular Oil Burner Guide used by thousands of Audel readers in past years.

AUTOMOTIVE

Auto Engine Tune-Up   (23181)

New revised edition. This popular how-to-do-it guide shows exactly how to tune your car engine for extra power, gas economy, and fewer costly repairs. New emission control systems are explained along with the proper methods for correcting faults and making adjustments to keep these systems in a top operating condition.

Automobile Guide   (23015)

Practical reference for auto mechanics, servicemen, trainees & owners. Explains theory, construction and servicing of modern domestic motor cars. FEATURES: All parts of an automobile—engines—pistons—rings—connecting rods—crankshafts—valve—cams—timing—cooling systems—fuel-feed systems—carburetors—automatic choke—transmissions—clutches—universals—propeller shafts—differentials—rear axles—running gear—brakes—wheel alignment—steering gear—tires—lubrication—ignition systems—generators—starters—lighting systems—storage batteries.

Diesel Engine Manual   (23024)

A practical treatise on the theory, operation and maintenance of modern Diesel engines. Explains Diesel principles—valves—timing—fuel pumps—pistons and rings—cylinders—lubrication—cooling system—fuel oil—engine indicator—governors—engine reversing—answers on operation—calculations. AN IMPORTANT GUIDE FOR ENGINEERS, OPERATORS, STUDENTS.

Foreign Auto Repair Manual   (23078)

Contains complete, service and repair data for the most popular imported makes, including Fiat, Hillman Minx, M.G., Opel, Peugot, Renault, SAAB, Simca, Volkswagen, and Volvo. Introductory chapters provide complete data on operation and maintenance of fuel and ignition systems.

Gas Engine Manual   (23061)

A completely practical book covering the construction, operation and repair of all types of modern gas engines. Part I covers gas-engine principles; engine parts; auxiliaries; timing methods; ignition systems. Part II covers troubleshootng, adjustment and repairs.

Truck & Tractor Guide   (23020)

A shop companion for truck mechanics and drivers—shop foremen—garagemen—maintenance men—helpers—owners—troubleshooters—fleet maintenance men—bus mechanics and drivers—farm tractor operators and mechanics. Covers gas and diesel motor principles—construction—operation—miantenance—repair—service operations—troubleshooting—engine tune-up—carburetor adjusting—ignition tuning—brakes—service of all parts.—1001 FACTS AT YOUR FINGER TIPS.

BUILDING AND MAINTENANCE

Answers on Blueprint Reading   (23041)

Covers all types of blueprint reading for mechanics and builders. The man who can read blueprints is in line for a better job. This book gives you the secret language, step by step in easy stages. NO OTHER TRADE BOOK LIKE IT.

Builders Encyclopedia   (23178)

Brand New. A book of terms used by members of the building and construction trade. A valuable book for the carpenter, plumber, electrician, steel erector, bridge builder, general contractor, architect, and others in the building and construction industry.

Building Construction and Design   (23180)

New from Audel. A completely revised and rewritten version of Audel's **Architects and Builders Guide.** New illustrations and extended coverage of material makes this treatment of the subject more valuable than ever. Anyone connected in any way with the building industry will profit from the information contained in this book.

Building Maintenance (23140)

A comprehensive book on the practical aspects of building maintenance. Chapters are included on: painting and decorating; plumbing and pipe fitting; carpentry; calking and glazing; concrete and masonry; roofing; sheet metal; electrical maintenance; air conditioning and refrigeration; insect and rodent control; heating; maintenance management; custodial practices: A MUST BOOK FOR BUILDING OWNERS, MANAGERS, AND MAINTENANCE PERSONNEL.

Carpenters & Builders Library—4 Vols. (23169)

A practical illustrated trade assistant on modern construction for carpenters, builders, and all woodworkers. Explains in practical, concise language and illustrations all the principles, advances and short cuts based on modern practice. How to calculate various jobs.
Vol. 1—(23170)—Tools, steel square, saw filing, joinery, cabinets.
Vol. 2—(23171)—Mathematics, plans, specifications, estimates.
Vol. 3—(23172)—House and roof framing, laying out, foundations.
Vol. 4—(23173)—Doors, windows, stairs, millwork, painting.

Carpentry and Building (23142)

Answers to the problems encountered in today's building trades. The actual questions asked of an architect by carpenters and builders are answered in this book. No apprentice or journeyman carpenter should be without the help this book can offer.

Commercial Refrigeration (23134)

Installation, operation, and repair of commercial refrigeration systems. Included are ice-making plants, locker plants, grocery and supermarket refrigerated display cases, etc. Trouble charts aid in the diagnosis and repair of defective systems.

Do-It-Yourself Encyclopedia—2 Vols. (23156)

An all-in-one home repair and project guide for all do-it-yourselfers. Packed with step-by-step plans, thousands of photos, helpful charts. A really authentic, truly monumental, home-repair and home-project guide.

Home Workshop & Tool Handy Book (23087)

The most modern, up-to-date manual ever designed for home craftsmen and do-it-yourselfers. Tells how to set up your own home workshop, (basement, garage, or spare room), all about the various hand and power tools (when, where, and how to use them, etc.). Covers both wood- and metal-working principles and practices. An all-in-one workshop guide for handy men, professionals and students.

Masons & Builders Guides—4 Vols. (23076)

A practical illustrated trade assistant on modern construction for bricklayers, stone masons, cement workers, plasterers, and tile setters. Explains in clear language and with detailed illustrations all the principles, advances and short cuts based on modern practice—including how to figure and calculate various jobs.
Vol. 1—(23072)—Brick work, bricklaying, bonding, designs.
Vol. 2—(23073)—Brick foundations, arches, tile setting, estimates.
Vol. 3—(23074)—Concrete mixing, placing forms, reinforced stucco.
Vol. 4—(23075)—Plastering, stone masonry, steel construction, blue prints.

Plumbers and Pipe Fitters Library—3 Vols. (23155)

New revised edition. A practical illustrated trade assistant and reference for master plumbers, journeyman and apprentice pipe fitters, gas fitters and helpers, builders, contractors, and engineers. Explains in simple language, illustrations, diagrams, charts, graphs and pictures, the principles of modern plumbing and pipe-fitting practices.
Vol. 1—(23152)—Materials, tools, calculations.
Vol. 2—(23153)—Drainage, fittings, fixtures.
Vol. 3—(23154)—Installation, heating, welding.

ELECTRICITY-ELECTRONICS

Electric Generating Systems   (23179)

New from Audel. Answers many questions concerning the selection, installation, operation, and maintenance of engine-driven electric generating systems for emergency, standby, and away-from-the-power-line applications. Private homes, hospitals, radio and television stations, and pleasure boats are only a few of the installations that owners either desire or require for primary power or for by standby use in case of commercial power failure. THE MOST COMPREHENSIVE COVERAGE OF THIS SUBJECT TO BE FOUND TODAY.

Electric Motors   (23150)

New revised edition. Covers the construction, theory of operation, connection, control, maintenance, and troubleshooting of all types of electric motors. A handy guide for electricians and all electrical workers.

Electrical Power Calculations   (23050)

275 TYPICAL PROBLEMS WORKED OUT. Presents and explains the mathematical formulas and the fundamental electrical laws for all the everday, practical problems in both AC and DC electricity. EVERY ELECTRICAL WORKER AND STUDENT NEEDS THIS MODERN MATHEMATICAL TOOL.

Guide to the 1968 National Electrical Code   (23166)

This important and informative book is now revised to conform to the 1968 National Electrical Code. Offers an interpretation and simplification of the rulings contained in the National Electrical Code. Electrical contractors, wiremen, and electricians will find this book invaluable for a more complete understanding of the NEC. Illustrated.

New Electric Library—10 Vols.   (23030)

For engineers, electricians, electrical workers, mechanics and students. Presenting in simple, concise form the fundamental principles, rules and applications of applied electricity. Fully illustrated with diagrams and sketches, also calculations and tables for ready reference. Based on the best knowledge and experience of applied electricity.

Vol. 1 (23031)—Electricity, magnetism, armature winding, repairs.

Vol. 2 (23032)—Dynamos, DC motors, construction, installation, maintenance, troubleshooting.

Vol. 3 (23033)—Electrical testing instruments, storage battery construction and repairs.

Vol. 4 (23034)—Alternating current principles and diagrams, power factor, alternators, transformers.

Vol. 5 (23035)—AC motors, converters, switches, fuses, circuit breakers.

Vol. 6 (23036)—Relays, capacitors, regulators, rectifiers, meters, switchboards, power-station practice.

Vol. 7 (23037)—Wiring, high-tension transmission, plans, calculations.

Vol. 8 (23038)—Railways, signals, elevators.

Vol. 9 (23039)—Radio, telephone, telegraph, television, motion pictures.

Vol. 10 (23040)—Refrigeration, illumination, welding, X-ray, modern electrical appliances.

Practical Electricity   (23160)

A newly-revised edition of an all-time best-seller. This updated version is a ready reference book, giving complete instruction and practical information on the rules and laws of electricity—maintenance of electrical machinery—AC and DC motors—wiring diagrams—lighting—house and power wiring—meter and instrument connection—transformer connection—circuit breakers—power stations—automatic substations. THE KEY TO A PRACTICAL UNDERSTANDING OF ELECTRICITY.

Questions & Answers for Electricians Exams   (23164)

Newly revised to conform to the 1968 National Electrical Code. A practical book to help you prepare for all grades of electricians' license examinations. A helpful review of fundamental principles underlying each question and answer needed to prepare you to solve any new or similar problem. Covers the National Electrical Code; questions and answers for license tests; Ohm's law with applied examples; hook-ups for motors; lighting and instruments. A COMPLETE REVIEW FOR ALL ELECTRICAL WORKERS.

Wiring Diagrams for Light & Power   (23028)

Brand-new updated edition. Electricians, wiremen, linemen, plant superintendents, construction engineers, electrical contractors and students will find these diagrams a valuable source of practical help. Each diagram is complete and self-explaining. A PRACTICAL HANDY BOOK OF ELECTRICAL HOOK-UPS.

ENGINEERS-MECHANICS-MACHINISTS
Machinists Library   (23174)

Covers modern machine-shop practice. Tells how to set up and operate lathes, screw and milling machines, shapers, drill presses and all other machine tools. A complete reference library. A SHOP COMPANION THAT ANSWERS YOUR QUESTIONS.

Vol. 1—(23175)—Basic Machine Shop.
Vol. 2—(23176)—Machine Shop.
Vol. 3—(23177)—Toolmakers Handy Book.

Power Plant Engineers Guide   (23052)

A complete steam-engineer's library in one book, with questions and answers. For all Engineers, Firemen, Water tenders, Oilers, Operators, Repairmen and Applicants for Engineers' License Examinations. 1001 FACTS AND FIGURES AT YOUR FINGER TIPS.

Practical Guide to Mechanics   (23102)

A Convenient reference book valuable for its practical and concise explanations of the applicable laws of physics. Presents all the basics of mechanics in everyday language, illustrated with practical examples of their applications in various fields.

Questions & Answers for Engineers
and Firemans Examinations   (23053)

An aid for stationary, marine, Diesel & hoisting engineers' examinations for all grades of licenses. A new concise review explaining in detail the principles, facts and figures of practical engineering. Questions & Answers.

Welders Guide   (23025)

A concise, practical text on operation and maintenance of all welding machines, for all mechanics. Covers electric, oxyacetylene, thermit, unionmelt welding for sheet metal; spot and pipe welds; pressure vessels; aluminum, copper, brass, bronze and other metals; airplane work; surface hardening and hard facing; cutting; brazing; eye protection. EVERY WELDER SHOULD OWN THIS GUIDE.

FLUID POWER

Practical Guide to Fluid Power   (23136)

An essential book for the owner, operator, supervisor, or maintenance man concerned with hydraulic or pneumatic equipment. A complete coverage of modern design, application, and repair of fluid power devices. Fully illustrated.

Pumps   (23167)

A new and detailed book on all types of pumps from the old-fashioned kitchen variety to the most modern types. Covers construction, application, installation, and troubleshooting.

MATHEMATICS

Practical Mathematics for Everyone—2 Vols.   (23112)

A concise and reliable guide to the understanding of practical mathematics. People from all walks of life, young and old alike, will find the information contained in these two books just what they have been looking for. The mathematics discussed is for the everyday problems that arise in every household and business.
Vol. 1—(23110)—Basic Mathematics.
Vol. 2—(23111)—Financial Mathematics.

OUTBOARD MOTORS

Outboard Motors & Boating   (23168)

Newly revised and up-dated. Provides the information necessary to adjust, repair, and maintain all types of outboard motors. Valuable information concerning boating rules and regulations is also included.

RADIO-TELEVISION-AUDIO

Handbook of Commercial Sound Installations   (23126)

A practical complete guide to planning commercial systems, selecting the most suitable equipment, and following through with the most proficient servicing methods. For technicians and the professional and businessman interested in installing a sound system.

Practical Guide to Citizens Band Radio   (23130)

Covers how to select, install, operate, maintain, and adjust all types of CB equipment. Also describes the latest equipment and FCC regulations. For everyone who now uses or plans to use a CB unit, as well as those who install and service such gear.

Practical Guide to Servicing Electronic Organs   (23132)

Detailed, illustrated discussions of the operation and servicing of electronic organs. Including models by Allen, Baldwin, Conn, Hammond, Kinsman, Lowrey, Magnavox, Thomas, and Wurlitzer.

Radiomans Guide   (23163)

A newly-revised and updated Audel best-seller, containing the latest information on radio and electronics from the basics through transistors. Covers radio fundamentals—Ohm's law—physics of sound as related to radio—radio-wave transmission—test equipment—power supplies—resistors, inductors, and capacitors—transformers—vacuum tubes—transistors—speakers—antennas—troubleshooting. A complete guide and a perfect preliminary to the study of television servicing.

Television Service Manual   (23162)

Now completely updated and revised to include the latest designs and information. Thoroughly covers television with transmitter theory, antenna designs, receiver circuit operation and the picture tube. Provides the practical information necessary for accurate diagnosis and repair of both black-and-white and color television receivers. A MUST BOOK FOR ANYONE IN TELEVISION.

SHEET METAL
Sheet Metal Pattern Layouts   (23045)

A practical illustrated encyclopedia covering all phases of sheet-metal work including pattern cutting, pattern development and shop procedure. Developed by experts for sheet-metal workers, layout men, mechanics and artisans, apprentices, and students. A MASTER BOOK FOR ALL THE SHEET METAL TRADES

Sheet Metal Workers Handy Book   (23046)

Containing practical information and important facts and figures. Easy to understand. Fundamentals of sheet metal layout work. Clearly written in everyday language. Ready reference index.

TO ORDER AUDEL BOOKS mail this handy form to

Theo. Audel & Co., 4300 W. 62nd
Indianapolis, Indiana 46206

Please send me for FREE EXAMINATION books marked (x) below. If I decide to keep them I agree to mail $3 in 10 days on each book or set ordered and further mail ⅓ of the total purchase price 30 days later, with the balance plus shipping costs to be mailed within another 30 days. Otherwise, I will return them for refund.

APPLIANCES
- ☐ (23159) Air Conditioning 5.95
- ☐ (23104) Gas Appliances and Heating ....$ 4.25
- ☐ (23016) Home Appliance Servicing 6.95
- ☐ (23133) Home Refrigeration and Air Conditioning 6.95
- ☐ (23151) Oil Burners 4.95

AUTOMOTIVE
- ☐ (23181) Auto Engine Tuneup 5.95
- ☐ (23015) Automobile Guide 7.95
- ☐ (23024) Diesel Engine Manual 6.95
- ☐ (23077) Domestic Compact Auto Repair Manual 5.95
- ☐ (23078) Foreign Auto Repair Manual 5.95
- ☐ (23061) Gas Engine Manual 4.50
- ☐ (23020) Truck and Tractor Guide 6.95

BUILDING AND MAINTENANCE
- ☐ (23041) Answers on Blueprint Reading 5.25
- ☐ (23178) Builders Encyclopedia 7.95
- ☐ (23180) Building Construction and Design 5.95
- ☐ (23140) Building Maintenance 5.50
- ☐ (23169) Carpenters and Builders Library (4 Vols.) 16.95
- ☐ Single Volumes sold separately ....ea. 4.95
- ☐ (23142) Carpentry and Building 5.95
- ☐ (23134) Commercial Refrigeration 6.50
- ☐ (23156) Do-It-Yourself Encyclopedia 8.95
- ☐ (23097) Home Modernizing and Repair Guide 3.95
- ☐ (23087) Home Workshop & Tool Handy Book 5.00
- ☐ (23076) Masons and Builders Guide (4 Vols.) 14.95
- ☐ Single Volumes sold separately ....ea. 4.00
- ☐ (23155) Plumbers and Pipe Fitters Library (3 Vols.) 12.50
- ☐ Single Volumes sold separately ....ea. 4.50

ELECTRICITY-ELECTRONICS
- ☐ (23179) Electric Generating Systems 5.95
- ☐ (23150) Electric Motors 5.95
- ☐ (23050) Electrical Power Calculations 4.50
- ☐ (23166) Guide to the 1968 National Electrical Code 6.95
- ☐ (23030) New Electric Library (10 Vols.) 35.00
- ☐ Single Volumes sold separately ....ea. 4.00

- ☐ (23160) Practical Electricity ....$ 5.95
- ☐ (23164) Questions and Answers for Electricians Exams 4.50
- ☐ (23028) Wiring Diagrams for Light and Power 4.95

ENGINEERS-MECHANICS-MACHINIST
- ☐ (23174) Machinists Library (3 Vols.) 16.95
- ☐ Single Volumes sold separately ....ea. 5.95
- ☐ (23026) Mathematics and Calculations for Mechanics 5.50
- ☐ (23056) Millwrights and Mechanics Guide 7.95
- ☐ (23052) Power Plant Engineers Guide 7.50
- ☐ (23102) Practical Guide to Mechanics 4.95
- ☐ (23053) Q&A for Engineers and Firemans Exams 4.95
- ☐ (23025) Welders Guide 5.50

FLUID POWER
- ☐ (23136) Practical Guide to Fluid Power 6.95
- ☐ (23167) Pumps 5.95

MATHEMATICS
- ☐ (23112) Practical Math for Everyone (2 Vols.) 8.95
- ☐ Single Volumes sold separately ....ea. 4.95

OUTBOARD MOTORS
- ☐ (23168) Outboard Motors and Boating 4.95

RADIO-TELEVISION-AUDIO
- ☐ (23126) Handbook of Commercial Sound Installations 5.95
- ☐ (23128) Practical Guide to Auto Radio Repair 4.50
- ☐ (23130) Practical Guide to Citizens Band Radio 4.95
- ☐ (23132) Practical Guide to Servicing Electronic Organs 4.95
- ☐ (23127) Practical Guide to Tape Recorders 4.95
- ☐ (23163) Radiomans Guide 5.95
- ☐ (23162) Television Service Manual 5.95

SHEET METAL
- ☐ (23045) Sheet Metal Pattern Layouts 11.95
- ☐ (23046) Sheet Metal Workers Handy Book.. 4.50

Prices Subject to Change Without Notice

Name _____

Address _____

City _____ State _____ Zip _____

Occupation _____ Employed by _____

SAVE SHIPPING CHARGES! Enclose Full Payment With Coupon and We Pay Shipping Charges.

PRINTED IN USA